Murderous remedy

In the rain a girl is running . . . desperately seeking an escape as powerful headlamp-beams fix on her fleeing figure. And later, in a hushed ward of her own hospital, young Dr Philippa Rowe lies with shattered limbs and severe internal injuries, unable, in her waking moments, to remember anything at all about her accident.

But next day a second ugly discovery is made: the dead body of Gil Bradshaw, an anaesthetist and senior registrar from the same hospital – a colleague of Philippa's. He died on the same evening that she was knocked down, in a locked house only yards from the road where her unconscious body was found.

As doctors and nurses – mostly her close friends, one an ex-lover – fight around the clock to save Philippa's life, Detective Inspector Montgomery confronts the questions: are the two accidents connected? If so, was it just the two victims involved? One doctor is dead, the other is suffering from amnesia, so neither can tell him whether some third party was hell-bent on killing them both.

Murderous remedy is both a satisfying novel of character and a highly ingenious puzzle.

Also by Stella Shepherd
Black justice (1988)

MURDEROUS REMEDY

Stella Shepherd

Constable London

First published in Great Britain 1989
by Constable and Company Limited
10 Orange Street, London WC2H 7EG
Copyright © 1989 by Stella Shepherd
Set in Linotron Palatino 10 pt and
printed in Great Britain by
Redwood Burn Limited
Trowbridge, Wiltshire

British Library CIP data
Shepherd, Stella
Murderous remedy
I. Title
823'.914 [F]

ISBN 0 09 469060 X

For my beloved husband John

Prologue

In the rain a girl was running.

Above, the September evening sky hung black, its only concession to sunset being a sullen glow of pewter over the distant hills. The narrow country road was empty, soundless except for the plash of her feet against its hard surface, and the rasp of each ragged breath.

At first she didn't hear the car. It had emerged from a gateway behind her and swung out into the road before the low warning growl of the engine reached her ears. Desperately she flung her head from side to side, seeking an escape from this one-way course where she was the hare. There were no pavements. To the right, a high brick wall stiffly denied sanctuary, while on the other side were brooding fields, dark and mysterious behind a vicious barbed-wire fence.

Gasping with effort, she tried to accelerate as powerful headlamp beams cut through the rain and flooded the arena with light, fixing on her fleeing figure. For a few more yards she held the centre of the road, then the closing swish of tyres activated her frozen brain. In a blind instinct for survival she jinked to the right, crossing the path of her pursuer.

It was too late. The throaty roar of the car mingled with a sickening thump as she was hit and catapulted over the front offside wing, to sail through the air, broken yet graceful, until the moment of impact with an unyielding road. She lay inanimate as a sack of potatoes while the car smoothly reversed back to the spot and lingered, idling, as if in slow appraisal of what it had done.

Rain pattered softly all around.

1

'Wake up, Philippa. Wake up!'

The voice sounded vaguely familiar, but for Philippa Rowe there were more immediate concerns: her head was pounding and nausea held her motionless in its grip. Every part of her body ached. Each limb felt as heavy as lead. She had no strength to move them; she didn't want to move them. Any change in her position and she would be sick.

'Philippa. It's all right. Everything's fine.'

There was more insistence now in the tone. Whoever it was was not going to give up easily. 'Can you open your eyes? Just for a minute. I want to look in them with this light . . . Philippa?'

She hung on to her pain-riddled cocoon of darkness. Light would be the final, intolerable insult. Let them come back later – a week, a month, whatever. But for now, leave her alone.

Suddenly there was a firm pressure against her upper eyelid. Someone's thumb was intent on forcing the lids apart. With a muted impression of outrage she tried to resist, but the person was too strong. Brilliant light burst in through the naked pupil, searing the retina and producing a frenzy of dancing dendritic images. She groaned and turned her head away.

'Good, good.' The voice sounded not only undeterred but horribly cheerful. 'Now let's try the other side.'

Her brain dredged up the word 'no', but somehow her larynx, tongue and lips seemed unable to articulate it. Everything was too much effort. Once again, she turned her head, this time more slowly. The pain was appalling. Somebody, do something. Please. But not that light.

The importunate probing resumed, and she submitted more out of sheer debility than conscious co-operation. An object seemed to be rasping against the back of her throat; she tried to

9

swallow but it wouldn't go away. No wonder she could hardly speak. Impressions were gradually lodging in her mind, indistinct memories forming and dissolving, eluding her sluggish attempts to bring them into focus and hold them there.

'Well done. We shan't be much longer.'

That voice. Male, slightly high-pitched. She knew it. She knew him. Oh, yes. Very well indeed. With a tremendous effort she licked her dry lips and forced past them three slurred words.

'Barnaby . . . go away.'

There was an astonished gasp close at hand, followed by a muffled background laugh.

He was there when she woke up again several hours later, blue-grey eyes peering down intently from behind his rimless glasses, their sharp expression at odds with his rounded pink cheeks. As Philippa surfaced reluctantly from the warm oblivion of sleep, his face was the first object her languid eyes focused on.

'Burby. Wh – h'p'd?'

Was that her voice? A faint croak, a disengaged mouthing of double Dutch. Her mouth was even drier than before. She tried again.

'Barnaby. What happened?'

He leaned closer towards her, and she heard a crash as his ophthalmoscope slid out of his pocket and hit the floor. She let out an involuntary cry of terror and tightened her limbs as if to draw herself into a ball. Her right arm didn't move.

'Sorry, Pippa.' Now he was scrabbling beneath her bed. 'I'm so clumsy, it's unbelievable. Oh, dear. The bulb's broken . . .' He chattered on as he picked up the pieces and levered himself rather heavily to his feet. Confused as she was, Philippa received a vague impression of a magician's patter. There was a word for it . . . she couldn't remember. In fact, there was a lot that she couldn't remember. How dreadful. Perhaps Barnaby would tell her in his own good time.

'You know where you are?' he asked abruptly.

'Yes, of course. The hospital.' She could recognize the pale green paintwork of Nottingham's District Hospital where she herself had worked for more than three years. The ward eluded her. She seemed to be in one of the small, anonymous single rooms.

10

'Cavendish Ward,' he supplied with disconcerting telepathy.

'I ... Cavendish Ward,' she murmured dreamily as her thoughts slid off into paths of least resistance.

'General surgery.'

'Oh.' Something was wrong with that. What . . . ? Ah; Barnaby.

'You're neurology,' she said with a hint of accusation. Gaining strength, she continued, 'You're the merchant with the flashing light.'

'Well, I did have. It won't do much flashing now. Listen, Pippa. You had an accident. You're in hospital under the care of the general surgeons. That's why you're on this ward. But we're also looking after you – Dr Gosling and myself. So are the orthopods. You had a variety of injuries, but nothing to worry about.'

Dr Gosling and Barnaby, his senior house officer. Neurologists. Two plump little figures in white coats pottering along the corridors of the District. Tweedledum and Tweedledee. So she was under their care . . . Oh, Christ.

'Did you hear me, Pippa?'

'Yes . . . thank you. I can't seem to take much in at the moment. I'm sorry.'

'It's all right. Plenty of time. Do you remember anything about the accident?'

Accident . . .

She thought hard. Events seemed disjointed. The haematology lab, her hospital flat . . . all safe and mundane. Nothing about an accident.

'No,' she said wonderingly.

'Are you sure?'

'Yes. I've no idea. Imagine – no idea. Do you know what happened, Barnaby?'

He fiddled with his tie, then ran a square hand through his centre-parted thatch of fair hair, leaving it sticking out in all directions.

'Hmm. Well, yes. That is, in the broadest context. You were knocked down.'

'Go on.'

'Doesn't that ring any bells?'

'No.'

'It was out in Sylvia Vale – Beechcroft Lane. Somewhere near where Gil lives; I've been up there once myself. Country road – a few houses and a farm.'

11

'But – that's impossible. I don't know that area. I've never been near there!'

'You were on Friday. The police have been calling it a hit-and-run. A WPC keeps popping in to see if you can give them any information.'

'I don't understand.' She screwed up her eyes, experiencing bafflement and the first stirrings of frustration. 'I don't understand,' she repeated emptily.

'You should rest now,' said Barnaby in soothing tones, preparing to leave the room.

'Wait!' she croaked, still fighting against the obstruction in her throat. 'You haven't told me anything. When did it happen? Who was I with?'

'Look, Pippa . . . when you're a bit better, I'll tell you everything I'm able to. But you really should sleep now.'

'Barnaby! Please – I must know. How can I rest when I don't?'

He sighed. 'I wasn't there, you appreciate. This is all hearsay. I gather you were hit by a car and run over on Friday night or early Saturday morning. A jogger found you lying in the road. No one else was around, and no one had reported the accident. You came here in the ambulance and – that's all.'

'That's crazy,' she muttered, as if to herself. Her eyes sought Barnaby's beseechingly. 'You're not making it up, are you? Some kind of peculiar joke?'

'Certainly not!' He sounded affronted.

'Well . . . where was my car? Sylvia Vale is miles away. I must have gone by car.'

'I haven't heard anything about that. Don't upset yourself, Pippa. It'll all come right. You've got a touch of retrograde amnesia – quite common after head injuries.'

Head injury! Neurologist! The implication of her useless right arm swooped down like a flock of black birds. Monoparesis; oh, no. And she couldn't swallow properly. Dysphagia! The terms came easily, reflexly, unlike other words where she had to stop and think. No wonder Barnaby was holding out on her; she was paralysed.

'Please . . . '

'What is it, Pippa?'

'Tell me – is there brain damage?'

Barnaby did not have a reputation for tact. Whatever he said was likely to be accurate. A pulse drummed in her ears as he screwed up his face into an expression of earnest consideration.

'I don't think so,' he said at length. 'Not from the way you've been asking questions. Your CAT scan was fine. There's just a hairline fracture of the temporal bone on the plain films. We're keeping you under routine observation.'

'Then why . . . My arm. I can't move it.'

'No, it's broken. Both forearm bones. Also your right tib and fib. And a few ribs. Sorry you asked?'

'No, I'm relieved. What's wrong with my throat?'

'You can blame the surgeons for that. It's a nasogastric tube. You'll also find a drip in your left arm. There were a few other injuries . . . They'll explain in due course. Nothing that time won't cure.'

'I see.' She felt deathly tired again with the effort of concentration and her headache was more pronounced. 'Thank you, Barny. Thank you very much.'

'Dr Rowe?'

Philippa opened her eyes at the sound of the light female voice. It was becoming easier each time to try to speak rationally and show an interest in her surroundings. Sister Markham had checked on her briefly after Barnaby had gone, and was now returning.

'Hello, Sister.'

'How are you feeling?'

'Oh, quite a lot better, thanks.' It was a polite lie, but hopefully would become the truth before too long.

'I promised you a few words with Mr Thornton. He's on the ward now looking at one of our ladies. Would you like me to wash your face?'

'Please. That would be marvellous. What time is it?'

'Nearly five o'clock. He's going down afterwards to sort out tomorrow's theatre list, so we'll just catch him.'

As Philippa submitted to the ministrations, she realized that a more important question had yet to be answered. Barnaby had said something about an accident on Friday night. In that case . . .

'Sister,' she asked hesitantly, 'what day is it today?'

Anne Markham gave a good-natured smile. 'Monday.'

'Monday!' Philippa was speechless, disorientated. Three whole days had vanished without trace.

'The surgeons patched you up on Saturday, before the orthopaedic team plated your leg.' Now Sister was straightening the
bedclothes with crisp, economical movements. She seemed to be
about Philippa's own age of twenty-nine, or even slightly
younger. Her face was wise and kind. 'Lots of people have been
asking for news of you. Dr Stannard has been here at least three
times, and when he's not here he's on the telephone!'

David . . . keeping tabs on her. Why? Their relationship had
been strictly professional since a bitter row six months before.
She had left their Sherwood flat and immediately moved back
into hospital accommodation. And now he had Audrey – vapid,
clinging Audrey.

She smiled ironically as Sister finished her tasks and stood back
from the bed.

'Who else?' she asked, pushing David Stannard to his habitual
place at the back of her mind.

'WPC Winger, for one. She's very interested in your recovery.
Barnaby Fletcher, of course.'

Professional concern, not personal.

'Coral and Maureen. They keep dropping by.'

That was better. 'You know them, Sister?'

'Oh yes. We go out for drinks every so often. Cocktails at the
Albany. Maureen loves the Jingle Belle. They told me you used to
have the flat below theirs.'

'Yes.' With David. Water under the bridge. She swallowed.
'Does – does my father know what happened?'

Anne nodded. 'He asked us to keep him informed.'

'He hasn't – rung back?'

'Not yet, Dr Rowe.'

'Please call me Philippa.' She clamped down on a feeling of
bitterness tinged with desolation. It was only natural that her
father would want to spend his time with his second family. It
was a long way to travel from Sussex for a visit. But the telephone? Was that so difficult?

'Perhaps we'd better catch Neil,' she said.

He entered the room five minutes later. Neil Thornton was a
highly competent surgical registrar, tall, brown-haired and attractive in a glacial kind of way. His eyes gave the clue to an
otherwise opaque character; they were blue and far-seeing, the
type one would associate with a pilot or driver. If he ever in-
dulged in humour, it was merely as an expedient but he did it

well. For this reason, he was one of the District's best after-dinner speakers.

'Hello,' he said. 'It's good to see you awake. Anne tells me you want a word.'

'Yes, I do,' said Philippa. 'Can you spare the time?'

'A few minutes. Fire away.'

'First, Neil . . . thank you. For whatever surgery you did. You must have saved my life.'

He waved a dismissive hand. 'Old Crowland did most of the work. I was assisting. Come to think of it, if we hadn't been on "take" you'd have ended up at the Victoria.'

'I'm glad I didn't. Most of my friends are here. I was wondering . . . what did you have to do?'

'You're sure you want to know now?'

'Yes.'

'Your liver was lacerated.' His lips compressed into a tight line. 'Your spleen was bleeding profusely.' He gave her a brief, considering look before continuing. 'I'm sorry, Philippa. We had to do a splenectomy on the spot.'

'Oh . . . was there anything else?'

'Possibly a bit of damage to the left kidney. We're keeping an eye on it.' He sounded offhand.

'Just the left one?'

'Mainly.'

'I see.'

'You're bruised round there, remember. Things will be sore for quite some time. Stewart has written up plenty of analgesics; you make sure the nurses give them to you.' He glanced at his watch. 'Most go, I'm afraid. I need to talk to Gil about tomorrow's list. Take things easy.'

'I don't have a lot of choice,' she smiled. 'Thanks again, Neil.'

Neil walked briskly into the small office adjoining Theatre One and acknowledged the greeting of Stewart Bridges, his houseman. Faint snatches of song emerged from the locker room next door as Mr Crowland, their boss, changed out of his sterile clothing.

'Where's Gil?' he demanded.

'I don't know,' yawned Stewart, scribbling on an X-ray form in his large, untidy writing. 'I bleeped him at four, and again at half-past. Pat says he should have been doing a gynae list this afternoon, but he never turned up.'

'He'd better not be ill again. He's anaesthetizing for my list tomorrow, and he'll need to see Mrs Peabody in advance.'

'"Fair, fat, fertile and forty."' Stewart chanted the classic aphorism listing the supposed attributes of gall-bladder patients. He lifted his head. 'May I assist? I haven't seen many cholecystectomies.'

'If your ward work's under control.'

A sullen expression passed over the houseman's heavy features, and Neil felt constrained to add a rider. 'Look, Stewart . . . you know as well as I do that "houseman" is just a polite term for general dogsbody. The wards are your primary responsibility. They've got to be smoothly run. If they're not, you're short of a reference. If they are and you've a bit of time, I'd be glad to teach you in theatre. Okay?'

'Yes.' Stewart reached across to a pile of notes and began to flick through the pages of the top folder. He was seven weeks into his first house job, and constantly chafing at the lack of surgical opportunities their understaffed and busy team afforded him. Still imbued with the ethos of the final-year medical student, he expected to be learning all the time; with ward work, he was arrogant and slipshod.

An increased volume of vocal heartiness heralded Mr Crowland's imminent egress from the inner sanctum. It was one of his favourite pieces, a sea-shanty from *Billy Budd*.

'"*We're towing to Malta*",' he roared in a resonant baritone, closing the door behind him while still fastening his shirt cuffs. '"*The Rock of Gibraltar, with only a halter, and Davy Jones' line below – so* pray *to the Devil below*!" What, is there no tea? Don't just sit there, Bridges. Ask Nurse what's-her-name – or better still, make it yourself. She's no good. Wish we had Nurse O'Donnell back. Don't forget the biscuits.'

As Stewart shuffled out, Vernon Crowland peered beadily at his registrar. 'Everything all right on your side? What does Bradshaw think about Mrs Peabody's cardiac problems?'

Neil answered with care. 'I'm afraid we haven't managed to discuss tomorrow's cases yet. He's elusive at present.'

'Hmm. Recurring pattern – pity. Jones is doing my list. If Bradshaw proves a weak reed again, he'll get you an SHO.'

'I'd prefer Gilbert. He has a lot more experience.'

16

'Well, here's the man to ask.'

Hugh Jones, the senior anaesthetics consultant, had just craned an enquiring head round the doorway. He had sparse grey hair and a long, thin nose which could sniff out beverages at fifty yards.

'We're talking about Bradshaw,' boomed Mr Crowland, waving him to a seat. 'Is the fellow AWOL again?'

'It would seem so,' said the other pettishly.

'Can you get us a replacement if he's not here in the morning?'

'If we adjust our rotas, I dare say. It's a nuisance, though.'

'I know. We'd prefer Bradshaw himself. What's the trouble this time, do you think? Stomach playing him tricks, or is it his bad back?'

'Back, maybe. That ulcer business cleared up years ago. But he's not usually discourteous. He does manage to ring . . . ah, what fortunate timing!'

Stewart Bridges awkwardly steered a trolley into the room and proceeded to pour out steaming cups of tea for all present. Neil accepted his with a wry smile; he knew that Stewart resented performing such menial tasks, and would infinitely prefer to see a nurse hovering attentively over the trolley.

'Well, now, Jones,' said Mr Crowland, leaning back and crossing his long legs, 'what's new?'

When both consultants had finally left the room, Stewart turned to Neil in a confidential manner. 'Gil Bradshaw,' he began. 'Didn't he do surgery once? I heard he worked with old Crowland.'

'Yes,' agreed Neil. 'That was before I came to the District. Apparently he had a lot of time off with a peptic ulcer and various other stress-related illnesses. He was never quite the right type for a surgical career. I think he was secretly relieved when he slipped a disc and was forced to pack it in.'

'So he retrained as an anaesthetist,' continued Stewart, enlightened. 'I understand now. I was puzzled about his age – fortyish and only a senior registrar. It didn't gel. And he still seems to be struggling. I wonder if they'll ever make him a consultant?'

'Unlikely,' said Neil.

2

Audrey Wentworth bit her thin red lip and stared anxiously across the table at the dark-haired young man sitting opposite. Her *boeuf bourguignonne*, so lovingly prepared with such exact measurement of each ingredient, might as well have been a boiled egg for all the attention he was giving it.

These evenings when she came round to David Stannard's hospital flat to fuss maternally about his eating habits and ensconce herself in his kitchen were the focus of her existence. If the onus of contact were left to him, weeks might elapse before he thought of ringing her, and their 'relationship', as she liked to consider it, would fizzle out, unnourished.

Audrey was determined to prevent that happening. The other medical secretaries in her office were highly impressed that she had netted herself a medical registrar. Barring two predictably envious souls, they were agog for details of David's affection; sometimes the sheer paucity of such titbits caused her to invent them. Not being entirely unintelligent, Audrey knew that she had caught him on the rebound from Philippa Rowe. No matter, as long as she could hold on to him!

Tonight, he was frustratingly distracted, with hardly a word to say for himself. She picked up a serving spoon and took the lid off the nearest tureen.

'More potatoes, David? Cauliflower?'

'What? . . . Oh, no thanks.'

There was a pause, and she felt the first simmerings of anger.

'Are you enjoying your meal, David?' she asked in more deliberate tones.

He looked up. 'Yes. Of course I am. Sorry, didn't I say so? It's very nice. You spent a long time preparing it, and I appreciate that. Forgive me if I'm not good company tonight. Truth is, I'm worried about Philippa.'

She hastily checked the stinging retort that sprang to her lips. So he had Philippa on the brain again. What was new in that? Philippa Rowe was the ghost which refused to be laid, present in thought if not in word during so many of their evenings together. She had walked out on David – her own choice – and he was unable to accept it. Why not? Why couldn't he see that it was all for the best? Why couldn't he be a man?

'Isn't she better today?' She strove to sound interested and sincere.

'Yes, in some respects. She's awake and talking . . . But they were terrible injuries, and she's not out of the wood yet.'

'Did she say what happened?'

'I didn't go in and disturb her. Everyone seemed to be wanting their two penn'o'th. But Barnaby told me that her mind's a blank as far as the accident is concerned.'

'She wasn't drunk, was she?' The steely dagger of her malice flashed out beyond her control.

An expression of dislike crossed his face. 'I very much doubt it.'

Aware that she had made a serious gaffe, Audrey quickly rose to her feet. 'I'll just clear up the plates if you've finished,' she said. There's syllabub next. Your favourite. May we have some music, please? You could put it on while I whip up the cream.'

It was difficult to create an intimate atmosphere in David's spartan, very masculine flat. She had brought a candle in her bag, but felt too reticent to produce it in the present climate. Maybe some soothing, classical music would do the trick. David had an enviable collection.

Once in the kitchen, she drowned the first faint strains of Gershwin's Piano Concerto in F by turning on the electric beaters at full speed. In one glass bowl an egg white was waiting. Another held the cream, which she was whipping savagely and failing to watch. Grated lemon peel soaked in a carefully measured quantity of white wine nearby.

Sugar. How much? David had a sweet tooth, but one had to be exact with these recipes. Perhaps just a little extra . . .

'Damn!' she muttered furiously, suddenly noticing that the cream had begun to separate. It was all his fault. He had upset her again, made her feel defensive as usual. She would be perfectly happy and relaxed without the corrosive jealousy engendered by the spectre of other girls. Any other girls, but particularly Philippa Rowe.

Salvaging the syllabub as best she could, Audrey piled it into tall glasses and carried them through into the small living-cum-dining room.

'Here you are,' she said brightly.

'Thanks, Audrey.'

They ate mechanically for two long minutes before David spoke again. 'I'm glad Philippa's under the care of Mr Crowland.

19

He's good, and I've absolute faith in Neil. Their houseman's a bit slapdash, unfortunately. I remember – I taught him when he was a medical student.'

'Perhaps Philippa will direct her own treatment.'

'Audrey, please. I don't think you appreciate the situation. At the weekend she was barely alive . . . she can't concentrate on anything just yet, and besides, she's not like that. She wouldn't interfere.' His face clouded over. 'It was awful to see her yesterday. All the drips, and tubes, and paraphernalia of hospital . . . It's different when it's someone you know. I felt – frightened.'

Well, don't go back then, if you find it so upsetting, she thought. He had absently finished the syllabub with no comment as to its quality. Another uncomfortable hiatus in the conversation loomed.

'How is Neil getting on with his motor-racing?' she asked. Neil was a good, safe topic. She had met him and his striking girlfriend, Vanda, at a hospital party in July, only to find that all their discussion seemed to centre on sports cars. It turned out that Neil spent every available Sunday at race-tracks all over the country, not merely watching but competing.

'Well up to a point. He's finding it increasingly difficult to fit in the time to practise and enter the races for this year's Championship. Surgery's more than a full-time job.'

'So is medicine. Some weekends I don't get to see you at all. I know how Vanda must feel.'

'Oh, Vanda's a tough nut. She can cope. She may be a surgical "widow", but she's very involved with the racing.'

'Where did he find her?' Audrey wrinkled her nose in distaste. 'I mean, she's not quite his *class*.'

'No, but she's the right image for the track. They met there, so I'm told. Brands Hatch. Vanda was doing a modelling assignment among the cars and mechanics, and she was asked to present the prizes. Neil won the Porsche race that afternoon.'

'I suppose she pretends to be interested just so she can get her hooks into him. Do you think she's after his money?'

David laughed. 'Sorry to spoil your elaborate theories, my sweet, but Vanda probably has more lucre stashed away than Neil! She's a very well-paid model. I'm not surprised . . . great body, long blonde hair –'

'Dyed,' snapped Audrey. 'And her voice sounds like a corncrake.'

20

'Not true. I'd call it seductively husky.'

'You would. Coffee?'

'I'll get it. It's my turn to do a bit of work.'

She trotted into the kitchen just behind him, and sat on a stool.

'What car has Neil got now?'

'The same. An old silver Porsche 911. He's devoted to it – spends hours checking it over with Arthur, that mechanic friend of his.'

'Won't he have to give up racing eventually?'

'Either that, or his surgical career. They're incompatible. It's funny – Neil's one of the most single-minded people I've ever known, yet on this issue he can't seem to choose. He wants to have his cake and eat it.'

'That's clear enough,' said Audrey. 'He'd like to hang on to both. Why shouldn't he?'

'He just can't. They'll both suffer. Apart from the time aspect, think of the financial side. Imagine maintaining a Porsche to racing standard – the price of a clutch, tyres, brake pads, steering brackets, or even something mundane like the oil filter! It all adds up. And you don't know the whole story. He was talking to me about Formula Ford recently. Formula Ford! That's a bottomless pit as far as money's concerned. Unless he can get sponsorship.'

'If he sticks with surgery, he'll never marry Vanda,' mused Audrey, cheering up slightly at the prospect of another girl having difficulties with her man.

They returned to the sitting-room with their cups of coffee, and David moved over to his small black and white television set.

'Is there a film?' Audrey asked eagerly.

'No. Snooker.'

'Oh, David, do you have to? Tonight?'

'It's not compulsory, but I thought it might be interesting. What else do you propose we do?'

The Piano Concerto in F was reaching the end of its *Allegro agitato*, and sounded boisterous, American, nothing like the atmosphere Audrey had hoped to create. His obtuseness was a pose. He knew perfectly well what she wanted, but was making her fight for every inch of it. Sometimes he allowed her to stay the night – a very rare treat. The humiliation and effort involved in bringing the situation about were hers alone. Other times, it was to no avail, because of work, or some flimsier reason. She balanced constantly on a narrow bar of uncertainty.

21

'I thought we might listen to more music,' she said, approaching the matter with caution.

'All right. What do you fancy?'

'Let me have a look.' She crouched in front of the nearest record case, opened it and began to read the titles. Her knowledge was strictly limited; many were pieces she had never heard of. She had a vague idea that Mendelssohn might suit her purpose, but could find nothing bearing his name. Reluctant to keep David waiting, she selected one at random and pulled it out of the case. Too late, she saw the writing across the back: 'To darling David, from Philippa'.

'Vaughan Williams, eh? Good choice.' His voice from behind her sounded quite normal. Audrey placed the record, 'Serenade to Music', on the turntable with a feeling of grievance seasoned with fatalism, then switched off a light and sat on the lambskin rug in front of the hard chair he occupied, leaning back close against his knees; unfortunately, the room did not boast any kind of settee.

The orchestra and voices were wistfully harmonic, evoking ethereal images of the night – moonlight and the soft rustlings of nature. It should have been perfect for Audrey's aspirations, but props alone could not save the play when the male lead refused to learn his lines. David's hand on her shoulder was light, casual . . . paternal. As Audrey sat with her coffee cup, hunched and miserable, she knew that only tolerance was holding him there.

She twisted round to look up at him.

'David?' she whispered, as if others were listening to the music.

'Yes?' he whispered back, not unkindly.

'I brought a few things with me – a bag. May I stay tonight?' There. She had asked him point-blank. There was no alternative.

He ran his finger along her powdered cheek. 'Sorry, Audrey. It's only Monday, and we're on "take" tomorrow. I think we both need some shut-eye.'

She turned her head away to hide her bitter disappointment. What was wrong with him? Why did she have to make all the running? Any other man would be delighted at such an offer – surely!

'We'll go out on Saturday, if you like,' he said with an air of propitiation. 'The new Italian place on Friar Lane. What do you think?'

22

'That would be very nice,' she answered dully. She would go, of course. Pride was an expensive commodity when pitted against indifference. As for now, there was only one tactic left to her.

'I must wash up,' she announced, scrambling to her feet.

'Nonsense. I'm not such a male chauvinist pig that I'd expect you to do the dishes after cooking all that lovely food.' He smiled at her. 'We can't have you missing your last bus, can we?'

Oh, he was hateful! Her lower lip pouted, and her damp pink hands clenched into fists. She felt like stamping her foot.

'Don't worry,' he said cheerfully. 'I was only joking. Get your coat – I'll run you home.'

'But the dishes . . .'

'I shall hand over your bowls and glasses on Saturday, sparkling clean. You won't need them any sooner, will you?'

She hesitated. 'No.'

'Good girl. Got everything? Right, let's be off.'

With her overnight bag lying forlornly on the back seat of his XR3i, Audrey tried to cut her losses and at least enjoy the drive. He handled the car very competently. The seats were comfortable, the engine note pleasingly quiet but suggestive of power. What a pity none of her friends was likely to be in the vicinity tonight!

He pulled up outside the terraced house she shared with two other girls, and looked across at her.

'Thanks for the meal, Audrey. Enjoy your week, and take care.'

'You, too.' She tilted her face determinedly in his direction and received a more satisfactory kiss than she had expected. A gentleman, she thought. Doing his duty.

'Good-night.'

'This is getting beyond a joke.' Neil Thornton's face showed an unusual irritation as he cupped his hand over the telephone receiver and peered up the short corridor leading to the outer doors of the theatre complex.

'Bradshaw not here?' Mr Crowland, resplendent in the regulation green outfit and boots, halted his stride by the anaesthetics room. Around them flowed the ordered bustle of porters and nurses passing by with trolleys, notes and X-rays.

'Perhaps we've made too many allowances for the chap,' he continued when Neil shook his head. 'He may have his problems, but it seems we're not helping him by being too forbearing. Ah well – Jones will have to come up with something.'

23

He stalked into Theatre One, and Neil chafed at the delay to the start of his list. If they didn't hurry, one of his more interesting cases might be switched to Mr Crowland. They couldn't overrun lunch; the theatres were booked for urology and paediatric bone marrows.

His ruminations were interrupted by the arrival of a posse of anaesthetists, fronted by the spare figure of Hugh Jones.

'Good morning,' Neil replied crisply to their greeting. 'Is there any news of Gilbert?'

The consultant gave a long-suffering sigh. 'No, nothing. You can have Dr Singh until lunchtime. I don't know who we can spare for the other team this afternoon. I wonder what can have happened? ... Dr Gale?' He turned to a young man with a boyishly unlined face and pristine white coat, who hovered at his elbow with an air of readiness. 'I think it's time someone checked on Dr Bradshaw. He may be ill again, and his phone could be out of order. Do you know his home number, or where he lives?'

'No, sir, but I can find out.'

'Good. I'd be obliged if you would do so, and give him a call. If there's no answer, go round to his house. Just express our concern, and ask when he thinks he'll be able to return to work. See if he needs anything. That's all.'

Milton Gale pedalled his bicycle eastward along the busy main road, whistling snatches of sea-shanties he had subconsciously imbibed from Mr Crowland. He felt ambivalent about this particular errand. On the one hand, he was missing useful anaesthetics instruction from Dr Jones who, although he had a dry, unengaging manner, was locally the best in his field. On the other hand, it was a lovely bright morning and he was enjoying the bonus of exercise in the open air.

Being a 'supernumerary' senior house officer – an offensive title if ever there was one – he was quite expendable for missions like these. In theatre, all his work had to be supervised until he reached the appropriate level of experience. Then, it would be chocks away for solo flight!

'"*Blow her away*,"' he sang. '"*Say farewell . . . long way to go . . .*"' What was the next part? '"*We're off to Samoa, by way of Genoa . . .*"' That was a bit tame. He began to alter the words. '*I'm off to Samoa, to get me a go-er, and I'm gonna throw her –*' An elderly lady looked at him askance from the pavement; feeling foolish, he pursed his lips and resumed whistling.

By the time he reached the borders of open countryside, the traffic had thinned considerably. Gil lived in an attractive location, he decided. And not really so far from the hospital – maybe twenty minutes by car. Left here, that girl from admin had said. Then left again along a narrow road . . .

Cows placidly chewed their cud in a field on his right. Susceptible to association, Milton dug into his pocket, found a sticky toffee of uncertain age, one-handedly removed its wrapping and thrust it into his mouth. Mmm. Life was good.

He speculated on Gil's unexplained absence from work. Since his own anaesthetics career spanned a mere handful of weeks, he realized that he was not in the best position to judge his senior registrar. Nevertheless, to him Gil had seemed reliable, pleasant and friendly, even if his demeanour was somewhat shy and self-effacing; in a hospital with its fair share of extroverts, a little reticence could be refreshing. He was thoughtful, too. Considerate. So either something was wrong with his telephone or he did need help.

One of the many rumours simmering blithely at the District hinted that Gil was very rich. Outwardly there was little to show for it. His green Maestro was modest in comparison with the more dashing conveyances owned by many of his colleagues. He favoured worn tweed jackets or a grey-green anorak which was splitting at the seams. Perhaps the money embarrassed him. It was said that he had inherited a sizeable chunk of wealth when his parents were killed three years before. (Nasty accident – something about a falling tree.) There was no one else to share it; he had been their only son.

Milton was looking forward to seeing the house where Gil had spent all his life. Nearly forty years with one's parents! And now they were dead. What did he do with his time? As an anaesthetics SR he had more leisure than ever he could have had on the surgical side. He wasn't one of the bright, gregarious crowd of junior doctors and middle-grade nurses who frequented the local pubs in droves. His pursuits were quieter, less overt. He was supposed to be an expert with tropical fish.

A break suddenly appeared in the wall to his left and Milton slowed his pedalling. Peeling gilt-painted hinge brackets protruded on each side of the gap, but there were no gates. A mossy drive wound in a left-hand curve to vanish behind an enormous dark shrubbery.

Milton halted, perplexed. This was Beechcroft Lane, and he had been told by the wages clerk that the first house he came to would be Number One, Gil's house; she knew the farmer at the other end of the lane. Assuming her information was correct, then this was it. Not at all as he had expected.

The drive was bumpy, so Milton swung his leg over the saddle and wheeled the bicycle round the worst of the ruts. As he reached the corner, the shrubbery came to an end and the rest of the garden straggled before him. He gaped. Where was the blaze of horticultural glory he had been anticipating? Where were the smooth green lawns, the arbours, the patios, the hanging baskets dripping with fuschias? His fertile imagination had been conjuring up these visions during most of the journey, and was now checked by blank disappointment. A heavy aura of neglect hung over this enclosure; it was grey, forlorn, a tangle of undisciplined plants and shrubs choking the life out of each other. Only the weeds, strengthened by the weekend's deluge, stood vigorous, erect.

His gaze panned in a slow arc to the house. It was large, certainly, a 1930s detached residence which must once have looked very fine. It was the type of house which would normally have provoked the mental response: 'stockbroker belt', plus a little envious admiration. But sadly, this one didn't come up to scratch. Several of the roof tiles were missing, a piece of guttering hung down at a crazy angle, and the paintwork was patchy and chipped.

There had been tubs, he noticed, half-barrels of elm made the traditional way by coopers who knew their trade. He looked into the nearest one. No flowers, just a pool of brackish water.

His feet dragged to a standstill, and with an unpleasant jolt he knew he was reluctant to proceed. Gil wasn't here. There was no sense of life about the place unless one counted the rude, triumphant weeds sprouting from every nook and cranny. Yes, there were curtains at the windows, drawn on the ground floor and in one of the bedrooms. Yes, there was a rolled-up newspaper jammed in the letter-box. These were mere trappings. The soul of the house had passed on.

With a profound effort, he walked up to the front door and propped his bicycle against the wall. A faded figure '1' just above eye level confirmed that he had come to the right house. Unease twisted his stomach, and the hand that reached for the newspaper fumbled its simple task, causing the paper to fall on to the doorstep and unroll.

The *Sunday Telegraph*. Today was Tuesday. *Tuesday*. And Gil never went away for the weekend.

Deliberately breaking the spell of his own dark premonitions, Milton seized the handle of a brass knocker shaped like a lion's head and gave a sharp rat-tat. The walls of the house seemed to absorb the flat sound, giving nothing back. He was about to try again when he noticed a bell push. Come on, Milton, he thought. Use your brains. He jabbed at it angrily, trying to suppress a mounting feeling of panic. This was wrong. All wrong.

The cold plastic vibrated under his finger and on the other side of the door the ringing was distant, remote. Irrationally, he carried on pressing, putting off the moment when he would have to make further investigation.

At length, he stopped. He looked hard at the letter-box, then sank to his knees in an inexorable, mechanical fashion. This time his hand made no mistake. He pulled the squeaking flap towards him and peered through the aperture.

Strange how correct instinct could be. Gil was not at home. Only his body lay there, sprawled at the foot of the stairs, the neck twisted at an impossible angle, his clouded eyes contemplating the regions beyond infinity.

3

'In here, sir.' The rookie uniformed constable, ashen-faced and striving to sound normal, ushered Detective Sergeant Brian Jackson past the shattered remains of the front door. 'It's – not very nice.'

'Corpses do have this tendency,' commented Jackson acidly. He was not happy either. Despite his training, a streak of fastidiousness in his otherwise rather yobbish nature led him to avoid, wherever possible, close encounters with death in its myriad forms. His stolid, imperturbable colleague William Bird could be relied on to cope, but unfortunately he was at the Crown Court with their immediate superior, Detective Inspector Montgomery. They might be hours yet; in the meantime, Jackson was in charge.

He frowned. There was an empathy between Montgomery and Bird which left him feeling permanently peripheral. It would be convenient to blame it on social links – William Bird, now a widower, had been a close friend of Montgomery's family for several years – but that would be inaccurate. Never once had the big man been heard to address Montgomery as 'Richard'; It was always 'sir', be it work or play. Yet Will was no crawling sycophant. He had an immense dignity for a sergeant who seemed to hold no ambitions for any other post. He and Montgomery formed an efficient team; often a telepathy resembling that of an old married couple was evident, a wordless knowledge which left Jackson excluded. Despite this, it was impossible to dislike William Bird.

That left Montgomery. A lean-faced man with cold blue eyes and a well-modulated voice, he had seen right through Jackson within a week of his joining the Nottinghamshire CID. Without ever referring to them directly, he had made it clear that he knew all about Jackson's laziness, his fiddled overtime claims, his liberal interpretations of the law, and his habit of blaming others for his own shortcomings. Such perspicacity had been painful to its object. All Jackson's vague discontents had immediately found a focus – Montgomery. One day it would be his turn to squirm . . .

Ignoring the body, he looked at the splintered wood surrounding two door locks and turned to the unlucky constable.

'This door's *destroyed*. Was that really necessary?'

'Sir – we had to get in. There might have been something we could do for him.'

'Oh, sure.' Jackson nodded sarcastically in the direction of the twisted form at the bottom of the stairs.

'We smashed that small window first.' The young man's voice was almost a whisper. 'But the door was deadlocked. Both locks engaged, in fact – the mortice as well. It wouldn't have been any use getting in at the back unless we knew where the keys were. Actually – ' he cleared his throat, ' – they were here after all.'

Following the line of his pointing finger, Jackson could just discern the gleam of metal next to the left-hand trouser-pocket of the body.

'Interesting,' he muttered, kneeling down as far away as he

reasonably could. Nine different keys were attached to a central ring; four of them undoubtedly belonged to a car. 'Did you find any others?'

'No. That is, no more were immediately obvious.'

'So you haven't been plastering this place with your sticky little fingers?'

'No, sir.' The constable sounded injured. 'We're waiting for the scenes-of-crime officers. Constable Rennie is in the kitchen with Dr Gale, who found the body.'

'Rennie!' Jackson brightened. Tim Rennie was a drinking pal of his, a rough-edged man who looked on life in the same way as he did.

'Stay here,' he ordered and walked along the hall towards the back of the house.

The kitchen was neat, tidy and somewhat old-fashioned. A fair-haired man in his twenties, who already sported a discernible beer-gut, leaned casually against the sink. In the far corner a boyish form crouched on a hard wooden chair, staring straight ahead, his eyes dark pools in a chalk-white, rigid face. He gave a small moan as Jackson entered, and his teeth chattered.

'Hi, Brian.' Rennie swaggered over to meet him. 'I thought they were sending a detective.'

Jackson gave him a playful punch, then jerked his head enquiringly at the seated figure.

'Dr Gale,' supplied Rennie. 'A gasman from the District Hospital. He's the poor bugger who found the body.'

His idea of *sotto voce* rivalled Big Ben; the young man swivelled his eyes in their direction.

'I have to go. I have to tell someone . . . When can I go?'

'As soon as Sergeant Jackson here has asked you a few questions.'

'But I told you everything. His name is Gil – Gilbert Bradshaw. He didn't turn up for work yesterday. Or this morning. We rang; there was no reply. The surgeons were getting impatient . . . I was sent . . . '

'Are you a friend of his?' Jackson stood with folded arms.

'Not really. Not a close friend. I've only been doing anaesthetics for seven weeks.'

'Is this his house?'

'Yes.'

'Does anyone else live here?'

'I don't think so. It was his parents' home, but they're dead now.'

'Had you been here before?'

'No.'

'What time did you arrive this morning?'

'About quarter to ten. The lists start at eight-thirty, but it took me a while to get hold of his address. I came by bike . . . I didn't hurry; we just thought he was ill.'

'What happened when you got here?'

The young man shrugged. 'I did the usual things. Knocked, rang . . . but something felt wrong. I don't know what, exactly. Perhaps it was too quiet. There was a Sunday paper in the letter-box. Sorry, I removed that before I rang. Because afterwards, I peered through . . . '

'Did you go round the back of the house at all?'

'No, there didn't seem to be any point. The front curtains were all drawn, so I assumed they would be at the back.'

'They were,' chipped in Rennie, 'but only on the ground floor.'

'What did you do then?'

'I left the bike and ran up the road to Number Three. It was quite a long way, because there's a field in between. I asked the woman there if I could use her phone. I told her there'd been an accident. It was all I could do to stop her coming back with me. PC Rennie was here very quickly, with the other constable.'

'The doors were locked, front and back,' said Rennie. 'So were all the windows. We didn't check the garage, but it's separate from the house. There seemed nothing for it but to break in.'

Rennie would not have weighed up the matter for long, thought Jackson. Direct action held its own appeal, a feeling of power, a satisfaction, well-remembered from his own days in uniform.

He turned his attention back to the young doctor.

'When did you last see Dr Bradshaw?'

'On Friday. Only briefly. I was in another theatre.'

'Did he seem anxious or depressed?'

'I really can't say. We passed in the changing room, no more.'

'What about earlier in the week? Was there anything unusual?'

'No. I saw him on and off. Tuesday – and Wednesday. He seemed all right.'

'What's your theory, then?'

The question was sudden and brutal. The juvenescent face,

30

which had been slowly regaining colour, registered a strong echo of its former blank horror.

'Theory?' His voice was thick. 'I – I don't know. I mean, he's fallen down the stairs – hasn't he?'

'Looks that way. But was it an accident?'

'I don't know,' repeated the doctor. 'I only found him.' He glanced around uneasily. 'I'd like to get out of here, if you don't mind. I must go back to the hospital. I appreciate you'll be wanting a statement . . . I'm perfectly willing. But – I want to go now.'

'Fair enough. You came by bike, did you say?'

'Yes. It's outside.'

'Well, I suggest you chain it up and leave it here. Constable Shaw will drive you back; you're not fit. Pick it up later – one of your friends can give you a lift.'

Surprised, his witness nodded.

As soon as he heard the engine note of the car, Jackson turned to Rennie.

'Any booze in here?'

'Nothing that you'd fancy.' Rennie walked across to a low cupboard, leaned over and opened it with a gloved hand. It contained three dark upright bottles and a partially filled wine rack.

'Sherry . . . port.' He twisted his neck to read the horizontal labels of the other bottles, unconsciously emulating the occupant of the silent hallway. 'Barsac . . . Sauternes. What lousy taste.' He straightened up again.

'Immature palate,' agreed Jackson. 'Did you put these two mugs on the draining-board?'

'No, they were here when we arrived. One of them has dregs of tea in, the other's clean.'

'No glasses around?'

'No. No more bottles, either.'

'Hmm. Bang goes my theory of intoxication. I suppose drugs are still a possibility.'

Rennie didn't answer directly. 'Look over the house,' he proposed, 'then see what you think.'

The ground floor was laid out along standard lines, with a central hall giving access to the rooms and staircase. At the rear, the kitchen and utility room were unremarkable, their few, simple items of equipment indicating a user with minimal needs. Two doors opened from the right of the hall. The dining-room, immediately adjacent to the kitchen, was a gloomy mezzotint, with furniture gleaming sullenly from velvet shadows. In the light from the hall Jackson could just make out a huge polished oak table and chairs, with a matching sideboard, all standing on a threadbare Turkey red carpet. Mustiness hung in the air, as if the last dinner served here had been years before.

He shook his head and opened the next door, careful not to disturb any fingerprints which might be on the handle. In this room the curtains of the side window were only partially closed, and a thin beam of sunlight slanted in through the gap. All four walls were stripped of paper. Bare floorboards drew the eye down their parallel lines to a cluster of furniture at the far end, where each individual shape was blurred by a ghostly shrouding of dust-sheets.

'Morning-room, I suppose,' muttered Jackson.

Across the hall, inches from the inert form lying there, was the door into the lounge. Avoiding the body, they went inside. This room also gave an impression of ghostliness, but for an entirely different reason. Glass fish-tanks occupied the whole of one wall, bathing the nearest portion of the ceiling with a lurid green glow. Faintly in the background, a sinister low-key bubbling sound could be heard.

Jackson was astounded. 'He liked his fish!' he exclaimed.

'Yes,' grinned Rennie. 'They're mighty hungry, too. Just try sticking your finger in.'

'No thanks! That one looks like a piranha.' He drew closer to the wall of glass, fascinated. Each tank was a miniature theatre with its own backcloth, elaborate set and troupe of players: here a cave, mysterious behind gently waving plant fronds, a wrecked galleon beside it, perfect in every tiny detail; there a windmill by a watery dyke, bulbfields stretching into the distance under a fresh spring sky.

The fish were not peaceful, however. While a small number performed their sinuous minuets at the back of the tank, the rest crowded forward, finning agitatedly, mouths gaping in appeal.

Jackson suddenly felt uncomfortable under the concentrated gaze of hundreds of unwinking eyes. Turning away abruptly, he seized a cord dangling by the nearest pair of curtains and gave it a firm, sustained pull. The curtains parted, light flooded in; the fish-tanks dulled and receded.

Slowly exhaling, he assessed the rest of his surroundings while disturbing nothing. As in the dining-room, there was an air of shabby gentility and under-use, but at least the presence of the fish ensured there had been some degree of occupancy, however sporadic. Where *had* Bradshaw spent his time when he was at home?

A small table in the corner attracted his attention. On the centre of its lace cloth stood a shrimp plant, drooping slightly. Two photographs flanked the plant, both with heavy gilt frames. One showed a wedding couple smiling shyly at the camera, wearing 1940s-style clothes; the man's features were pleasant but irresolute, the woman's somewhat sharper. In the other frame the same couple, twenty-odd years on, were standing on a lawn with a young graduate, their smile this time the complacent pride of parents the world over.

It was Gilbert, of course. Even in death the resemblance to his father was clear enough. But here, at one of his moments of greatest achievement, he didn't look particularly happy. Anxiety lurked behind the brown eyes, and worry-lines already crossed the young forehead. The expression on his face, with its weak chin and thinning hair, seemed to be a compound of eagerness to please and crushing knowledge of inadequacy.

And now it didn't matter any more. Whatever struggles he had undergone were lost in the vast indifference of time; like his parents, he was dead.

Detective Inspector Richard Montgomery completed his close scrutiny of the body and rose smoothly to his feet.

'You're sure about that, Dr Greaves?' he asked the elderly man perched on the second stair. 'Friday night or early Saturday morning?'

'As sure as I can be. Looking at the marbling of the veins, and that anterior abdominal wall . . . he's been here a good three days, possibly four. I can't find any other injury, apart from his broken neck. No evidence of a ligature, for instance. Will Frobisher be doing the PM?'

'I hope so, if he's available. It's a suspicious death. There may be drink or drugs involved . . . Thank you. We'll be in touch.'

He stood, thoughtful, as the doctor walked rather arthritically out past the splintered front door. This case was not all it seemed. Superficial analysis would place the three options accident, murder and suicide in that order, with 'accident' covering a wide variety of sins. But on Friday night a girl, another doctor from the same hospital, had been almost killed less than a quarter of a mile from this very house. That had been someone else's case; he knew only the sketchiest of details. Nevertheless, it would be quite incredible if the two incidents were not connected in some way.

Giving orders for the body to be removed (which would enable Jackson to emerge from the wainscot) he slowly climbed the stairs. A fingerprint expert was still beavering away below, but the staircase and upper floor had now been examined.

He entered a room and nodded at William Bird, his sergeant.

'Anything out of the ordinary, Will?'

Arguably, the room was. Once a bedroom, it had been converted into a study-cum-den, boasting a desk, two hard and two comfortable chairs, and numerous bookshelves bracketed to three of the walls. The fourth wall had been partially covered by strips of wood veneer, hiding discoloured, uneven plasterwork. On a table abutting the wall, a fish-tank gurgled softly, its tranquil green sporadically emitting flashes of silver.

'No, Sir.' Sergeant Bird moved away from the bookshelf and indicated the aquarium. 'I've fed the fish. Poor little devils, they were starving.' He sucked in his rounded, rosy cheeks. 'The light was on, same as the tanks downstairs. That might help us with the time of death.'

'Unless he leaves them on all the time for the benefit of the fish.'

'No – you'd get an overgrowth of algae. Nobody with his knowledge of fish would do that; the tanks are in beautiful condition.'

'True, Will.' Montgomery sat on the nearest hard chair, stretched out his long legs and steepled his fingers. 'Dr Greaves has finished now. He reckons the death occurred late on Friday or early on Saturday. Let me go over the current position with you . . . ' He gave a mirthless smile. 'We have a man wearing his ordinary daytime clothes, lying dead at the bottom of his stairs, eight feet from his doubly locked front door. The back door is both locked and bolted. There is no sign of a forced entry through any of the windows, which also have locks, albeit old ones.

34

His keys are on the floor by his left trouser pocket. There are spares in the back of the kitchen drawer. His watch, regrettably, hasn't stopped. The credit cards and money found on his person appear to be untouched. He is a professional man of forty, yet no one finds his body for nearly four days. All a tragic accident, you might think, but for one thing.'

'That hit-and-run.'

'Yes!' Montgomery's blue eyes snapped. 'There's a link. There has to be. We must find out about that incident. Everything there is to know – what the girl remembers, who may have witnessed something, whether she was associated with Bradshaw in any way . . . Who found her after the accident?'

'A jogger from Number Five up the road, so I'm told. I don't know many details, but Brian's going to check it out later.'

'Good. I think our strategy has to be the collection of all relevant background information relating to Gilbert Bradshaw and the girl, Philippa Rowe. Character, friends, lifestyle, the lot. If there isn't much on the hit-and-run, we'll appeal on local radio and in the newspapers. Television even.'

'It rained heavily last Friday night,' said Sergeant Bird. 'There'll be no tyre tracks to see.'

'I know. And I suspect we'll be whistling for witnesses. This is a very lonely road. But two incidents, same time, same place – !'

For half an hour they leafed through the papers and box files in Gilbert Bradshaw's study. He had been a tidy, methodical man, a fact which made his shabby environment jar all the more on the searchers. Alongside his medical books were tomes on stamp collecting and the care of tropical fish, with scores of copies of the *National Geographic* magazine.

His bedroom was pale blue and sparsely furnished. The only features of interest were a cased violin standing at the bottom of the wardrobe, and a locked metal document file. The key was not to hand.

'There might be a will in here,' said Sergeant Bird, tapping the file with his stubby finger.

'Mm,' agreed Montgomery. He stood up from the desk. 'Where's Brian now?'

'Outside getting a breath of air.'

'Let's go and join him. I think it's time we took a look at Bradshaw's car. Presumably it's in the garage.'

Jackson was pacing the cracked patio outside the lounge window; he started guiltily as they approached.

'Tell me again about Milton Gale,' Montgomery said to him. 'Was there anything suspicious in his behaviour? The person who raises the alarm often proves to be the guilty one.'

Jackson shook his head vigorously. 'Not this fellow. He was in shock – white, trembling. I thought he was going to be sick at one point. He said the hospital had sent him. They could have sent anybody.'

'Well, we'll make sure of that. Has anyone looked in the garage yet?'

'I haven't.'

'Right, I've got the spare set of keys here. Let's see that his car is where it should be.'

They stood in front of the garage door, which was of up-and-over design and distinctly weathered. Grasping the keys in his left hand, Montgomery gave the top portion an experimental push; to his surprise, it reluctantly began to move.

'The only thing that wasn't locked,' Jackson observed. They flexed their knees and pulled at the lower rim of the door. Gathering momentum, it slowly swung up to the horizontal, enabling them to see inside.

Long strips of wood veneer were stacked against the left-hand wall. On the right were crude shelves bearing an assortment of paint pots. But the focus of their attention was the car itself. A four-year-old green Maestro, it was an average type of car, as mild and unassuming as its owner had been. But the offside headlight was smashed, an empty socket of crumpled chrome, while the bumper bar below was distorted by a large ugly dent.

Philippa regarded her two visitors with affection. Coral Chapman and Maureen O'Donnell had been not only neighbours but good friends during her time with David. Since she had returned to a hospital flat there had been less social contact between them, but they often met in the course of their work, in corridors or the canteen, and exchanged greetings or news.

Both were nurses of a very modest height, but there all points of resemblance ended. Coral's aureole of flame-red hair epitomized her whole personality. She was talkative, lively, fun-loving, a prominent figure at many of the hospital parties and outings. Vibrant colours were her trade-mark, and if they shocked, all the better.

Maureen, by contrast, was unobtrusive, slender and mousy with a soft Irish brogue. Nursing was a true vocation for her; no job was too demeaning, no patient's behaviour too difficult. She loved the continuity of care afforded by ward work, and for this reason had returned to Clifton Ward after a successful year in theatre, despite the blandishments of Vernon Crowland. She was a good listener – which was rare among her friends – and kept her own counsel. She was devoted to Coral.

'We knew you'd be swamped with flowers,' Coral was saying cheerfully. 'And we thought you might not be ready yet to read a book or do a jigsaw. You can't eat chocolates or fruit – so here's something else.' She handed over a dainty package wrapped in turquoise paper printed with squirrels.

'Thank you,' said Philippa, holding it awkwardly in her left hand. 'I don't suppose you'd help me with the wrappings, would you? It looks very pretty – seems a shame to open it.'

Maureen, now seated, took the parcel and removed the outer layer of paper. Inside was a thin membrane of tissue paper, which she loosened. 'Try now,' she said.

Philippa's probing fingers extricated a small carved onyx horse. 'Oh, he's lovely!' she cried. 'He can have a place of honour on the locker.'

'It might be a she,' teased Coral.

'We'd better not go into that. Thank you, both of you.'

Lying half propped-up on pillows, Philippa still felt very weak. Although she had been fully conscious for less than thirty-six hours, she had expected to recover much more rapidly. The nausea, headache and mental confusion frustrated her, although she strove to appear bright and agreeable when friends came. She was grateful for the good sense of Anne Markham, who restricted the visits to a few minutes each. Even then, they were exhausting.

'How are things in the flat?' she asked.

Coral pulled a comical face. 'Oh, the plumbing's gone funny, the grill plate has buckled and the rent's about to go up. All good stuff. So, we said, "blow it!" and went and bought some new curtains.'

'Typical,' laughed Philippa. 'Can you afford them?'

37

'Just about. Maureen manages to restrain some of my wilder excesses, or we'd be constantly in hock.'

Maureen blushed. 'How do you feel, Pippa?' she asked, her level voice not quite deflecting from the concern in her face.

'Getting better bit by bit. It's weird being on this side of the blanket, so to speak.'

'We'll bully Anne and make sure she looks after you properly,' announced Coral, then looked up as Sister Markham herself appeared. 'We're just talking about you.'

'Good things, I hope,' smiled Anne. 'Sorry to interrupt, but there's an Inspector Montgomery here who'd like to see Philippa.'

'It's all right. We weren't going to outstay our welcome.' The two girls stood up simultaneously.

'Take care, Pippa. Let us know if there's anything you need.' Coral touched her hand briefly while Maureen stood the little horse on the bedside locker.

'Good-bye. We'll be back tomorrow.'

Philippa acknowledged their valediction with a limited smile, the best her muscles could fashion. Ordinary conversation was such an effort; it would be so much easier to slip into that ever-ready twilight state of floating images, where all things lacked substance and concentration was unnecessary.

Who was this inspector anyway? What did he want? She had told WPC Winger that she knew nothing about the accident. As the door opened, she wearily hoped he wouldn't stay long.

'This is Inspector Montgomery,' said Anne calmly, and vanished again.

A man in a smart grey raincoat stepped into the room. He had dark hair greying at the temples, and steely blue eyes. His lips were narrow, the chin firm and the cheekbones well-shaped. Philippa estimated his age to be around forty. Height – five feet ten or eleven inches. Her mind registered surprise. Here was not the beefy physiognomy she had expected ... In fact, she liked what she saw, barring the rather pale hue of his skin.

'Dr Rowe – I'm sorry to disturb you like this. May I sit down?' He had an educated voice, with the barest hint of a Nottingham accent.

'Yes.' She indicated one of the chairs with her free hand, and tried to improve her position in the bed.

'I know WPC Winger has been in to see you a couple of times

about the accident. Have you been able to recall anything since you last spoke?'

'No. I'm sorry. I've really tried hard, but it's all a complete blank.'

'What is the last thing you remember doing?'

'I'm not sure. I know that must sound silly, but it's the truth. I don't seem to be able to concentrate for any length of time . . . '

'Has anyone attempted to jog your memory?'

'Oh yes. Barnaby Fletcher – he's the neurology SHO; he's in and out all the time asking me things. Some people from my own department came – that's haematology. They reminded me that I'd been teaching Michael Wylie to inject his own factor eight. He's a haemophiliac, and it saves him coming to hospital every time he has a bleed. It rang a bell . . . I could vaguely remember doing it. But that was Thursday lunch-time. Everything else has just – *gone!*'

Her voice rose slightly and he leaned forward as if to calm her down.

'Don't worry, that's quite natural in the circumstances. It'll come back. There's no rush.'

She wasn't sure whether to believe him. Why was an inspector here if he didn't want information? And why – her head began aching more fiercely – was he here at all for a common or garden hit-and-run?

'Is there something special you need to know?' she asked him.

He gave her an unfathomable look. 'Yes and no. I've something to tell you, something not very nice. But I'm also hoping you'll be able to answer one or two questions afterwards which will help us clear up the problem.'

'What – is it?'

She felt she didn't want to hear, but he hadn't come for chit-chat.

'Gilbert Bradshaw, the anaesthetist. Do you know him?'

'Yes.'

His blue eyes were watchful. 'I'm afraid he was found dead at his home this morning.'

Disbelief made her numb. 'Dead? I – I don't understand. How – what happened? Did he have a heart attack?'

'No. It seems he fell downstairs. I'm sorry to burden you with this when you're not well yourself, but his death raises some important questions.'

'I – go on.'

'Well, you've probably been told that your accident occurred within four hundred yards of his house.' He raised an eyebrow.

'Yes.'

'And that it took place on Friday night or early Saturday morning?'

'Yes . . . '

'That is when Dr Bradshaw met with his death.'

'Oh.' She could think of nothing to say. She felt like a defective computer, accepting input but unable to process.

'Inspector . . . ' Philippa moved restlessly. 'I understand what you've said, but I can't explain it. Not just now. There's no mental picture at all . . . I'd never been to Gil's house before; at least, I thought not. I didn't even know him very well.'

'Had you ever disagreed with him, or incurred his anger?'

'No. We were – just colleagues.'

'He was never your boyfriend?'

'No.'

'Do you have a car?'

'Yes. A Fiesta.'

'Where is it now?'

'I asked Barnaby to check. It's where I usually park it – outside the Doctors' Residence.'

'Have you ever had a lift from Gilbert Bradshaw?'

'No.'

'Do you know what car he drove?'

'Er . . . no. I've never really noticed. There are several places to park.'

'How do you think you got to Sylvia Vale?'

'I don't know. Truly.' All the discomforts of her broken bones and surgical manipulations were pressing in on her, vice-like. She couldn't take any more. 'Please, Inspector – may we talk tomorrow? I might have remembered something by then. I am trying, but – it's so difficult.'

'Yes, of course. I hope you'll be feeling better.'

He paused by the door. 'One more thing. We'd like to take your fingerprints as soon as possible, just for elimination. It won't be a long procedure.'

'Whatever you need to do.' Her eyelids drooped, and she barely heard the door close.

While Montgomery was interviewing Philippa, Coral and Maureen huddled in anxious discussion with Anne Markham in the tiny ward office.

'She looks awful,' stated Coral frankly.

'I know,' said Anne. 'Her kidneys are failing. She's hardly passing any fluid. Neil's very worried.'

The two small nurses stared at each other in dismay.

4

'Let me ask you something, Barnaby.'

It was Wednesday morning, and Philippa still felt sick and drained, but an issue had to be cleared up.

'Yes?' He blinked at her owlishly from the bottom of the bed.

'Don't take this amiss, whatever you do. I appreciate all the attention you're giving me.'

'This is beginning to sound alarming.'

'No, just a genuine question . . . My head injuries are relatively minor compared with the other things. Strictly, they're neuro-surgical anyway, but since there's no case for moving me to neurosurgery's regional centre, I come under the auspices of neurology here – Dr Gosling and yourself.'

'That's right. Is that the problem?'

'No. I told you, I'm very grateful for your care. Since I woke up, you've come to see me approximately nine times – in two days!'

'Really?'

'You know you have. And you must have lots of other patients. Once or twice you've done physical tests, but *every* time you've asked me what I remember. Then you've grilled me about numbers, dates, addresses and who the Prime Minister is.'

'I'm only being thorough, Pippa.' He held his fingers stiffly like a garden fork, and ran them through his thick hair. The end result resembled a great crested grebe.

'Oh, yes, I don't dispute that. But why the overkill? I can't help feeling there's a reason you haven't got round to divulging. And I'd like to hear it.'

'You're quite wrong, Pippa.'

'And you're a hopeless liar. Please tell me, then I can try to co-operate.'

41

'Well . . . ' He looked sheepish. 'I've been gathering data for a paper on concussion, with specific reference to retrograde amnesia.'

'Good for you, Barny. How many cases do you have so far?'

'One or two.'

'Which?'

'Er, one . . . you.'

As he fussed around with his notes, Philippa considered Barnaby's career to date. He had always been the clumsy one of the year at medical school, and there had been a collective sigh of relief when he had relinquished his earliest aspirations towards a neurosurgical consultancy in favour of neurology. Even so, he was formidable when let loose with a tendon hammer. Blessed with neither charisma nor good looks, he had astonished everyone two years before by carrying off the District Hospital's pride – Sister Hampshire from Intensive Care. Now there was a cherubic infant to complete his domestic bliss.

'It isn't very easy, you know,' he grumbled somewhere near her right knee, ' – eliciting tendon reflexes when half your limbs are immobilized. The arm's solid with plaster, and I don't know what to do with this leg . . . '

Philippa wondered whether or not to inform him that the orthopaedic surgeons actively encouraged movement at the knee and ankle, since the bones between were safely plated. An instinct of self-preservation kept her silent; his inaccuracies with the tendon hammer were likely to prove painful.

She smiled. It was ridiculous, attributing sinister motives to Barnaby's other actions. He just didn't have the guile.

When he had gone, Philippa lay back and transferred her thoughts to Gil Bradshaw. The news of his death had been shocking, all the more so because of the possibility of a connection with her accident. Why had she been near his home? He was an acquaintance, a colleague, not even someone from her own department. She had seen him perhaps twice a week, either in theatre, if she happened to be doing bone marrows under anaesthetic, or in the canteen. He hadn't frequented the hospital bar, and had only rarely appeared on communal outings.

Gil had been a solitary man, with a shyness that belied his age. Yet anyone taking the trouble to draw him out, as Philippa had done on occasions, caught rewarding glimpses of a sincere and amicable nature.

So he had fallen down his stairs, poor Gil! How could that be anything to do with her own collision with a car?

Philippa rolled unhappily towards her left side. Hypothesis: – had she, for some reason currently obscure, been a guest in Gil's home and inadvertently caused his fall? Had she then run away in panic, and blundered into the path of a car? Surely not. She would have telephoned for help from the house, and stayed to do whatever she could.

Might he have frightened her in some way, causing her to flee, then fallen because of his own agitation? That was even more absurd. Gil had been gentle and kind: violence would have been totally alien to him.

A third party, then. The mysterious X. But Inspector Montgomery had given no hint of such a person. Unless . . . fingerprints 'for exclusion'? Perhaps. But who? And more important, what would they all have been doing out there? What did she have in common with Gil? Medicine. Nothing else.

Philippa coughed, and caught her breath as pain lanced through her lower chest from the broken ribs. Her physical condition was miserable, but her mental state depressed her more. She was plagued by a lurking fear that her memory might never return. The questions would fester, and never be answered . . .

'Hello, Philippa.'

She started, again painfully, then relaxed with an embarrassed smile.

'Stewart. Sorry, I didn't hear you come in.'

'No, you were too busy coughing. Are you bringing anything up?'

'No.'

He slouched to the foot of the bed and picked up the TPR chart.

'Small temperature spike,' he commented. 'Are you keeping your legs moving?'

'As well as I can.'

'No pain in the left calf?'

'No.'

He took her pulse, then embarked on an examination which was thorough by his lights. His conversation was restrained, but Philippa could appreciate the awkwardness of his position – a houseman looking after a registrar.

43

'Your laparotomy wound looks all right,' he said gruffly, 'and there's no obvious evidence of a DVT although the swelling at the fracture site makes it difficult to assess. But I'm going to order a chest X-ray; there are signs of consolidation at the left base.'

'It hurts to cough,' admitted Philippa. 'I suppose that's because of the ribs.'

'Yes. And the pleura. We'll probably be changing your anti-biotics today.'

He perused her fluid balance chart, and made a few sketchy notes.

'Stewart?'

'Mm?'

'What's my blood urea?'

'Sorry. Can't tell you.'

Won't, you mean, she thought. 'I just wondered if it was still rising, that's all.'

'Everything's fairly stable.'

It was the sort of diplomatic answer she would have given a patient. 'Thank you. I'll carry on with the Hycal.' She indicated a bottle of concentrated glucose solution on the locker top. 'At least they do it in several flavours.'

'Is it staying down?'

'Just about.'

'Any problems, and we'll go back to the dextrose drip. The cannula is staying *in situ* for the antibiotics.'

'You're the boss.' She didn't want to delve too deeply into their treatment strategies. Her interference would not be welcome and, besides, her brain was only able to cope with simple things at this stage. She would try to be a good patient – tolerant, grateful, and not relentlessly inquisitive.

Stewart sought out Neil in the side room of Willoughby Ward and walked with him back to the office.

'How's Philippa?' Neil asked.

'Pyrexial: temperature spike of thirty-nine degrees, now thirty-eight. Clinically there's some consolidation at the left base, so I've ordered a chest X-ray. I can't find anything else to account for it.'

'Well, make sure you treat it seriously. This is one we don't want to screw up. Swabs of everything, sputum culture – if there is any – and blood cultures. Then take an ECG. When you've excluded a pulmonary embolus, consider changing her anti-biotics, but keep the cover broad spectrum.'

'Will do. Are you off to theatre?'

'Yes. Mr Barton's hernia's first on the list.'

Stewart looked longingly at his watch. 'I'll join you – as soon as I can.' He hurried back to Cavendish Ward.

'We've organized a radio appeal, coverage in today's *Recorder*, and posters all round the site.' Sergeant Bird ticked off the points on his blunt fingers then looked expectantly across the desk at Montgomery.

'Good. That road's isolated, but there's a fair chance that some-one heard something without realizing its significance. Pity we lost four days.'

'Enquiries were made,' said Jackson, 'but not very thoroughly. After all, the girl was alive and we didn't know about the other incident. PC Crabtree went to Numbers One, Three and Five, and then to the farmhouse. He couldn't get a reply from Number One – not surprisingly – and didn't feel any urge to peer through the letter-box.'

'Did you see the jogger yourself last night?'

'Yes. Executive type from Number Five. Mr Pettifer. They're a real yoghourt and muesli crowd there. He was out at six-thirty in his tracksuit, and found the girl lying about three hundred yards from Bradshaw's gatepost, on the same side of the road. Appar-ently her clothes were saturated, and the rain had stopped some hours before. He pulled her off the road and sprinted back to his own house to raise the alarm.'

'Then?'

'The ambulance and PC Crabtree arrived almost simul-taneously. Life and limb had to come first, so he was only able to make a few observations. In any case, she'd already been moved by Mr Pettifer. She wore a tweed skirt and a lambswool jumper, which was torn at the front. There were no tyremarks, either on her or on the road, because the rain had washed them all away, but glass was scattered at the spot where she was initially found.'

'Thank you, Brian. So what we're left with is this: Philippa Rowe was knocked down on Friday night. She's single, and works as a registrar in haematology at the District Hospital. She tells me that she barely knew Gilbert Bradshaw, yet that tea-mug with dregs in it on the draining-board was covered with her fingerprints. There were also several inside his Maestro.' He leaned forward, resting both elbows on the desk. 'No one else's were found either in the car or the house.

'Regarding the car – you both saw the dent. It looks recent, but Forensic will hopefully be more precise. They've found some threads caught on the offside jacking point. These will be matched against Philippa Rowe's clothes. Assuming for the moment that was the vehicle involved, what was the chain of events? Did Bradshaw try to kill Dr Rowe? How did he meet with his own death? Is there any evidence at all to indicate the presence of a third party?'

'He was lying in a locked house,' said Sergeant Bird thoughtfully, 'with the keys some distance from the front door. If someone else was present at the time, how did they get out? You can set a deadlock and slam the door behind you, but a mortice is a different kettle of fish: you've got to turn the key when the door's closed. So if you're outside the house, how do you get the keys back inside?'

'Throw them through the letter-box.'

'I'm not sure. It was a deep box, but still a small aperture for that purpose. He was lying eight feet away, and the keys were immediately adjacent to his pocket. It would be difficult to make your throw as accurate as that. I think we should test it.'

'The spares were in a kitchen drawer,' added Jackson, 'And the window locks were all set on the inside. It's my bet he was alone.'

Montgomery nodded his agreement. 'It seems more likely, certainly. We're still waiting for the drugs reports, but there was no trace of alcohol in the body. So – was it an accident, or suicide?'

'An accident would seem like a hefty coincidence,' said Sergeant Bird, 'unless he had hit the girl with his car, thought he had killed her, and was rushing around in a panic.'

'Tripped up, you mean.'

'Yes. Something like that.'

'What about suicide?'

'Crazy method; no guarantee. There must be fifty better ways.'

'Yes. He had a lot of pills in the house – painkillers for long-standing back trouble, so I'm told. That's just one option.' He tapped his fingers on the desk. 'But the practical details are still wrong, aren't they? We have evidence that the girl was in his car and in his house some time recently, probably on that night. She was found nearly four hundred yards from his front door. How come, if she was with him in the house?'

'Perhaps he made a pass at her, and she ran away,' said Jackson.

'Or perhaps she was dumped there,' mused Sergeant Bird.

'Apropos your point, Brian, from what little I've heard of the man it would be totally out of character, although I'll grant you some inadequates do try to assert themselves in devious ways. We need to speak to more of his colleagues to be sure. As to the scene of the accident – wherever it was, he'd hardly leave her just up the road from his own drive. His home remains the nearest one to the spot where she was found. Barring some complicated frame-up, it would seem most likely that she was actually knocked down there, especially if you remember the glass. So which way was the Maestro travelling? To or from the house?'

'Assuming she was in the house that night,' said Sergeant Bird, 'she must have left it and been followed by the car. Maybe they had an argument and she was walking to the nearest phone box. That's on the main road nearly a mile away. Even though she was found on the wrong side of the road, it's so quiet there that the Maestro could easily have crossed over in order to knock her down.'

'Callous and calculated, put that way.' Montgomery was frowning. 'I'd envisaged a more hot-blooded scenario. Let's say she was running, as Brian suggested, from something very unpleasant. Exactly what, it's our job to find out. If she'd been walking, he wouldn't have needed a car to catch her.'

'Unless she'd incapacitated him.'

'Or killed him.' Jackson's eyes gleamed as the idea took root.

'If that's the case, we're chasing our tails,' said Montgomery with a sigh. 'Bradshaw was supposed to have been driving the car. There are no other prints.'

'If she was running for help,' objected Sergeant Bird, 'why didn't she go the *other* way, to the nearest house?'

'Ah. That rather bears out her story, doesn't it? She claims to be unfamiliar with the area. Number Three is across a field and screened by trees; if she ran down Bradshaw's drive, she would have been confronted with the choice of a narrow, lonely road winding deeper into the countryside, or the same road leading eventually to a major road with cars, houses and people. She would have seen that on the way in . . . so she turned right.'

'Do you think her memory will come back?' Jackson chewed carelessly at the end of his pen.

'I hope so. It's our best chance of sorting this out. I'm going to the hospital again shortly, and I shan't be fobbed off. I'll find out what the outlook is for the girl.'

'May I raise a hoary old chestnut?' William Bird bore a passing resemblance to one himself.

'By all means.'

'Well, we're concentrating on the girl, which is perfectly reasonable, but the dead body is Bradshaw's. Supposing someone else was involved, someone clever enough not to leave any traces? Who actually *benefits* from Bradshaw's death?'

'I can give you an answer to that, but it doesn't help us much. The document file you found did contain his last will and testament. It was dated five years ago, and he left everything to his parents. Of course, they're dead now. I had a brief word with Pendle of Pendle, Rathbone and Blair. They've been solicitors to the Bradshaws for forty years, which is convenient. They have a copy of the will, and confirm that it's the latest one. At present, they're advertising for claimants; there are no close relatives to speak of. I'd like one of you to have further words this week, and find out the value of the estate.' He yawned. 'Time for tea, lads.'

Sergeant Bird brightened perceptibly.

5

The girl looked much the same to Montgomery. She was pale and sallow, her face devoid of vitality, which made character assessment difficult. The dark eyes held no sparkle, and strands of black hair straggled into a limp page-boy cut beneath a startlingly white surgical dressing. She didn't seem to be at the point of death, but on the other hand, her air of lassitude was worrying.

'I'll keep this as short as possible,' he promised when they had exchanged greetings and he was seated next to the bed. 'We were talking about Gil Bradshaw yesterday.'

'Yes.'

'I need to know more about him. What was he like? Who were his friends?'

She lifted a hand and ran the wrist across her forehead. 'I'm not the best person to ask. I only saw – his professional side. He was kind and gentle, good with the patients. I think that's because they were at a disadvantage, often semi-sedated – so he didn't feel shy with them, whereas he did with some of his colleagues. It was hard to get him to come out of his shell.'

'And his friends?'

'I – I don't know. There didn't seem to be anyone particular. Barnaby, perhaps. That's Barnaby Fletcher. They sometimes discussed tropical fish. Otherwise – ' she shrugged, ' – I can't say.'

'Fletcher . . . thank you. Who else do you suggest I speak to?'

'The senior surgical staff knew him fairly well. Try Mr Crowland. Gil was on the surgical ladder for several years, but eventually had to give it up because of his own ill health. You need a lot of stamina to survive long hours of standing. He changed to anaesthetics; they may be able to tell you something helpful. The senior consultant is Dr Jones.'

She sank back against the pillows, and stared at him tiredly.

'Can you describe the inside of Dr Bradshaw's house for me?'

'I told you before, I've never been there.'

'You're sure?'

'Absolutely.'

'And has anything come back to you about the accident?'

'No.'

'All right. Thank you for your time.'

He stood up. She muffled a cough.

'Inspector?'

'Yes?'

'Do you think it was suicide?'

'What makes you ask that?'

The girl's eyes seemed to sink deeper into her skull.

'He was never happy. Poor Gil . . . I never saw him really happy.'

Montgomery was glad to find that Sister Markham was on duty. He encountered her by the doorway of the clinical room, and immediately requested a quiet chat.

'In here,' she said, indicating a small interview room round the corner. 'This is where we see patients' relatives.'

The low chairs had plastic-covered seats, but were comfortable. A fading print of Van Gogh's *Sunflowers* adorned one wall, and a regiment of spider plants paraded across the windowsill. The air was stale with cigarette smoke.

'Which doctors are in charge of Philippa?' he asked.

She gave a wry smile. 'It'd be easier to tell you which aren't. She has multiple injuries . . . The surgeons have overall responsibility; this is their ward. Mr Crowland is the consultant, and Neil Thornton is his registrar. However, the person with the most direct patient contact on the ward is Stewart Bridges, the houseman.'

'Heavy, rather sullen-faced chap?'

'That's him.'

'I'd like a word with Mr Crowland, if you can contact him for me.'

'I'll try, but I'm afraid he may not be available. I believe he's at a meeting in the Victoria Hospital.'

'I'd be obliged if you'd try, anyway. If you can't get hold of him, Dr Thornton would do.'

'Mr Thornton. Would you like some tea while you wait?'

Montgomery warmed to this capable young woman. People rarely offered him refreshment on duty; something in his face seemed to put them off. Sergeant Bird, on the other hand, was usually inundated with platefuls of cake or biscuits – he who least needed any extra ounces.

'Thank you.' He forbore to mention that he had drunk some scarcely an hour before. He had a sneaking curiosity about hospital tea; like British Rail tea, it was an institution in itself. Ever ready to broaden his experiences, he decided to take the plunge.

The third spider plant from the right had just received an unexpected treat when Neil Thornton walked in. He was clad in green theatre clothes, and had a bleep tucked into the waistband of his trousers.

Montgomery stood up and tendered his hand.

'Mr Thornton, I'm Inspector Montgomery. Thank you for sparing the time to come.'

'Pleasure. I'm just between cases.' His grip was firm, and brief. Montgomery took in the details of his face with a single casual-seeming glance. It was a strong face with a forceful chin, straight nose and well-proportioned forehead. The hair was brown, parted on the side, and short. The blue eyes were direct.

They sat down on opposite sides of the small room.

'I've come to enquire about Philippa Rowe,' said Montgomery. 'I gather your team is in charge of her treatment. How is she?'

Neil paused for a moment, as if deciding the level at which to pitch his explanation.

'When she was admitted,' he began in deliberate tones, 'I wouldn't have given tuppence for her chances. The liver was torn, the spleen had a delayed rupture – we had to remove it completely and transfuse large quantities of blood – and both kidneys were damaged. Several bones were broken, including the lower ribs. She was lucky not to have had a pneumothorax. The head injury, ironically, proved to be the least of the problems; she sustained a hairline skull fracture and concussion, but nothing else. Oh, the odd cut and bruise, but nothing really serious.

'We patched her up with emergency surgery, and she survived the critical first few hours. I've got to emphasize, though, that we can't be sure of a full recovery just yet.' He gazed across a low coffee table at Montgomery. 'In cases of multiple injury like this, the patient is vulnerable to a variety of complications, infections and thrombosis being only two of them. Someone thought to be improving can deteriorate and die in an alarmingly short period of time. Where Philippa is concerned, we have the added worry of her renal function. Her kidneys are not working at the moment. The cause may have been crush injury, haemorrhage, shock, or any combination of these. The net result is the same – acute renal failure.'

'Can't you treat that?'

Neil Thornton smiled grimly. 'Indirectly. The cause is past history, but our job is to limit the deleterious effects on the rest of the body. If she's passing very little fluid, we give her very little fluid. We don't give her the wrong sort of proteins which will break down into poisonous substances she can't get rid of. You understand? Essentially, we wait and see. If the kidneys are going to recover, they'll do so and one day she'll start passing gallons of fluid. Then we have to reverse our strategy, and keep up with the loss by pouring fluids into her.'

'And if they don't recover?'

'The poisons go on building up. They come from tissue breakdown; we try to suppress the process with hypertonic glucose solution, but it can't be entirely avoided. We'd have to dialyse.'

'I see. So overall, what you're saying is: she's still critical at present.'

51

'Yes.'

'We must talk to her, though – find out as much as we can about the accident.'

'I appreciate that. Just keep it to a minimum.'

'How well do *you* know her, Mr Thornton?'

'Not terribly well. In hospital life you cross most people's paths at some time, but usually on a superficial plane. If I want a haematology opinion, I ask Philippa. If I see her in the Mess, we might discuss a television programme, or the latest piece of idiocy in hospital politics – no more. I know Dave Stannard, who was her boyfriend, much better.'

'Boyfriend?'

'He was. They've split up now, but they were close for three or four years.'

'Is he a doctor?'

'Yes. General medicine.'

'Does he work here?'

'Yes.'

Montgomery made a mental note of the name.

'About Gilbert Bradshaw. You've heard what happened, I'm sure. Did you see much of him?'

'A fair amount. He anaesthetized regularly for our Tuesday list.'

'What was your opinion of him?'

'Professionally or socially?'

'Both.'

'His work was adequate – no, I amend that; he was a good anaesthetist. But the big problem was reliability. He had a lot of time off because of various illnesses, and of course over a period of time that tended to colour people's judgement of his professionalism as a whole. I felt he was unlucky, but to a degree we make our own luck, don't we? There were occasions when he could have tried just a little harder to overcome his difficulties. Instead, he succumbed. He had a low threshold for opting out.'

'What were his illnesses? Did he have a psychiatric condition?'

'Not that I know of. They were purely physical things. A peptic ulcer that kept flaring up, and a slipped disc which eventually needed surgery. Presumably he had a GP who can give you more details. The orthopods here fixed his back; Mr Lightfoot's team.'

'Thank you. Are you sure all this didn't make him depressed?'

Neil Thornton shrugged. 'Who can say? He showed no signs of

clinical depression, but he could have been languishing at the other end of the spectrum. He was a quiet man – kept things to himself.'

'Did you ever see him in his off-duty hours?'

'No. Our interests didn't overlap at all.'

'Who were his friends?'

'I've no idea. Sorry, but that's the truth. Barnaby Fletcher might be able to fill you in. I used to hear them comparing the merits of tropical fish in the Mess.'

'You've never been to his house, then?'

'No.'

'Was Dr Rowe a special friend of Bradshaw's?'

'Philippa? I don't think so.'

'Any other female?'

'I can't really imagine it, but anything's possible.'

'Was he well off?'

'I beg your pardon?'

'Did he have a lot of money?'

The young surgeon sitting opposite looked momentarily wary, then a grin began to form. 'You must have been applying your ear to the hospital grapevine, Inspector. Stories about Gil's legendary wealth have flourished here for years, and no one knows whether there's any truth in them. Now the tongue-clackers are waiting to hear what size of estate he left. Gossip for its own sake ... He never looked the part, you see. That's what they can't understand.'

'Ah, Tell me – how did his death affect you personally?'

'I don't quite follow.'

'Were you shocked, surprised, sorry for him?'

Neil considered. If he found the question offensive, no sign of emotion disarranged his coolly handsome features. He might have been in the middle of a rather tedious *vica voce* exam.

'Yes, no, yes. That is, like everyone, I was shocked. You don't expect a colleague of forty to drop down dead, or fall, or whatever happened. Surprise isn't quite the same. Gil was one of life's losers; you could sense it even if you didn't know him well. Now he's lost in a particularly final way, and somehow it's hard to feel surprise. It's as if it was always on the cards – inevitable. As for being sorry for him – yes, I always have been. He engendered that feeling in others. Ask around; you'll find that half the hospital was sorry for him.'

Montgomery studied the young man who pronounced his judgements so dispassionately. There was a cold kind of honesty in the way he refused to simulate regrets he did not feel. Hand-wringing was not his style. Possibly he was already looking ahead to Gilbert Bradshaw's replacement, someone who wouldn't let his colleagues down so often. It was an ill wind . . .

The bleep tucked in Neil's waistband emitted a series of piercing sounds. He smiled and stood up, signalling the end of their interview.

'That'll be theatre, I'm afraid. Sorry I can't be of any further assistance.'

'You've been very helpful,' said Montgomery.

They paused in the corridor before going their separate ways.

'I'd be grateful if you'd keep me informed about any major changes in Dr Rowe's condition.'

'Of course.' Neil Thornton looked down suddenly, the tanned skin around his mouth and nostrils pinching into whiteness. 'It's a miracle she wasn't killed, you know. An absolute miracle.'

Montgomery knew genuine anger when he saw it. His embryo opinion of the registrar underwent its first reversal.

'What do you think of this?'

Coral pirouetted energetically in front of her friend, and the new green circular skirt whirled out in a rich tier of colour. Beneath its flowing folds, her legs were shapely; for a small girl, she was perfectly proportioned.

'It's very nice.' Maureen was sewing in her favourite armchair, spotlit by the standard lamp which was the best illumination their flat could offer. Behind her, the new floral curtains shut out the blackness of night.

'You see I took your advice.' Coral sat down on the hearthrug, sunny and satisfied, and hugged her knees. 'I was tempted to order the orange one, but you were quite right – emerald is much better. Look at all the material! It's very '50s . . . funny how fashions repeat themselves. A perfect excuse for hoarding.'

The expected rejoinder didn't come, and she glanced upwards to see if Maureen was listening. The Irish girl's face was pensive, her attention neither on Coral nor on the meticulous repair she was effecting at the elbow of one of her jumpers. Coral knew Maureen disapproved of her mail-order sprees; perhaps that was the trouble. Well, personal expenditure was her own concern!

'How was Clifton Ward today?' she rattled on. 'Was Sister in another of her moods?'

'No.'

Coral waited a few seconds, then scrambled to her feet. 'Have you got a headache?'

'No ... I'm fine.' With an effort, Maureen seemed to rally herself. 'That's a lovely skirt, Coral. Elegant, but exciting as well. Is it for anything special?'

'Just the next Mess party. They've seen all my other clothes.' She undid a button at the waistband, then changed her mind. 'I might as well keep it on. What time is it ... half-past ten? There's not much of an evening left when we work a "late", is there? Are you on an "early" tomorrow? Oh, good, so am I. I suppose we'd better go to bed soon, then. Do you fancy some toast?'

'Please. Let me make it.'

'No, you're busy. Back in five.'

She danced out of the room and returned within the stipulated time carrying a small tray; a background aroma of charcoal wafted through from the kitchen. 'That stupid grill plate,' she said.

Coral ate her slice quickly, dextrously trickling the butter into her mouth and avoiding the spillage of crumbs. After a polite murmur of thanks, Maureen had lapsed into silence again, and intermittently nibbled the corner of her piece like a cautious mouse. Something was evidently on her mind, and she was in no hurry to divulge it.

'I do love this flat,' said Coral, throwing her head back to study the ceiling plasterwork, 'despite its little annoyances. I think it's diabolical to put the rent up yet again. For what we're charged, we might as well be buying a place.'

'They can't lose.' Maureen's voice was soft. 'The demand for rented accommodation is so high.'

'Well, I think it's monstrous!'

'We could always go back to the Nurses' Home.'

'Are you crazy? We loathed the Nurses' Home! All that noise ... people staring if a man dared to cross the threshold, and listening at doors ... everyone knowing everyone else's business. Oh, no. I'm not spending any more time in there. I've grown out of that.'

'Yet sometimes here, Coral – going in to work on dark mornings ... or if you're out and the flat is empty and quiet ... '

'There's Mrs Sharma below, with all her family, not to mention

55

Robert on the ground floor. And the new man in 1B is friendly enough.'

'I know, but it's not the same. It was much nicer here when Pippa and David were downstairs. Just knowing they were nearby – it felt safe. And we saw so much more of them. I really enjoyed Pippa's dinner parties with beautiful gypsy music, and David lost in a great tangle of spaghetti, and Pippa laughing . . . She never laughs now. I mean even before the accident. I haven't seen her laugh for months. They shouldn't have split up. He should have made her come back.'

'He was upset,' said Coral reminiscently. 'Perhaps his pride was hurt as well.'

'But look at them now! They've got hospital flats at opposite ends of the campus. It's so sad. If it was me, I don't think I could cope with that.'

'Mm.' Maureen was unlikely to be faced with such a situation, thought Coral. Left to herself, she would stay in every night with a book, or perhaps the radio. She could relate beautifully to male patients in her nursing capacity, but was quite incapable of sustaining a sociable conversation at parties and dinners. She had never had a boyfriend; her idea of a dirty weekend was cleaning out the bathroom. It was all rather a waste.

Coral took a last crunch of toast. 'I'm for bed,' she said.

'Packing your box of tricks again?'

Vanda Pitts glanced up from her task to see Neil standing in the bedroom doorway, a brandy balloon in each hand.

The question was rhetorical; he came forward into the room and placed the glasses on the bedside cabinet. 'Thought you might like one of these. Remy Martin.'

'Oh – thanks,' she said. 'I don't suppose you've seen my amber bracelet, have you? It matches this.' She extricated a small labelled box from the half-filled model bag on the bed, opened it, and held up a chunkily cut necklace which winked and glowed in the light. Scattered around the bag were similar items of jewellery, headbands, make-up, underwear and tights.

'In a word, no . . . but if you're looking for your eyebrow pencils, they're in the fridge.'

'Yes; I was going to sharpen them.'

He nodded, used to these peculiarities by now, and began a careless examination of her possessions.

'Leave that alone!' she snapped, rescuing a seamless black bra. 'You'll disarrange everything.'

'It looks pretty disarranged already,' he observed.

'Really? That's your ignorance. All these items are ready for packing in a specific order – there's no redundant space in the bag. I'm not taking another. It would be too much to handle with the portfolio, and I shan't be leaving *that* behind. You never know who you'll meet at a shoot.'

He sipped his brandy and sat down on the bed. 'Make the most of your opportunities,' he mocked. 'Most models are over the hill at twenty-five.'

'Well, that gives me two more years to make my fortune,' she answered, unruffled, folding and stowing with deft precision.

'You're not doing so badly as it is.'

'Neither are you.'

'Great little team, aren't we?'

She didn't answer. There was a subterranean sarcasm in the comment which hit at the root of her one area of insecurity. Vanda had been a cocky child from one of the seediest parts of London's East End, her only assets being personal ones – a face and figure to burn the trousers off any red-blooded male she encountered, and an unexpectedly high IQ. At school, she had ruthlessly ironed out her accent by imitating teachers from outside the area and by listening to BBC broadcasters. She had taken on any extra job she could find, exchanging the certainty of academic qualifications for sufficient funds to pay for a grooming course at model school, which taught her the best ways to channel her love of self-projection. As Neil had implied, a model's youth was not to be squandered.

When the real work started, she quickly noticed that quiet girls failed to thrive. Personality seemed to be as important as looks in this most public profession. Vanda gritted her teeth and survived the humiliation of being someone's third choice, the ego-sapping indifference of many clients for whom models were ten a penny, the long hours spent in freezing, barn-like studios modelling bikinis in February. Privations only made her more determined to succeed.

And then – the classic lucky break. After three years of catwalks, catalogues and sporadic editorial work, she became the Coco Palm Soap girl, and their television advert triggered a flood of demands for her services. Income soared; her dismal Paddington bed-sit was superseded by a spacious Chelsea flat. She began to frequent the West End wine bars and entered into a series of brief, unsatisfactory relationships.

It soon became clear that her class was against her. The business executives she met were either dandified 'Hooray Henrys' with whom she had nothing in common, or lecherous married men intent on sleazy gropings. Those from the Middle East were the worst – all gifts and flattery until the savagery of the night, the implacable insistence on a partner for unspeakable acts, a whore bought and paid for.

As her career flourished, Vanda's personal life had become more desperate. True, men were queuing up to be seen with her, but most of them she despised and the rest found nothing appealing beneath her carefully manufactured veneer. They knew her as a parvenu.

Just when her hard glaze of confidence was beginning to crack, she had met Neil at Brands Hatch. There was an immediate physical attraction, and more. Here was someone with the same ingrained self-interest, the same disdain for idleness, the same unbending arrow of ambition. It was a shock to find that his sexual appetites also coincided with hers. They were deeply compatible, and yet ... Neil's background was solidly middle class, and the fleeting occasions on which she had met his family had not been a success. He took her to the rowdier hospital parties, but not to the quiet dinners where there was a danger of conversation with consultants. The old problem was still alive and kicking.

If only he would give up surgery in favour of racing she would fit in with his lifestyle, without a doubt. Her glamour would enhance his image, and his triumphs bolster hers. Conversely, however, marriage to a surgeon would bring her the respectability she secretly craved. It was a conundrum.

Vanda closed the bag, removed a batch of cards from a wallet and began to check through them. Neil had taken his shoes off and was now stretched out on the other side of the bed, hands behind his head. His manner was serene; he never evinced regret when her visits to Nottingham were at an end. He accepted her punishing modelling schedule as a fact of life, like his own hospital rota. If she could be with him, all well and good; if not, never mind.

But there was something he didn't know about. Her face had

been dominating magazines and television screens in the UK for more than three years now, and her agent Teri Golding was anxious to avoid the effects of over-exposure on her long-term career. A six-month assignment in Milan was on offer: Teri's network of contacts included the prestigious Candelli Model Agency. It was a wonderful opportunity – new fields to conquer and high rates of pay. Vanda intended to accept, but six months was too long to be away from Neil. If, as she suspected, he was just beginning to tire of her, it would provide him with the perfect excuse to sever the threads. More than anything, she wanted to avoid that.

He stirred beside her and took the cards from her hand. 'Equity card,' he said, 'model cards . . . good picture, this three-quarter view. The words aren't very complimentary, though – "*Grösse, Oberweite, Taille, Hüfte*" – they say you're gross, overweight, tall and hefty.'

'Neil, you wretch! That's one of my German ones. It means: "height, bust, waist, hips". You'll find French and Italian versions there, too.'

'So there are.' He tapped them into a straight pack and returned them to the wallet, then watched her as she quickly filled a suitcase and placed it with the model bag next to the wardrobe. 'Are you driving straight to the shoot tomorrow, or calling at your flat first?'

'The studio's in a Docklands warehouse,' she replied. 'I'll see what the traffic's like, and how much time I've got . . . God, I could do with a cigarette.'

'Not in here.' His voice was calm, authoritative.

She bridled. 'Who says so?'

'I do.'

Vanda pulled a silver cigarette case and lighter from her handbag and faced him challengingly. 'Isn't this your cue for a homily on the evils of smoking?' she asked, her accent slipping a bit. 'Go on – tell me about cancer and bronchitis and heart disease.'

His chiselled profile remained expressionless. 'You sound sufficiently well informed to me,' he said. 'I don't care one way or the other.'

A small chill passed down Vanda's spine. It was true. He didn't care – not for one soul, not for thousands. He regarded surgery as a scientific exercise, and his pursuit of excellence was merely a reflex. If asked to lament premature deaths due to smoking, his answer could be predicted – they were saving the country millions of pounds in pensions and geriatric facilities.

Clutching the offending items, she walked with dignity through the lounge into the kitchen, where she lit the cigarette and drew on it deeply. Up yours, Mr Neil Thornton, she said to herself. Vanda Pitts does what she wants to do.

The smoke was dry in her throat. She remembered an article he had shown her once on the cosmetic effects of smoking – the yellowed teeth, the wrinkled skin. Hardly the most sensible habit for a model. Had that been his way of trying to reach her in an area she would find more relevant than that of the distant possibility of illness? Or had it been a stark reminder that when the bloom had gone, this particular rose would find itself on the compost heap?

Her breath came and went more quickly, and with a smothered curse she stubbed out the half-smoked cigarette in a saucer where it lay, broken and ugly. Stay cool, Vanda, she murmured. You've got everything you need: youth, good looks, money in the bank. What's so special about him?

She tossed her blonde head, but her feet gave the answer, treading noiselessly over the thick carpet towards a room with a large and well-sprung bed where he was waiting for her.

6

Mr Crowland's entourage threaded its circuitous way through the hospital corridors early the next morning, assaulted by regular blasts from his repertoire.

'"Oh hang at open doors the net, the cork . . ."'

Stewart Bridges, shuffling at the rear, rolled his eyes towards Neil and shrugged.

'Peter Grimes,' he was informed in a whisper.

Stewart contemplated his list of patients, then frowned, more puzzled than before.

'The opera,' hissed Neil. 'Benjamin Britten.'

No more enlightened, the houseman shook his head.

Moments later they erupted into Philippa's room and congregated at the bottom of the bed. The air held a light floral scent, the temperature chart showed a gratifying return to normality, and their patient looked both comfortable and alert. Stewart prepared to receive a verbal pat on the back.

'Any complaints, Dr Rowe?' Mr Crowland's tone was roguish.

'What would happen if I said "yes"?'

'You'd be sorry. We'd take away your Hycal.'

'Oh no, don't do that. It's the only thing that actually tastes pleasant.'

'Well, tell your kidneys to start working properly and we'll be able to give you steaks.'

'On the NHS?'

'Mince, then. But for now, I'm afraid we must stick with the regime.'

Philippa made a face.

Following a long discussion of symptoms, signs and X-ray findings, Mr Crowland held out his hand for the treatment card. Sister Markham extracted it from the Drug Kardex and passed it to him. Silently he perused the list of drugs prescribed.

'We won't be needing this ... or this,' he said after a short pause, then smiled at Philippa. 'It's all going very nicely. If it wasn't for your orthopaedic problems, we'd have you up and about. Keep your limbs moving as much as possible. This young fool – ' he indicated Neil ' – is racing again at the weekend, so he may be joining you in plaster.'

'No danger,' said Neil firmly.

The atmosphere was cheerful as they left, and Stewart stood expectantly in the corridor waiting for accolades. Anne Markham closed the door.

'What the *hell* do you think you're playing at?' Mr Crowland's anger was all the more potent for being suppressed, and his houseman shrank away in alarm.

'And you should know better!' He swung round on Neil.

'What's wrong, sir?'

'This!' He stabbed at the treatment card with an irate forefinger, bending the thin cardboard. ' "Gentamicin", ' he read. ' "Cefuroxime". Truly an inspired choice of antibiotics!'

'I – I thought it would cover a broad spectrum of organisms, Sir,' faltered Stewart. 'We haven't yet had a positive culture.'

Neil, who had noted the error immediately, tightened his lips and waited for his share of the blame.

'Four doses of each,' continued Mr Crowland. 'Four doses.

And the girl has renal failure. She can't excrete them. Don't they teach you anything at medical school?'

'I was going to do gentamicin peak and trough levels tomorrow,' muttered Stewart miserably.

'Oh, I see. To show you how well you've overdosed your patient. Very useful.' He thrust the card into Stewart's large hands. 'Go away when this round has finished and read some pharmacology. Adverse drug reactions, contra-indications. I don't want to see this happen again.'

It was three hours before Neil had an opportunity to lambast his junior.

'You bloody fool,' he said tersely as the white-coated figure of Mr Crowland vanished into the distance. 'Whatever possessed you to prescribe those drugs for Philippa?'

'I don't know ... I didn't think. She said she was allergic to penicillin.'

'Cephalosporins can cross-react, you know – ten per cent of cases. But that's another matter. Regarding her renal failure, one dose of gentamicin would have been enough to start with. It goes round and round if there's no effective excretion. You ought to know that. Do I have to watch *everything* you do from now on?'

'No.' The houseman's head and shoulders drooped, and he slunk away to the clinical room. Anne came out of her office almost immediately.

'I'm sorry, Neil,' she said. 'I should have spotted that myself.'

'Don't worry, Anne. It's one of those things. It's just a pity we didn't find out before old Crowland ... Murphy's Law.'

As he left the ward, Anne had the impression that his pride had been stung. Neil was such a perfectionist, it must have been galling for him to be saddled with a houseman like Stewart.

Her reflections were interrupted by the advent of a now familiar figure. It looked as if Inspector Montgomery, once more in his grey raincoat, was returning to conduct further interviews.

The haematology staff had been fulsome in their praise of Philippa, thought Montgomery as he left the warren of laboratories in an out-of-the-way wing of the hospital and trod the shining green corridors leading to Cavendish Ward. Her consultants had described her as 'bright' and 'very sound' (although surely the prospect of an 'unsound' doctor wandering round was not an edifying one). The SHO had chosen the terms 'sensible' and 'reliable', while to the lab technicians she had been 'good; always supportive, never high-handed'. There had been a general feeling that she took life a little too seriously, but they were a jolly crew of workers who could extract a laugh from the most unwilling candidate with their banter. In the warm light of their attentions, Philippa had thawed like all the rest.

As a character reference, this was perfectly satisfactory. Unfortunately, it left Montgomery no nearer to any link with Gilbert Bradshaw. The consultants scarcely knew him, the SHO had only started his job in August, and the technicians had no call to be in the vicinity of theatre. It was disappointing, but one got used to that in police work. Perhaps the anaesthetists would be more help. Or the surgeons.

First of all, he was going to see Philippa again. Somewhere in her head lay the key to this mystery. There might have been no crime at all – just a common, sordid domestic squabble culminating in an accident. But until that was proven, he would pursue the truth with tireless determination.

The sister of Cavendish Ward smiled at him as he paused by Philippa's door. What was her name? Ah, yes. Markham. Anne Markham. He gave her a little nod, then entered the room. Somewhere in the background a lunch trolley lurched and rattled on its way from the kitchens.

Two faces swung round to observe him as he crossed the threshold. Philippa was propped on top of the bed this time, and sitting beside her was a small girl with elfin features and a puffball of flaming red hair. His interest sharpened as a memory note twanged like a plucked string in the back of his mind. She had an elusive familiarity, an imprint, an essence which refused to be catalogued. He would hardly forget such hair, or those cat-like amber eyes in a porcelain face. It was something more subtle. She wore a nurse's uniform, the cap denoting staff nurse status. That told him nothing at all. Where . . . ?

Montgomery allowed none of these thoughts to project from his impassive features.

'Sorry to disturb you at lunch-time,' he said to Philippa.

'What lunch?' she asked jokingly. 'I'm not sorry. I'm glad you're here, to take my mind off the nauseating smell of that lamb casserole outside. This is Coral Chapman, a friend of mine. Coral – Inspector Montgomery.'

They acknowledged each other politely and Coral scrambled to her feet.

'I was just going,' she said in a resolute voice which contrasted with her petite figure. As she skirted the bottom of the bed, Montgomery made up his mind.

'I'd like a word with you, too, if possible,' he told her. 'Can you wait on this ward?'

She gave him a sunny smile. 'Yes, if you'll tell Sister Ramsbottom it's all your fault if I'm late back on duty.'

'Done.'

She whirled out in a Titian blur of russet, leaving the two remaining occupants of the room feeling slightly breathless.

'Before you ask,' said Philippa, 'nothing has come back about the accident. I'm sorry if that means a wasted journey. WPC Winger was in today, as well.'

'Don't worry,' said Montgomery easily. 'I'm interviewing a whole cross-section of hospital personnel. Perhaps you'll tell me about your friend.'

'Coral? She's a nurse on Byron Ward, a staff nurse. I've known her for two years. She shares a flat in Sherwood just above one where I used to live.'

'What is she like?'

'Pretty extrovert. Always in the middle of things like parties or concerts or visits to the cinema.'

'Did she know Gilbert Bradshaw?'

'I don't think so. She never worked in theatre. Maureen did.'

'Who is Maureen?'

'The girl she shares the flat with. Quiet, shy, Irish.'

'Thank you. You make my job easy ... Were you in the flat below with David?'

She started, and a thin flush seeped across her cheekbones before retreating to reveal a tight, hostile set to her facial muscles.

'That's common knowledge, as you seem to have found out.'

'Why are you angry?'

She didn't deny it. 'Because I don't see the relevance of your question. Because I imagine David is one of your "cross-section of hospital personnel", and I don't like the idea of you and him discussing me. He has nothing to do with the accident, so why drag him into it?'

Her lower lip quivered slightly; she splinted it with her teeth and looked away. Montgomery felt a pang of compassion for the girl. She tried hard to project a strong exterior, but beneath that her emotions were perilously close to the surface. This was the doctor that other people described as 'sensible', 'serious', 're-liable'. She had been crushed to within an inch of death and was now helpless in the grip of frustration and pain.

He lifted the little onyx horse from the locker top and examined it admiringly.

'David might just have some clue,' he answered in calm tones. 'Something he doesn't realize himself at this point. You may have dropped a hint as to why you were going to Sylvia Vale on Friday night – a word in the canteen, maybe. It's up to me to see anyone who can help.'

She turned her face back towards him. 'You're right. I'm sorry. But David won't be able to tell you anything. We weren't on speaking terms before the accident, and afterwards . . . we've talked about it, puzzled over it, and I'm sure if he knew anything useful he'd have said.'

Instinctively, Montgomery felt that it would be more fruitful to question Coral on the subject of David and Philippa's relation-ship than Philippa herself. Nevertheless, he had to try.

'How long were you two together?'

'Four years.'

'Why did it end?'

Her eyes glinted. 'How do these things usually end? It wasn't high drama, just a morass of prosaic little differences, and failure to compromise. He was thoughtless once too often . . . I couldn't stand it any more.' She gave a small bitter laugh. 'I dare say he sees it from an entirely different angle, with me the villain of the piece. Well, it's all in the past now, anyway.'

'Was it a mutual decision?'

'No. I left.'

'I see . . . do you think he harbours a grudge?'

Philippa was startled. 'Good Lord, no. Not that kind of grudge. Not if you're implying . . .'

'What am I implying?'

'You know . . . that he would harm me. He wouldn't. He's not like that at all.'

'What is he like?'

'Kind. Gentle, but not weak. Intelligent . . . slightly selfish.'

'Is he a sportsman?'

65

'Yes, when he gets the time, which isn't often in general medicine. Football, squash, swimming.'

'Thank you. I think that's all I need to know for the present. I won't be coming back unless you remember something specific, or we find some evidence ourselves, but WPC Winger will keep in contact. We all wish you a speedy recovery.'

Coral Chapman proved to be as forthcoming as Montgomery had hoped. Ensconced in a tiny sitting-room, with no fear of Sister's reprisals for tardiness, she revealed an avid love of gossip.

'They were so well suited,' she affirmed, nodding her head as if to emphasize the point. 'You know that feeling you get with some couples – that they *belong* together. Well, Pippa and David were like that. Maureen was hoping she'd be asked to be a bridesmaid. Pippa's an only child, you see. She has two stepbrothers now, but they live down south and they never visit . . . I suppose they think anything north of Watford is still wallowing in the Dark Ages.

'Their flat was nice, you know. They'd decorated it together, and it had . . . elegance. Not cheap modern furniture, but classical reproductions, and one or two genuine antique pieces. Guess what he did when she left? He went and *sold* them. Except for the sideboard he gave to Maureen and me. That was really generous, because it's one of the antiques . . . But, imagine! You build things up, then knock them down again. He's gone back to that cramped little row of boxrooms and broom cupboards they dare to call a hospital flat. You couldn't swing a cat in any of them. Not that you'd want to, of course . . .'

'That's very interesting,' Montgomery chipped in. 'He must have been upset.'

'Oh, he *was*. Really upset. He couldn't believe it at first; he thought she was just trying to teach him a lesson. Then she paid the landlord three months' rent, and he knew.'

'Did he feel she'd made a fool of him? Was he angry?'

'No. More sad. He does have a girlfriend now, Audrey, but I'm sure he wouldn't have looked twice at her in other circumstances. She caught him on the rebound.'

'What about Philippa?' Is there anyone special for her?'

'No, she's been concentrating on work and exams. It's made her – dull. She's lost her sparkle. More than that . . . she seems suspicious of men now. Cynical.'

66

'Whatever happened?'

'I don't know. I wish I did! It was something to do with a dinner party. Neither of them has said exactly what caused the split . . . I don't like to ask outright.'

She was probably bending the truth there, Montgomery reflected. He could well imagine this flame-haired sprite 'asking outright', and for once being denied. His earlier impression of *déjà vu* had faded to a niggle; the more closely he observed Coral, the further the memory withdrew to the outer reaches of recall. Like an elusive word, it would come suddenly, unheralded, and for now he had to accept that.

'When was this?' he asked.

'Six months ago. He's been going out with Audrey for three.'

'Ah. Tell me, Coral, how well did you know Gilbert Bradshaw?'

For a split second her fingers stiffened, and a look almost of panic darted across the back of her eyes.

'I didn't know him, not to speak to, anyway. It was more – by repute. I heard other people talking about him.'

'What did they say?'

'That he was always ill . . . and money couldn't buy everything.'

'He was well off, then?'

'So I gather.'

'What was their attitude towards him?'

'A kind of pitying contempt.'

'Was Philippa a special friend of his?'

'She never said. I don't think so.'

'Do you think your friend Maureen would be able to tell me more about him?'

'Oh, no,' she said hastily. 'Maureen knows much the same as I do.'

'Are you sure?'

'Yes.' Noticing his frown, she went on: 'Maureen's very shy. Official things upset her, even simple memos from the hospital hierarchy. I'm sure she doesn't know anything that would help your investigation.'

'Nevertheless, we may need a few words with her,' said Montgomery firmly. 'What is your address?'

'Flat 3, Devonshire Mansions, Hillside Road, Sherwood. Don't frighten her, Inspector, that's all I ask.'

'Don't worry. It probably won't be necessary, but if it is, we have female detectives.' Or there was Sergeant Bird, who had a gift for gaining the confidence of young people.

He rose as if to leave, but Coral asked him brightly, 'Do you have any children, Inspector Montgomery?'

'Yes.'

'Girls?'

'One girl, one boy. Thirteen and fifteen.'

'What does the girl want to do?'

'She's still deciding. Art college is the latest idea.'

'Not nursing?'

'She did mention that once.'

'Don't let her be a nurse. It's a moral trap. You find that you love the job, but it won't allow you to live decently. The pay is awful. Your friends leave . . . they go to America or Saudi Arabia and earn huge salaries. People say to you: "If you're dedicated, that shouldn't matter." But why should they exploit your dedication? I love England, I don't want to go. But if I remain in nursing I'll never be able to afford a home of my own. Tell her, Inspector. Make sure she knows.'

Montgomery hesitated over the reflex male rejoinder, 'You could always get married.' There was something hard and desperate in this small girl, some chip on the shoulder not fully explained by her words. Instead, he said mildly, 'Isn't the pay now better than it used to be? I understand it's pretty good at the top of the scale.'

'Yes, if you want to be a pen-pushing *administrator*,' she spat. 'Matrons went out of fashion long ago. These days you have nursing officers and a variety of directors who swan about making lists and arranging meetings. All talk and paperwork. You should see them at a cardiac arrest. They don't know *anything*. That's not nursing!'

David Stannard had much more self-possession than his erstwhile neighbour. His steady gaze and unruffled expression reminded Montgomery of Neil Thornton, but there was a warmth in the young physician which the blue-eyed surgeon lacked. David's own eyes were brown, with very clear whites which belied his many late nights on duty or in the research lab. He was tall and slim.

'Sorry about the cramped surroundings, Inspector,' he said,

leading the way into yet another poky interview room, this one belonging to Manvers Ward which held general medical patients. 'I'd open the window, but I don't suppose we want the gardeners to hear our conversation.'

Montgomery flicked ash off an orange plastic chair and sat down gratefully. His legs were beginning to tire, but he had no intention of displaying the fact.

'No,' he agreed.

'What can I do for you?' asked David.

'I'd like to discuss your friend, Philippa Rowe.'

'Her accident, you mean?'

'No. Her character, her lifestyle, her other friends. I understand that you and she were very close for a time.'

'Yes. Four years. Quite a "time".' His deep voice foundered on a splinter of pain.

'Was she an excitable girl?'

'No. Calm, strong, hard-working – hardly ever neurotic. That's why – '

'Go on.'

'I was going to say, that's why it was such a shock when she left our flat. I presume you already know about that.'

'I do, but I'd like your version.'

'I'm afraid the reason's a mystery to me. We had a little mix-up over a dinner party, but that was more an amusing fiasco than the stuff of break-ups.'

'Did you try to talk her into coming back?'

'Talked myself hoarse.'

'And Philippa?'

'Enigmatic – the Mona Lisa had nothing on her. She said if I didn't know what the problem was, then she'd made the right decision.' He gave a small embarrassed laugh. 'I don't know why I'm telling you this. It's supposed to be therapeutic, talking to strangers – the bus-stop syndrome – but it's not what you've come for.'

'On the contrary, it's all useful for the complete picture. Did you ever physically fight?'

'No . . . well, occasional rough-and-tumble, like most couples, but never in earnest. She has a lot of inherent dignity.'

'Did she mention anything at all to you about a proposed trip to Sylvia Vale last week? Or did she talk about meeting or visiting Gilbert Bradshaw?'

'None of those things. I've racked my brains for clues. Pippa has no idea why she was found there. She wasn't a special friend of Gil's, although I think she made more effort with him than a lot of us did, I'm ashamed to say. She's good with lame ducks; they find her reassuring. She instils confidence, a sense of worth, by listening and then being constructive.' He grinned suddenly. 'With one notable exception – yours truly.'

'You don't look like a lame duck to me,' said Montgomery drily. 'And you have your consolations.'

'Yes, indeed. The devoted Audrey.' David's tone was gently ironic.

'Did you ever visit Gilbert Bradshaw in his home?'

'No.'

'Did any of your colleagues?'

'He tended to keep to himself. He could be painfully shy at times, even though he was older than all the other juniors. Let me think ... maybe Barnaby. Yes. Barnaby Fletcher; neurology SHO. They shared an interest in tropical fish. Ugh!'

'You're not keen on fish?'

'No. Nasty, slimy things. They look at you with those great big eyes ... It's just a quirk. Some people don't like cats; I think they're terrific.'

'Tell me about Barnaby.'

David Stannard raised his eyebrows. 'Which aspects of Barnaby?'

'Any that come to mind.'

'That might take too long. In a nutshell, he's a bit of a joke – for God's sake don't quote me. He was the clumsiest student in our year. He resat all his exams. He set his heart on neurosurgery, but luckily his general surgical house job was such a disaster that he was forced to give up that idea. Now he roams the hospital as neurology's latest recruit – or last resort – leaving a trail of devastation wherever he goes. Luckily he can't do much permanent harm in that specialty.'

'It sounds just as well. Is he jovial about his shortcomings?'

'Er, regrettably, no. He's in deadly earnest most of the time. He often doesn't know when he's made a mistake. His cloud of oblivion's all right for him, but it does rebound sometimes on other people.'

'Do you think he is capable of violence?'

David looked genuinely shocked. 'Barnaby? Never.'

'Fair enough. Tell me about his saving graces. There must be some.'

'Oh, yes. As I said, he's earnest, and actually he means well. He's devoted to his wife and baby. He keeps photographs to show anyone with even a flicker of interest. In a strange way, we'd miss him if he weren't here.'

Montgomery made a mental note to allocate the interviewing of this stolid-sounding person to someone else.

'Inspector.' David's face wore an expression of strained concern.

'Yes?'

'I've been wondering for days now ... Is this unfortunate business with Gil anything to do with Pippa's accident?'

'You tell me.'

'How can I? I don't know! It just seems ... too much of a coincidence to be a coincidence, if you see what I mean.'

'Yes.'

'You don't give much away, do you?'

'That's not my job. I'm merely a collector of information at present. Just for interest, what were you doing last Friday night?'

David stared in amazement, then gave a small shrug.

'Me? Nothing unusual. We'd been on "take" Thursday night – that means a constant stream of emergency admissions. I was fairly tired on Friday, but you don't like to waste the whole evening sleeping. What did I do ... ? I went to the canteen for a bite to eat, then watched television in the Mess. After that I had a quick shower and joined a group of hospital people in the Mortar and Pestle. I suppose it would have been about nine o'clock by then. We all stayed until closing time.'

'What was the programme you watched?'

'Some nature thing. That's right, a documentary on bamboo rats. Quite enlightening.'

'You like nature programmes?'

'Some of them. I can't get excited about molluscs, for instance, or fish, but I can watch creatures with fur. I would have preferred the detective serial on the other side, but ours is a democratic Mess.'

'What else did you see?'

'Part of a silly quiz game. I was reading the paper by then, so I didn't take much notice.'

'Mm. Who else was in the Mess?'

'It's hard to remember. People come in, then they get called away again. I think Stewart was there. Stewart Bridges. He's a surgical houseman. A couple of anaesthetists . . .' He gave the names. 'Some students I don't know very well.'

'What about the crowd at the pub?'

'Oh, the usual people. Tom Allsopp from Casualty, Tony Spitz from surgery. There were a lot of medical students, and several nurses.'

'Coral Chapman?'

'Yes, Coral. Have you met her?'

'Our paths have crossed.'

'She's a nice kid under all the talk. A good nurse, too, like Maureen. I'm glad they're being so supportive towards Pippa.'

Montgomery recalled Coral's vehement views on the state of the nursing profession.

'Do you like your job, Dr Stannard?' he asked mildly.

'Yes, I do. I still feel enthusiastic about medicine, and enthusiasm breeds energy. I'd be sorry if I lost that. Very sorry.'

Montgomery nodded non-committally. 'What about your enthusiasm for Philippa? Have you lost that?'

A distant expression materialized on David Stannard's face, the eyes two dark empty tunnels.

'You've hit on it, Inspector,' he said thickly. 'My big problem. I still love her.'

7

'Barny, you *didn't*!'

The assembled group shrieked and rocked with laughter while Barnaby blinked uncertainly, his mouth hovering between the purse-strings of deep offence and a flattered smile acknowledging their appreciation of the wit he must have somehow displayed. Optimistically, he treated them to a wide, vacant grin.

Philippa's friends were clustered round her bed for the evening visiting hour. Although individually they sneaked in and out of the room whenever they could spare the time, *en masse* they tried hard to observe the hospital conventions and only allowed themselves to be noisy when there was already a hubbub from the main ward next door.

A bare two days before Philippa would have hated such an invasion, but now she welcomed it. Too much introspection was a torment; the antiseptic hours crawled interminably from dawn to dusk.

She was humbled by the obvious affection of her friends and colleagues. A token visit from each would have been reasonable, but many had come almost daily. She knew how busy they were, yet there was never any sense of impatience or rush. Tonight David, Coral and Maureen had spilled into the room full of good humour, followed within minutes by the more pompous tread of Barnaby, who was on call for neurology. Half asphyxiated in the strait-jacket of his newly starched white coat, he had just re-counted his latest diagnostic misadventure.

As the laughter subsided, Philippa adroitly changed the subject.

'How's young Paul getting on?' she asked Barnaby kindly.

His moon face glowed. 'He's on to solids now,' he said. 'When I hold out his teddy, he reaches forward to take it from me. He's always trying to sit up . . . if Becka supports his back, he can do. Then he chuckles, because he knows he's achieved something.'

Maureen appeared to be hanging on to his every word, her expression soft, benign, maternal. Coral, by contrast, was no more than tolerant. Barnaby's next move could be anticipated.

'I've got some pictures here . . .' He dug into one of the capacious lower pockets in his white coat and drew out a blue plastic 'granny's boasting book'.

The photographs were dutifully passed around. As usual, the infant languished at the extreme edge of each print, plump and placid like a fledgling Buddha, or greeting the camera with an open-mouthed salute, a silent, toothless crow of triumph. Philippa sighed as she received the booklet from David. Young Paul was already showing a marked resemblance to his father, reassuring in some respects, but surely a handicap if it went much further. Any compliment on the subject of familial features would be two-edged in the circumstances. She stared at the blurred pictures, with their poor composition, and tried to think of a pleasant comment to make.

David forestalled her. 'I like the soft focus – very atmospheric.'

Warily Philippa watched for Barnaby's reaction, and was re-lieved to witness his gratification.

'I thought so, too,' he said happily.

73

'What exciting news have you got, Pippa?' asked Coral when the treasures had been safely deposited back in the pocket.

'Not a lot, I'm afraid. It's very boring in here, but at least it's quieter than the ward. The nurses feel obliged to wake everyone at six o'clock, whether they need it or not. There's a sort of barrack-room discipline in operation – not that you could sleep through the noise of the trolleys anyway. I've decided it's all a stimulus for people to get well, so they can go home and get some peace!'

'That'll teach you,' said David briskly. 'We don't want any malingering.'

'Take no notice of him,' advised Coral. 'He's just jealous because no one considers him worthy of all this attention.'

'Most understandable,' smiled Philippa.

'However,' Coral went on, 'I'm a bit put out myself. I was looking forward to decorating your leg plaster with obscene graffiti, but there isn't one to decorate. I still haven't grasped why.'

'Ah. Mr Lightfoot and his team decided to do an open reduction of the fracture, with internal fixation. That means he operated to align the bones properly and screwed a plate across the fracture line – I think it's stainless steel. Later, there will be an external splint, but for now I can move my knee and ankle, and stop them getting too stiff. It also makes things easier for the nurses, the general surgeons and everybody else.' She glanced ruefully at her right arm, which was bent through a right angle and imprisoned within a hard shell of plaster of Paris extending from the axilla above to the base of the fingers below. 'I only wish they'd done the same here. This cast really gets in the way.'

'There you are, Coral,' invited David. 'Virgin territory. Have you got a felt-tipped pen?'

'That's different,' she demurred. 'It would look *untidy* on the arm.'

David shook his head mockingly. 'Women ... I suppose there's logic there somewhere – ' He broke off at the sound of a sharp, peremptory tap. Before anyone could speak, the door swung open.

Audrey surveyed the occupants of the room through an arboretum of over-mascara'd eyelashes. She was dressed for maximum confidence in an acid yellow suit and pale blue silk scarf, a combination of colours she had recently seen in the window of a large international store and had immediately concluded were the latest fashion. The suit she had bought forthwith; the scarf, a present from David, had already been in her possession.

It had taken courage to get this far. Sick-rooms and their occupants normally disgusted Audrey. She plied her typewriter a safe distance from the wards, and the often harrowing details she entered into letters and summaries were only so many words as far as she was concerned. For David's sake she pretended to feel more involved than she did, but secretly she despised the trusting people whose illnesses and traumas provided her with her livelihood.

Tonight, though, she had worked herself up to a pitch of righteous indignation and resentment. David's casual offer of dinner on Saturday had been slowly rankling ever since he had made it. Apart from his research, which required attention at sporadic hours, he wasn't on duty again until the following Monday. So what was he doing with his time? Why couldn't he spend more of it with her?

Philippa was one answer. Audrey had half-expected her to look shrivelled, yellowish, unattractive, like other patients she had seen when the instance was unavoidable. She had not only expected, but hoped that that would be the case. What she saw was disappointing. Philippa had indeed changed – her decisive features now blurred into a pale copy of their former selves, the keen brown eyes faded like velvet – but her plight engendered no revulsion. At this hour, people were with her because they wanted to be. Audrey recognized everyone present to some degree; it seemed to her that they formed a protective wall, surrounding Philippa with their friendship, and perhaps even more . . .

Her throat tight, she advanced towards the locker, letting the door swing back with a creak. She set down a plant with such impetus that the little onyx horse almost fell over. It was a cactus, as spiky as her manner.

'I brought this for you,' she said brusquely to Philippa.

'Thank you. That's – very thoughtful.'

The other members of the group were slow to recover. Barnaby, standing at the foot of the bed, was polishing his glasses. Coral and Maureen sat with their backs to the door while David, opposite, occupied the only other chair in the room. No one spoke.

'I thought you might be here, David,' Audrey rushed on before the silence could become more embarrassing. 'I was talking to Susan at lunch-time about our booking for the Trattoria Sorrento. She says it's very nice.' Jerkily she skirted the bottom of the bed and placed a proprietary hand on David's arm. He stood up with some reluctance and offered her his chair.

'Maureen and I have been there,' volunteered Coral to keep the conversation going. 'The food is good, but watch out for one of their waiters, the one that looks like a dwarf. His English is very poor. We asked for two prawn cocktails and he brought us corn on the cob; I suppose the names sounded similar to him. When we refused them, he went into a kind of paroxysm. It took ages to sort out – Italian curses flying everywhere.'

'He probably had to eat the corn himself later when the staff had their supper,' commented David. 'He'll listen more carefully in future.'

'We'll watch out for him,' said Audrey graciously.

'Speaking of food,' said David, 'would any of you ladies like to give me a few simple recipe tips? You know, cheap, nutritious meals. The canteen isn't always convenient.'

'But you can cook,' stated Coral. 'We've eaten your spaghetti.'

'Man cannot live by spaghetti alone,' he intoned.

'Well, you're pretty feeble if you can't manage anything else after spending years in a flat.'

'I can grill steak,' he recalled. 'Or bacon and egg. And then there's chilli con carne . . .'

'Typical,' groaned Coral. 'The standard repertoire of men. Can you do an omelette?'

'No. They're so soggy in the canteen, it puts me off trying it myself.'

'That's a pathetic excuse. The trick is to whisk the egg whites separately until they're really stiff. Then it'll come out light and fluffy.'

'More like a soufflé,' sniffed Audrey.

'Yes.' Coral was unrepentant. She turned back to David. 'What else? You could buy wholemeal pastry from the supermarket and make cheese and onion pasties. Or a quiche – hot or cold with plenty of salad.'

'All I've got at the moment is a can of corned beef, a tin of soup and a few vegetables, most of which have shrivelled because I kept them too long.'

'Wonderful. What has survived?'

'Just the onions, I think. And a bag of potatoes.'

'Easy, then. Cut your corned beef into cubes and fry it with the onions and very little added fat. Meanwhile, peel and boil your potatoes. Mash them when they're ready, season, and mix in the rest. If you've a dash of sauce or a bit of tomato purée, add that as well. Or perhaps some herbs. Then return it to the frying pan if you want to brown its bottom.'

Audrey looked round the room despairingly, but failed to find an ally. 'That all sounds frightfully Heath Robinson,' she articulated in disapproving tones. 'Cookery is an exact science. Flavourings are subtle, and need to be treated with care. They should always be measured.'

'Rubbish,' snorted Coral, abandoning all pretence at social niceties. 'Cookery is simply common sense. Trial and error. Using what's available.'

Audrey seized David's arm again, digging in her sharp finger-nails. 'I'll buy you a recipe book, darling,' she said sweetly, 'then there won't *be* any errors.'

'Except he'll give up because he doesn't happen to have any root ginger or know what cumin seeds are,' muttered Coral.

'About this corned beef tin,' said David delicately. 'I usually find that the strip breaks off before I've opened it. I hate those fiddly little keys.'

'Chill the tin. Take off the top *and* bottom with a rotary tin opener. Press the meat out on to a plate.' Coral's succinct advice pre-empted Audrey's by a hairsbreadth, and the faint pull of tension was once more discernible in the room.

'What do you cook, Barny?' asked Philippa.

'Oh – ' He looked slightly bemused. 'I don't. Becka makes all the meals.'

'Lucky devil,' said Coral. 'We have a rota.'

'A flexible one,' added Maureen.

'I noticed that the nurses have booked the Wollaton Room for a party next month,' said David. 'Are you in charge of the punch-bowl again, Coral?'

'Not this time. I thought I'd keep a low profile in view of the fiasco last Christmas.'

'What's this?' Barnaby leaned forward.

'Oh, some idiot spiked the punch with frusemide. The heaviest drinkers were desperate for the loo; the more fluid they lost, the thirstier they got and the more they drank, so it was a vicious circle. I think a few of them thought I did it.'

'Are you still one of the organizers for the charity swim?' enquired Philippa.

'Yes. I take it badly that you've opted out by breaking your leg.'

'Charity swim?' The belated echo came from Barnaby.

'It's for St Catherine's Hospice,' explained Maureen. 'Anyone connected with the hospital is invited to join a sponsored swim in about five weeks' time. The committee is made up of members of the Friends of St Catherine's, but Coral is a kind of liaison officer, whipping up support among medical personnel.'

'Whipping? If there's whipping involved, I'm in,' said David. Audrey glared at him.

'You're in anyway,' answered Coral. 'We're expecting at least fifty lengths from you.'

'Pippa could have done that easily. Pity . . . Have you asked Neil? He's your man for swimming. Or any sport.'

'No, I haven't broached it with him yet. What about you, Barnaby?'

'Er . . . I can do a few widths with goggles on. Maybe as many as seven.'

'That would be fine. Thank you.' Coral's lips were quivering. Perhaps she was visualizing Barnaby thrashing across the pool while everyone else was swimming lengths, or perhaps she was refraining from a comment about the natural buoyancy he carried around his waist.

Audrey knew that her own two lengths of elegant breaststroke would be inadequate, but she waited in vain to be asked. She was out of place in this group, without a doubt, but nothing short of a volcano was going to propel her from the chair. As David's girlfriend, they would just have to start accepting her.

'Will you be swimming?' she asked Maureen brightly.

Maureen's small heart-shaped face flushed crimson.

'Maureen's volunteered to be one of the stewards,' Coral answered for her. 'She can't swim, but I intend to teach her before this year's finished.'

Audrey nodded, pleased that someone else was suffering discomfiture, sorry because the someone wasn't Philippa.

Voices sounded in the corridor outside.

'That's Neil!' cried David. 'What a stroke of luck. Call him in, Coral.'

Coral hooked her shoe round the door, which Audrey had left ajar, and pulled. Sure enough, Neil Thornton and his houseman were standing in the entrance of the clinical room opposite, poring over a bulky file of case notes.

'Have you a minute to spare, Neil?' asked David.

The registrar hesitated. 'Yes. But we've an emergency on the way up from Casualty.'

'Just quickly, then. You too, Stewart. Would you be prepared to take part in the sponsored swim for St Catherine's?'

'When is it?' Neither Neil's handsome face nor Stewart's lugubrious one registered much interest.

'Five weeks' time. Don't worry, it won't be a weekend; I know we can't compete with Donington Park or Brands Hatch. It'll be a Wednesday night.'

'All right. Be glad to – unless we're on "take". I'll check the rota.'

'Thanks, Neil. We appreciate that. You'll probably be our best swimmer. Stewart?'

'Okay,' he mumbled. 'Same proviso.'

'Great. We'll let you get on with healing the sick.'

'Actually – ' Neil paused in the doorway and scrutinized David thoughtfully. 'We've got a woman in a side room on Clumber Ward with infected leg ulcers. Not one of today's patients; she's been here for weeks. The microbiologists think the organism is a form of MRSA. You've done a microbiology job, haven't you? Can you tell me anything about it?'

'Well, it's a bug which has caused trouble since the 1960s, because of its resistance to almost all the commonly used antibiotics. Initially the outbreaks were in London and Australia, but now the spread is virtually world-wide. I thought most of the British hospitals affected were in the North East Thames region. Is your patient from down there?'

'No, but we have a new student nurse on Clumber Ward who has come from Essex. She's being screened as a possible carrier.'

'If it *is* MRSA, you'll all have to be screened – anyone who's been in contact with the patient. It's a nasty bug – some strains are now only sensitive to Vancomycin, which leaves us only one jump ahead.'

Neil looked gloomy. 'We'd better continue to have her nursed

79

in isolation, then, and institute special precautions for the visitors . . . more work for Clumber Ward; it's the last thing they need.'

'Let me know what happens. The hospital may have to notify the body which monitors communicable diseases.'

'Will do. Thanks.'

They left with the briefest of valedictions, and Maureen turned to David. 'What does MRSA stand for?'

'Methicillin-resistant *staphylococcus aureus*. It's probably the penalty for our being too cavalier with antibiotics in the past. I wrote a paper along those lines when I was working in the microbiology lab.'

'How's your present research going?' enquired Coral.

'Oh, don't mention that if you want to keep me on the right side of raving insanity! When I'm not wandering round the wards in the middle of the night taking blood samples from volunteers, I'm up to my neck in papers.'

'Why not get whoever's on call to take the blood?' asked Audrey.

'Because David's not like that.' Philippa's voice held strength and authority.

Audrey smothered her incredulous rage at being gainsaid so flatly by the fragile-looking figure on the bed, and answered in tones of reason: 'But the houseman's on duty anyway. It's annoying when David has to leave the flat just to take a blood sample.' Her words were carefully chosen to bolster the impression that she spent most evenings, if not nights, with David. In fact, the event she described had occurred only once.

'The houseman has a thousand and one things to do,' said David quietly. 'The research is my responsibility, and will hopefully lead to my MD, so unless the circumstances are exceptional, I do it myself.' He wandered over to the window, rested his forearm on the sill, and looked out over the darkening roofs. 'I don't mind the patient contact, it's the library work I hate – wallowing in Index Medicus and Medical Subject Headings, ordering photocopies from obscure journals and having to wait weeks before they arrive . . . it took me a long time to understand why they couldn't produce *Ibid* for me.' He grinned round, but only Philippa smiled while the rest waited expectantly.

'"Some fell on stony ground,"' he muttered. 'Sorry.'

'Ah!' cried Barnaby, his eyes gleaming. 'I get it. *Ibid*. Hah! I made the same mistake once. I tried to put a bet on *Bar* at the Cheltenham Races.'

'Really, Barnaby, you do hide your light under a bushel,' simpered Audrey, totally missing the joke.

David sighed. It was proving to be a long visiting hour. Roll on the bell.

At eight o'clock a sharp jangling from the main ward cut through their stilted conversation, and Coral and Maureen gathered their belongings together preparatory to leaving. David had been studying Maureen's face with growing amusement. Usually pale, tonight she had seemed bright-eyed and glowing, though still virtually tongue-tied. It wasn't just the brief embarrassment following her exposure as a non-swimmer, either. He had seen that look before when his younger sister had developed a 'crush' on some pimpled youth while she was at school. No doubt about it, little Maureen was in love.

Curiously he considered the choices available. Barnaby came high on the list. With any other girl, he would barely have rated space as a footnote, but his social ineptitude might well have struck a chord of empathy in a sensitive soul like Maureen. And one had to remember – the nubile Rebecca Hampshire had married him without a qualm. Maternal instinct had a lot to answer for.

Next, there was Stewart Bridges. An almost categorical 'no'. Shuffling along corridors, peevish and unlovely . . . no woman in her right mind could be languishing after him. Neil? Tall, with good features, but repellently unemotional.

That left himself. Without undue lack of modesty, it did seem rather likely. He had known Maureen for two years now as a friend, and felt that she trusted him. Many people were unable to prise open the oyster shell of her reserve, consequently they failed to appreciate the gentle character inside. She had never had a serious relationship with a man as far as he was aware, and surely everyone had to start some time?

His mouth began to tug itself into a visible smile.

'David, what are you standing there for?' His reverie shattered as Audrey yanked at his arm. 'The bell's rung twice; we have to go.'

She was wearing the scarf he had given her in a moment of

weakness two months before. Soft blue silk, almost iridescent. Staggeringly priced, too, with the name *Gucci* printed in flowing italics across the corner ... Audrey had been delighted, and he had felt like Judas. He had bought one a year before for Philippa, a deep royal purple which had complemented her dark colouring. Pure lack of imagination had prompted him to present a similar one to Audrey. He had never dreamt that a situation might arise when she would be wearing it in Philippa's presence.

Philippa took care to hide the Gucci signature, while Audrey always arranged her scarf for maximum exposure of its pedigree. There, in one illustration, was the difference between the two girls. Pippa had nothing to prove.

In midnight's quiet blackness, Philippa tuned her ears to catch sounds of life from the corridor outside. It was odd how, in a hospital containing hundreds of people (thousands during the civilized hours), she could feel so isolated in this side room. If her thoughts had been tranquil, she would have received the benefit of its very real advantages – no creaking beds whose occupants tossed, turned and snored, no banal conversations with equally banal women indulging to the full their fixations with death and disease. But they were not. Ideas both dismal and disquieting competed for her attention, and the lack of any distraction gave them a fertile breeding-ground.

Her family was one problem. Somehow she had hoped that this accident would have brought them together, shown her that she had been wrong to imagine that they were indifferent to her estrangement. She had tried to co-operate – so hard. But her father's hasty remarriage less than a year after her mother's death from cancer had left Philippa feeling betrayed for the two of them. Mother had given up her career, done everything for him, and was now consigned to a small square photograph at the back of the mantelpiece, a photograph nobody even bothered to dust.

That second marriage had changed everything. Philippa found her new stepmother shallow, her conversation trite and trivial; in reciprocation she was considered intimidating. The early advent of two noisy stepbrothers clanged down the coffin lid on the camaraderie she used to share with her father; he no longer had time for her. Medical school at seventeen had removed her from their sphere altogether. The 'parental contribution' to make up her grant cheque had never materialized, owing to her father's misguided economic theories, and the remainder barely stretched to cover the most basic necessities. The compressed nature of the Nottingham course beyond the first summer gave Philippa no opportunity to take on temporary vacation work. She had struggled for the sake of a few pounds.

Insidiously, the estrangement progressed. After her second student Christmas, she ceased to spend regular holidays in a household where she was made to feel like an interloper. Love for her father was slowly diluted by contempt for his weaknesses, his inability – or worse, unwillingness – to stand with her and take her part.

But they were all the family she had. And the sum total of their concern for her was an embarrassed, whispery telephone call from Valerie, her stepmother, brought to Philippa's bedside courtesy of the plug-in 'trolley phone'. Valerie could be relied on to do whatever was fitting in a given circumstance, especially if she could be seen to be doing it. The call, no doubt sandwiched in the middle of a list of other irksome duties, would be ticked off with relief, and the matter regarded as dealt with.

Treacherous tears pricked behind Philippa's eyelids as she contemplated the rather sinister glow of the corridor night-light, through the small window above the door to her room. What was the use of success in her chosen career when her personal life was a desert? She could almost imagine herself becoming an eccentric spinster with strong views on everything and no one to discuss them with. Yet she valued her independence highly; it reared above the foothills of minor relationship troubles like a mountain, pure and stark; it was something to keep in view, something solid, a focus in times of doubt. Her mother had been a doormat, first assimilated into, then annihilated by, her father's identity and ambitions. Philippa dreaded repeating her story. Demolish the mountain, and the desert would be complete.

Coral would understand her point of view, she thought. Maureen had a loving family in County Clare; she had crumpled, much-read letters in her uniform pocket and the comfort of giggling, sisterly telephone calls. Paradoxically Coral the gregarious was less secure, despite her manner. There was no friendly family safety-net for her. She was an orphan.

Her background held some similarities to Philippa's own. Both had been only children in the original family units. Both had had a dominant parent, in Coral's case her mother. Mr Chapman had died in a mining accident when Coral was ten, and her mother, scion of another social class, had supported them both with secretarial work until her tragic death from cardiac valvular disease just after Coral had started nursing. No relatives had come forward to offer help or advice; the original *mésalliance* had resulted in a polite but profound alienation.

Coral was as extravagant as her bank manager would allow, behaviour Philippa intrinsically disapproved of but could understand. She herself was now in the fortunate position of being able to afford a few small luxuries without worrying about their cost; Coral was still enmeshed in budgeting and balancing, envy and cheap emulation, constantly unable to manage on her modest salary.

Shifting in the bed to ease the nagging discomfort pulsing up from her leg, Philippa's thoughts reverted to her own immediate situation. So far she had lain back, docile and accepting, merely glad to be alive. But while memory stubbornly refused to return, other parts of her brain were working overtime to make up for their previous stupor.

Her physical state was starting to provoke insistent questions. Would she dance again? Skate? Play tennis? Even walk properly . . . ? How did one manage without a spleen? As a haematologist, the functions of that mysterious organ were well known to her. It acted as a filter, removing bacteria, worn-out cells and general debris from the bloodstream. It generated antibodies to fight off infection. In special circumstances, it could revert to its embryonic role and actually produce blood cells.

Without a spleen she was vulnerable to sepsis. Her defences against pneumococci were probably permanently impaired. She would have to be careful travelling in tropical countries, because it had an important role in combating protozoal parasites. She would . . .

Philippa gave herself a mental shake. Such thinking was negative and ungrateful. Mr Crowland and Neil had saved her life; thank heavens for their skill. Now it was up to her to get better and make everyone's efforts worthwhile.

She watched the dull glow of the night-light again, trying to bore herself into sleep, but her brain was not yet ready to settle down. It was interesting how easy some medical facts were to recall. They were safe, sober, unaffected by emotions such

as fear – or guilt. But as for other things ... the events of
Friday ...

Philippa still accepted the concussion theory. Amnesia
commonly followed head injuries, even mild ones. She was convinced that hers was real, not the hysterical type where people
couldn't face their unpleasant experiences. Her nature was not
like that; she had no truck with mirages and self-deception.

But in that case, why was she beginning to dread her memory
returning? That had once been her most fervent desire; now she
was less sure. Gilbert Bradshaw was dead, and she had been
right outside his house. Perhaps even in his house. The police
had told her very little, but their continual appearances had worn
away at her composure, like water against limestone, leaving a
raw area of doubt. Was it possible ... could she actually be a
killer?

8

'There's a bit of news from Forensic,' said Montgomery, beckon-
ing his two sergeants into the office, 'but otherwise information is
thin on the ground.'

They settled into chairs as he continued: 'First, the glass found
on the road where Philippa was lying. It's consistent with the
type used for Maestro headlamps. Enquiries among people who
frequented the same hospital car-park as Bradshaw have turned
up no one who can recall seeing any damage to the Maestro last
week. Haslam and Grange had a chat with a particularly garrulous porter whose main job is to prowl the car-park looking for
vehicles without parking permits; more and more staff are
coming in cars these days, so they've got to be strict. He's in the
best position to have noticed anything amiss with the "regular"
cars. Someone's Citroën had been in a scrape, but the Maestro
was fine.

'Next – and more damning – there was a thread of green
lambswool caught on the offside jacking point of the Maestro. It
matches Philippa Rowe's torn jumper perfectly.' He paused.
'Mere confirmation of what we already suspected. It's difficult to
come up with any evidence indicating the presence of a third

party, yet I'm not satisfied with our theories for Bradshaw and Philippa Rowe alone; they just don't make sense. For instance, I've been told that one of Philippa's fingerprints was on the inside door handle of Bradshaw's bedroom, but the bed was untouched and she flatly denies any relationship.'

'Maybe he tried to force her,' suggested Jackson. 'He might have been high on drugs.'

Montgomery shook his head. 'I was just coming to that. The serum analyses have drawn a blank except for traces of paracetamol and another substance called dextropropoxyphene. These are the components of a tablet bearing the generic name of Coproxamol, which is a great favourite among arthritis sufferers and others with chronic pain. Bradshaw had a bottle of them in his bathroom cupboard, and they were prescribed by his own GP. It fits with the back pain. Apparently aspirin-based preparations and most of the other anti-inflammatory drugs are not recommended for people with ulcers. That wouldn't leave him a lot of choice. The laboratory findings are perfectly reasonable.'

'Nothing else?'

'Neither gram nor dram.'

Jackson was disappointed. 'I don't know . . . quiet type, no friends . . . I bet he had a secret. If not drugs, then some perversion . . . wait! The body was nearly four days old. A drug could have broken down by then.'

'Not the major narcotics. Metabolism stops at death. Morphine's been found in bodies exhumed after months in the ground.' He looked at them both and shrugged. 'So far, we're stumped. Our publicity's been greeted by a resounding silence. Bradshaw's death and the hit-and-run are firmly linked by his own car, but that doesn't seem to lead us anywhere.

'We've got enough background information on the working lives of Bradshaw and Philippa Rowe to fill a fair-sized book, but it's bland, pappy stuff. He was a bit of an invalid, and she was "sensible". No tantrums, dark passions or secret grudges – unless you can count David Stannard, the rejected boyfriend. I spoke to him yesterday. Seems a straight enough young man. Neither Bradshaw nor Philippa appears to have been a threat to anyone.'

'Dead end,' said Jackson glumly.

'Not necessarily; we just have to scratch a bit deeper, that's all. But with our current case load, it won't be easy.'

'This David Stannard,' began Sergeant Bird, 'has he an alibi for last Friday night?'

'Of sorts. Not the watertight kind concocted for a premeditated crime. He'd been on duty the night before, so he spent Friday evening lazing around. Said he watched a documentary on bamboo rats and part of a quiz programme in the Mess, then had a shower and joined a group of his colleagues at the Mortar and Pestle around nine o'clock. He stayed until closing time.'

'Did anyone see him in the Mess?'

'He was vague about that bit. People were coming and going all the time. He mentioned Stewart Bridges, the surgical houseman who is looking after Philippa, and two anaesthetists, but the rest were conveniently nameless – members of the shifting pool of medical students. I haven't had time to see any of them. You can. Check that they actually *were* watching the nature programme, and not the other side.'

'Yes . . .' Sergeant Bird looked thoughtful. 'That kind of programme would be a lucky chance for anyone wanting an alibi, wouldn't it? No plot, like a drama, but a specific subject you could read about in the library. The same goes for a quiz show, but for the opposite reason. There's so much going on that no one could be expected to remember the questions.'

Brian Jackson was visibly perking up. 'Too right! If no one can confirm his presence in the Mess, that leaves two clear periods when he could have driven out to Sylvia Vale and caused mayhem. Suppose he's been following Philippa around, gripped by pathological jealousy? Bradshaw offers her a lift, to go and see his fish or something quite innocent, then Stannard bursts in and knocks him down the stairs. The girl is terrified, and runs out on to the road. Stannard grabs the Maestro keys from Bradshaw's pocket, drives after her, hits her, then runs over her for good measure. Thinking she's dead, he returns the car to the garage, sets the deadlock on the front door, engages the mortice from the outside, then chucks the keys in through the letter-box to point suspicion at Bradshaw. Simple!'

'Mmm.' Montgomery steepled his fingers. 'Why didn't he lock the garage door to complete the deception?'

'In a hurry.'

'The pressure would have been off him by then. His greatest urgency would have been the minute Philippa fled the house. And you suggest that he wasted time rifling Bradshaw's pockets

87

in the hope of finding car keys – which could have been put down anywhere – in order to drive a car which was probably safely locked in the garage. It was a dark, wet evening. Philippa could have hidden by then, or reached help. Wouldn't he have leapt into his own car, or followed on foot?'

Jackson's mouth set stubbornly. 'I imagined him parking outside the grounds and creeping up to the house. Besides, he'd have been reluctant to damage his own car. Bit of a giveaway.'

'Looked at coolly, yes. But you've outlined a scene where split-second decisions needed to be made. Follow the girl and reason with her? Or mow her down? The decision to follow. The decision to kill – which he must have thought he'd done. Which car to take? Surely the most instantly accessible. And there's nowhere to park on that narrow country road, neither is there any space at the bottom of the drive. I would have thought he'd jump in his own car, parked outside the house. He may have driven up beforehand quite openly and knocked on the door.'

'Has anyone seen Stannard's car?' enquired Sergeant Bird.

'No. There's another job for you. In addition, I want you to see a doctor called Barnaby Fletcher. He may be able to throw some light on Bradshaw's home life. His name cropped up two or three times during yesterday's interviews. They shared a common hobby – tropical fish.'

William Bird nodded his acquiescence. 'I know a bit about those myself.'

'You would,' said Jackson, not entirely good-humouredly. His jaundiced eye slid round to Montgomery. 'And me?'

'I'd be grateful if you'd go and see Mr Pendle in person – the Bradshaw family's solicitor. Find out Gilbert Bradshaw's exact financial circumstances and how they might have been affected by his death. Something doesn't add up in that quarter. The house is clearly run down, yet his colleagues seemed to be under the impression that he was a rich man. See if there's any more news of possible beneficiaries. We might unearth a motive yet.'

When Jackson had gone, Montgomery transferred his attention back to the bulky figure of Sergeant Bird, who was frowning over his notepad.

'What is it, Will? Something we haven't covered?'

'No, Sir. It's those keys . . .' He scratched the side of his forehead. 'I don't think it's possible, throwing them accurately through the letter-box like that. They were right against the dead man's pocket, nearly ten feet away . . . Yet parts of Brian's scenario seemed feasible, even likely. I feel that there's a third person in this, somewhere.'

'So do I. Someone with a quick brain, who knew how to avoid leaving the place strewn with clues. Let's go out to Sylvia Vale and conduct some experiments. I fancy a breath of fresh air.'

'Now?'

'Why not? It may prove to be the key – literally.'

Sergeant Bird was a competent but unexciting driver, which meant that Montgomery could relax in the passenger seat. His own performance had more flair, but even he was reduced to infancy when compared with his wife Carole's tearaway young cousin Mark, who had a disquieting predilection for fast cars. Once, in an unguarded moment, Montgomery had commented to Mark that he would be safer on a racing circuit than the open road – not to mention standing more chance of keeping his licence. The penalty for this folly was now at hand; a promise had been extracted from him to spend the forthcoming Sunday at Donington Park Racing Circuit with Carole, cheering on any passing blur which might conceivably represent Mark in his Fiesta XR2.

William Bird gave a sigh of contentment beside him. 'Beautiful countryside,' he said. 'People imagine Nottinghamshire's just mining and industry, but they should see this. Fields and rolling woodlands, villages of red-roofed cottages . . . tranquillity everywhere you care to look.'

It was a warm, torpid day, one of the last of the Indian summer, the kind to view through half-closed eyes. Montgomery was doing exactly that.

'Have you any special plans for the weekend, sir?'

'You're a thought-reader, Will. I was just contemplating Sunday's obligations. Young Mark has finally pinned me down; I'm going to watch him at Donington.'

His companion chuckled. 'You might even enjoy it. Regular racegoers get hooked on the excitement, the general noise and bustle.'

'We get enough of that in the station. I'm hoping for a sunny day – something like today – and a bit of tasty food. I reckon if I make a fuss between now and Sunday, Carole will pack a specially good spread in order to propitiate me.'

'You ought to be ashamed. Petulance is a two-edged weapon; she might not pack any at all!'

'True. She will if you come, though. How about it?'

'That's blackmail, sir – I'd be delighted.'

'Good. The day may prove to be tolerable after all . . . Isn't this our entry?'

The car made a neat left turn into the rutted driveway of Gilbert Bradshaw's deserted home. Even in sunlight the straggling shrubbery looked mournful, while on either side of the drive the weeds stood mockingly erect. As they pulled up in front of the house, a wisp of cumulus temporarily blotted out the face of the sun. Both police officers felt a dragging sense of oppression.

'Let's not hang around,' said Montgomery, eyeing the newly repaired front door and the curtained windows flanking it, blind sentinels, guardians of darkness and death. 'Have you got the keys?'

'The car keys are down at Forensic, but I can attach some of mine to make up the weight. Just a moment . . .' With a slight effort, Sergeant Bird snapped the requisite number of keys on to the key-ring then tossed the resulting bunch in his hand assessingly. 'That's about right.'

They opened the front door and knelt down by the outline in the hall.

'Here,' said Montgomery, pointing to the position of the left hip. 'This is what you've got to aim at. Try five times, then I'll have a go.'

Sergeant Bird's disappearance was followed by a squeak as the letter-box opened. A moment later, the keys sailed through the air in a gleaming arc to land noisily two feet short. Montgomery made a small chalk mark.

'Try again.'

This time, there was a clatter outside, followed by a muffled cluck of annoyance.

'Sorry, sir. Hit the edge of the box. It's not so easy.'

Only one of the chalk marks proved to be close to the target. Sergeant Bird stared down philosophically at the end of his efforts, then crouched on his haunches with a little difficulty as Montgomery took his turn.

The inspector's throws were more consistent, but once again the necessary degree of accuracy was lacking.

'It would be perfectly straightforward in the open air,' he commented, 'But being confined to that narrow aperture wrecks everything. Our murderer, if he exists, could hardly pick the keys up and have another go – he'd be locked out.'

'There's something else,' said Sergeant Bird in his measured way. 'The point you made earlier. If we've got a character who was cool enough to reverse the Maestro back into the garage, and set not one but *two* front door locks in an attempt to imply that Bradshaw was on his own and had locked up for the night, why didn't he complete the picture and lock the garage, too? The key was on the ring. An extra four seconds, if that.'

'I don't know,' sighed Montgomery. 'This third person is still an abstraction as far as tangible evidence is concerned. All we've proved with the keys today is that it's very difficult to throw them to a precise spot through the letter-box. We can't say someone *didn't* do it. It could have been a lucky shot. Or perhaps Bradshaw *was* on his own. Maybe he simply forgot about the garage door.'

Sergeant Bird shook his head. 'No, I can't agree with that last bit. He seems to have been a neat individual at home. Papers filed, everything tidy from the kitchen to the bathroom cabinet. The window locks were engaged. The back door was locked and bolted, the front as we know. Nothing excessive, sadly, in this day and age; it just reflects a careful disposition. A man like that would lock his garage.'

'Unless he was in a hurry to barricade himself in the house!' exclaimed Montgomery with a flash of inspiration.

Sergeant Bird considered, rolling the chalk between his finger and thumb. 'Running for his life? I like it – but nobody forced an entry. And the only alternative is square one – panic at what he had just done . . .'

They returned to the car with relief, glancing back once at the house with its peeling paintwork and chilling air of soullessness.

'There's a clue here,' said Montgomery. 'And we've missed it.'

His companion gunned the engine. 'What happened to the fish?' he asked.

'A dealer in Ilkeston is looking after them. That reminds me – get as much as you can out of Barnaby Fletcher. He's the doctor who shared Bradshaw's interest in tropical fish. Draw him out in your inimitable manner; he seems to be the only person who was ever invited to this house.'

'A dubious privilege,' he added in a low voice as they drove away.

David Stannard peered out across the crowded dining-room and spotted Neil at a corner table with Tony Spitz, a registrar on one of the other surgical teams. Audrey always spent her lunch hour in the office, eating sandwiches and gossiping with her girl friends, a fact for which he felt disloyally grateful; mealtimes were his best opportunity for informal discussion with colleagues from different specialties.

He made a bee-line in their direction, and they both smiled acknowledgment as he transferred his plate and cutlery from the tray on to the table.

'Hi, Dave,' said Tony. 'What've they fobbed you off with this time? Smells exotic.'

'I don't know. I just pointed. These days they have to placate vegetarians, Muslims and goodness knows who else, so it's a bit of a lucky dip. I think it's called dhal.'

'Indian spiced lentils,' said Neil, pushing fishbones tidily to the side of his plate.

David sampled a cautious mouthful. 'You're right.'

Tony was called away before they could converse further, leaving David and Neil some distance from the nearest pair of ears.

'Is there any more news on your suspected MRSA case?' asked David quietly.

'Yes. It's confirmed.' Neil took a sip of water. 'That nurse was the carrier – she has eczema on her hands. So you can imagine the consequences: everyone on Clumber Ward's got to be screened.'

'Just make sure you keep it down there,' said David, only half joking.

'We'll do our best. I'm still trying to teach Stewart that sterile technique doesn't begin and end in theatre.'

'How's your racing going? You always seem to swing the right weekends off.'

'Proof of the virtues of forward planning. If I don't compete, I can't get the points, and this year I intend to win.'

'Has anyone agreed to sponsor you yet? Didn't you approach a computer software firm?'

Neil gave a rueful grimace. 'Yes. That one was almost in the bag, then their sales figures fell and they got cold feet. I politely pointed out that advertising was surely even more important now, but they vacillated and finally said "no".'

'I'm sorry. What about the big local industries?'

'Sure.' There was irony in the tone. 'Raleigh bicycles. Nottingham lace. John Player cigarettes – just the thing for a doctor to advocate. There's a voluntary freeze on tobacco sponsorship in motor sports at present anyway, and it won't stop there . . . that whole concept is on the wane, I'm convinced.'

'You've missed the obvious one: Boots.'

'No – I'm waiting to hear from them.'

'Well, good luck. May your bank manager always be amenable.'

'He is – but he won't be when he hears what I *really* want to borrow.' Neil began to attack his apple pie. 'I want to break into Formula Ford, and soon. Next season. Then I've got to catch some promoter's eye in a big way, because making my mark as a driver won't be enough; I'll need a lot of hard cash to persuade one of the established Formula Three teams to take me on.'

David could feel his eyes widening. 'Formula Three?' he echoed.

'Well, of course that's just a stepping-stone to Formula One.'

'Grand Prix racing.' David nodded, his voice holding the bright, agreeable lilt one uses when speaking to the hopelessly deranged. He waited a moment. 'You're serious?'

'Absolutely.'

'But – ' He groped for inoffensive words, then gave up. 'Aren't you too *old*?'

'I'm twenty-nine. In terms of driving skill and stamina that's not over the hill; Derek Bell won his fifth Le Mans at the age of forty-five – in a Porsche, incidentally – and you know that race is one of the most gruelling in the world. It's a marathon. But in terms of racing career impetus, twenty-nine *is* old. I open the *Motoring News*, and there are all these twenty-two-year-olds grinning out from the pages, fully established in Formula Three.'

'You said "career". What about your surgical career?'

'I don't find it a challenge any more. Most of the work's routine, let's face it. I could return to medicine in some form later on, while if I miss the boat in racing, that's that. End of story.'

Neil meant what he said, that much was clear. He had recited

93

his objectives calmly, with no apparent sense of their enormity beyond an impassive appraisal of the financial strings attached. And something in his manner instilled confidence in the listener; one *knew* he was going to succeed. Lack of funds only constituted a temporary setback.

David sat with his cutlery poised while Neil steadily ate pie.

'I'm sure you'll find what you're looking for,' he said. 'Especially if you win this season – sponsors will be falling over themselves to offer you contracts. But in the meantime, have you thought of asking Vanda if she'll help? I bet she'd love to.'

A distinctly Arctic chill emanated from the blue eyes opposite. 'I'm taking nothing from Vanda,' he snapped.

'Sorry,' mumbled David, aware that he had committed a *faux pas*.

Neil left shortly afterwards, and David slowly finished his dhal. If Neil did switch completely to racing, it would be a significant loss to surgery; Vernon Crowland wouldn't be at all pleased. And yet he felt he understood why. Ask a mountain climber why he risked life and limb hauling himself up some inhospitable peak, and he would say: 'Because it's there.' It was the same for Neil and racing – the lure of bigger and better championships, an end point to aim for, something to achieve.

With anyone else, one might have suspected that he craved the razzmatazz associated with the circuit, but with Neil that was definitely not the case. He eschewed the glamour aspects completely; in fact, he was mildly contemptuous of them. He never took advantage of his relationship with Vanda and her public world. His ego was self-contained, unassailable. Trappings were for the plebs.

David smiled as a neat association of imagery occurred to him. Neil was like his car, a glorious silver fifteen-year-old Porsche Carrera RS ... smooth and sleek, cold and powerful ... dangerous.

As Brian Jackson pushed open the venerable mahogany front door of Pendle, Rathbone and Blair (Solicitors and Commissioners for Oaths), to enter their small green-carpeted lobby, a peevishly raised voice reached his ears.

'... it's *illiterate*, that's what. Look at this paragraph – three sentences blurred into one. No punctuation at all! And these words ... this one ... and this. The spelling is abysmal. Utterly abysmal. "Attend" with one "t". "Convenience" spelt with an "a". I could continue for half an hour, but I trust the point is made. Your work may satisfy Mr Blair, but I assure you it falls a long way short of *my* expectations. We aren't one of those upstart outfits advertising cut-price rates in the *Recorder*. Ours is a respected firm; the quality of our staff should reflect the quality of our clients. Anything less is insulting. Do you understand what I'm telling you? Good – then please type these letters again. I'll sign them at four.'

Jackson felt a twinge of sympathy for the recipient of this onslaught, having suffered similar castigations from Montgomery in his time. He hoped the speaker would not prove to be Pendle, since that would bode ill for his own interview. Entering a brightly lit reception area, he caught sight of a thin man with crinkled grey hair and narrow chin turning away from the desk with an air of impatience and vanishing through a door at the rear.

The blonde girl seated behind the desk pulled a face at his retreating back then pouted childishly before she noticed Jackson. He gave her his most charming smile.

'Hello. I'm Sergeant Jackson. I rang up this morning to ask if Mr Pendle could spare me a few minutes of his time. He's expecting me at two-thirty. Er – I don't suppose yours was the sexy contralto on the telephone?'

She simpered, and attempted a coquettish attitude, but was intellectually unable to respond to his badinage beyond the monosyllable 'No'.

'A pity,' said Jackson, sighing inwardly. 'Still, I imagine she isn't a beautiful blonde. Perhaps that was Mr Pendle just leaving as I came in?'

The girl's face hardened, and its expression became aggrieved once more. 'No, that was Mr Rathbone. He's Conveyancing. His own secretary is away just now. I do Mr Blair's letters. He's Divorce.'

'I see. Well – if you'd be kind enough to tell Mr Pendle I'm here . . .'

The idea seemed to strike the girl as a novelty, but she recovered and indicated the empty row of seats down one wall of the room.

'Right away, sir,' she chirruped mechanically. 'Please take a seat. There are magazines on the table.'

As she pressed a series of buttons on the telephone, Jackson wandered over to the table and idly sorted through copies of *Key Note* which were arranged in an artistic sprawl. On a small stand at the back were various printed leaflets with inspiring titles such as *It's Never Too Soon To Make Your Will* and *Understanding The Decree Nisi*. He had no intention of waiting indefinitely.

'Sergeant Johnson is here,' the girl shrilled into her receiver. There was a pause, then: 'Yes, Mr Pendle.'

'He'll see you now,' she said to Jackson in confidential tones. 'His office is on the first floor at the front.' No nonsense about showing him the way, even in this establishment.

'Thanks.' Jackson winked at her, and escaped with relief into the lobby.

A door swung open as he reached the top of the stairs, and Arthur Pendle waited courteously on the threshold. He was a tall man in his early sixties, with a round, shrewd face and a brown suit which achieved the miracle of looking both smart and comfortable at the same time. His thinning hair gave hints that he had once been a redhead, while a pepper-and-salt moustache surmounted his smile.

'Good afternoon,' he said, offering his hand. 'I'm Pendle. I believe your name was Jackson this morning?'

'Yes.'

'The correct version, I should imagine. I apologize for Miss Silkin's error. Do come in. You want to talk about Gilbert Bradshaw, I gather?'

'Yes. Thank you for sparing the time.'

'No matter. Please sit down ... Yes, I was discussing the Bradshaws with your Inspector Montgomery on Tuesday. Tragic affair. An unlucky family, I'm afraid. Sometimes it seems quite inequitable, the way these things strike. So random.'

Jackson, who had sunk appreciatively into a leather-covered high-backed chair, took surreptitious stock of his surroundings. Here in Mr Pendle's office was the quasi-Dickensian interior he had expected to encounter on entering the building. Somehow the bright clinical reception area had come as a rude shock, an unwelcome reminder that firms of solicitors ran a commercial enterprise like anyone else, a business with outgoings as well as enormous fees. Perhaps young blood now had a say in the style of their presentation, and had chosen to project an image of untrammelled efficiency. A pity Miss Silkin could not deliver.

The first-floor landing, though, was the gateway to tradition. This high-ceilinged, quiet room had brown velvet curtains, sturdy legal tomes on real oak shelves, and a mahogany desk with tooled leather inset, bordered by gold leaf. There was even an inkstand. No mawkish family photographs or coffee mugs.

Mr Pendle's light and pleasant voice had ceased on a faint note of enquiry. Jackson smoothly replied: 'Unlucky. Wasn't it Napoleon who always asked his generals whether or not they were lucky? He rated that quality above all others.'

The solicitor nodded approbation, and Jackson was pleased with his contribution; he had first heard the sentiment expressed by Sergeant Bird approximately one week before.

'Well now, Sergeant Jackson,' said Pendle, settling in his chair. 'What precisely would you like to know?'

Jackson concentrated. 'First, we need some background on Bradshaw senior, an explanation for the anomaly between an apparently prosperous family and a house which is, frankly, run-down. Then there's the will. Both wills, in fact. I did wonder whether Gilbert's father had left his money outside the immediate family for some reason – making Gilbert pay his way, perhaps, while allowing him to keep the family home. That might account for Gilbert's obvious struggle in maintaining the place. And his own will ... did he make another after his parents died?'

'Hmm. Quite a lot there. We'll start with Thomas Bradshaw's financial situation. You may know that he was a stockbroker, a prosperous, well-respected one. He built up an excellent reputation over many years, and one would have described him as solid rather than flashy. Cautious people trusted his advice to the letter. Shortly after Gilbert was born, Thomas and Marion moved from West Bridgford out to Sylvia Vale, and bought the house they were to live in until their deaths. I arranged the conveyancing myself, although latterly that aspect of my work has devolved on Mr Rathbone. There was a mortgage, of course, since houses in the area were expensive even then, and this was duly paid off. Young Gilbert was sent away to Winchester, but he was unhappy there and actually returned to a local grammar school.'

He paused. 'Seven years ago Thomas Bradshaw made a profound error of judgement. Do you remember United Cobalt? What an attractive issue that was! I almost subscribed myself. And how prodigiously it sank!

97

'Tom behaved in a way which was totally alien to his character. "A madness," he later explained it to Marion; she told me that. Without her knowledge he had borrowed heavily and bought a huge block of those shares. When they were rendered worthless, he had lost not only his wealth, but more important, his reputation. One ill-considered act destroyed him. He was haunted by shame, by the knowledge that other men had been ruined because they had followed his advice. Poor Tom – he couldn't have punished himself more if he'd been an embezzler.

'His isolation from long-standing friends was entirely self-imposed. Young Gilbert came to me with an idea for sorting out the mess. They had already sold their paintings and all the best items of furniture. The shortfall was considerable, and the interest rates crippling. Their obvious remaining asset was the house. We decided that it should be mortgaged in Gilbert's name. His father was incapable of work, and while it grieved him to pass the burden of failure on to his son, he acknowledged the sense in it.

'For Gilbert's part, he was happy to be given an opportunity to repay all his parents had done for him, and make up for disappointing them in the past. He had a steady job, albeit not an especially lucrative one at that time, and had no difficulty in being accepted as mortgagor. We completed the transfer of ownership; a life insurance policy was incorporated into the arrangement, not for any sinister reason, but more by way of a little belated caution. A few months later, Gilbert decided to make a will – his first – in his parents' favour. Their own will, naming him as virtually sole beneficiary and executor, had been drawn up twenty years before, and remained unchanged. So you see, Sergeant Jackson, there was no question of Gilbert's being deprived of money by his parents. They were a very close family – perhaps too close.'

'It was just an idea,' said Jackson. 'What you've said fits the facts nicely. Where does that leave us with Gilbert's will?'

Mr Pendle gave a small, regretful sigh. 'The elder Bradshaws were both killed outright when a falling tree crushed their car three years ago. It was a freak accident in a storm – your people know all about it. Gilbert apparently never saw fit to revise his will. He was thirty-seven at the time, in reasonable health, and presumably had no one special he wished to leave his estate to. That will cannot now take effect, since the legatees have prede-

98

ceased him. To all intents and purposes, then, he has died intestate. A common situation, I assure you.'

'But surely there's a legal formula to cover this eventuality?'

'That is so. The rule of law now designates those individuals entitled to the property. As I said, a common enough occurrence. The difficulty is in finding them. We have had recourse to the usual channels of communication – the local and national press. An erstwhile domestic helper has been tracked down; she left their employ when the financial crisis occurred. Her name is Marjorie Hanson, and she was one of the witnesses to Thomas Bradshaw's will. She gave them twenty-two years of service. Her work took place in the mornings, and so she was not in an ideal position to assess their social and family matters, but she did hint at the existence of relatives on the distaff side. There appears to have been some kind of schism, dating back well before the United Cobalt disaster.'

'Interesting,' mused Jackson. He lifted his head. 'These potential beneficiaries – is the pecking order as one would expect?'

A glimmer of amusement flickered in Pendle's grey eyes. 'You could say that. In the absence of a surviving husband or wife, children, or parents, we move on to brothers and sisters of the whole blood. If they are themselves deceased, they may be represented by their own offspring.

'The next category embraces relatives of a remoter degree – brothers and sisters of the half blood, then grandparents – not applicable in this instance – uncles and aunts of the whole blood, and finally uncles and aunts of the half blood. Once again, their own children may represent them.'

'I see. So a half-brother, say, comes before an uncle or a cousin.'

'Yes.'

'And if no designated relatives are found, the estate passes to the Crown?'

'Yes again, but in point of fact the mechanism is not entirely rigid. If there is a dependent or some such person whom the testator would clearly have wished to benefit, provision may be made, even if that person is not a relative as described. Sponsoring an orphan abroad, for example.'

'Ah.'

'So there you have it. Was there anything else you wished to discuss, Sergeant Jackson?'

'No. I'm obliged to you. You've made it all very clear.'

'Good. Then you won't mind my asking a question, will you?'

'I can't promise to answer, sir.'

'That is appreciated. When he rang me, Inspector Montgomery described Gilbert Bradshaw's death as "suspicious". Since you are pursuing his legal affairs in this way, I must assume that no outsider has, as yet, been implicated. Do you therefore imagine that a *relative* may have had some connection with the death?'

'We don't know,' said Jackson candidly. 'That's what we have to find out. Anything's possible.'

Mr Pendle stood up and escorted him to the door. 'How very disturbing,' he said.

Jackson lingered briefly in the lobby, mentally debating whether or not to extend the courtesy of a 'good-bye' to Miss Silkin. Through the glass-panelled door, he could see her examining a strand of her blonde hair at close range, presumably checking it for split ends. The bright reception room was silent. No clients pored over *It's Never Too Soon To Make Your Will*. No typewriter clacked. (Had she finished Mr Rathbone's letters already, or was this just a break?)

Perhaps those upstarts in the High Street were providing more competition than Mr Rathbone cared to admit. Everyone had their problems, even the apparently prosperous.

Jackson quickened his stride and left.

9

'In here . . . er, sorry, no. Perhaps not.' Barnaby Fletcher's wide pink brow was creased with anxiety as he blundered out of the Doctors' Mess, Sergeant Bird at his elbow.

'Not very private,' he explained, the words tumbling out in erratic bursts. 'Some people are having tea. I don't know . . .'

'Is there a canteen?' asked Sergeant Bird pleasantly. 'We could have a quiet cuppa ourselves. If your colleagues usually come to the Mess, we won't be disturbed.'

'Er, yes. Yes!' Barnaby gasped with relief. The very name 'Detective Sergeant William Bird' seemed to have thrown him into a state of dithering incompetence, even though the absence of uniform meant that his companion would not be remarked upon.

In a distant corner of the canteen, several yards from the nearest occupied table, Sergeant Bird took a satisfying bite of Bakewell tart and prepared to allay the young neurologist's fears.

'It's just routine,' he said casually, dabbing at his mouth with a napkin. 'We're trying to trace anything which might shed light on the reasons for Dr Bradshaw's accident – anything at all, a word, an appointment . . . As you know, we've interviewed some of your friends already, and we understand that you knew Dr Bradshaw fairly well.'

'I – yes, that's true, He was very good to me. I wanted some fish for Rebecca, my wife, to relax her when she was pregnant. Oh – not to eat; I meant tropical fish. I thought that it would give her something interesting to watch while she was at home. They're so peaceful and friendly. That's why Gil liked them.'

'Did he help you choose the fish?'

'Not in the beginning. I – er – made a few mistakes myself first. I thought it was all straightforward – a tank, a heater, a filter, some plants, a bit of food. Oh, and the fish, of course. I didn't want to bother anyone else. But then I had – er, the odd problem. The tank got choked with algae, and I thought I'd better clean it all out and start again. Unfortunately I, er, didn't have a fish-tail gadget for the siphon tube and – well – three of my neon tetras suddenly disappeared. It didn't, er, do them any good. Then I moved the tank to get the last of the water out. The other fish were in buckets by then. You're not supposed to do that – move the tank. Not unless it's a plastic one, or is sealed with one of those glass-bonding adhesives. Er, it started to leak. Quite badly, in fact. No water pressure holding it together, you see. I rang Gil up and he came over immediately. That was very kind of him. It was a Sunday.

'He did a temporary repair on the tank, then put me straight with respect to quite a few things. Apparently you don't have the lights on all the time – it encourages algae. And my tank had been in the window, getting all the sunlight. The heater was in the wrong place, too. It was hanging down the back. He said I'd get stratification that way, and the catfish would be too cold at the bottom. They *were* rather languid. He showed me how to build up gravel banks, where to put the heater – everything. I didn't like to tell him about the neons, but Becka let it slip. He was ever so cross.'

Sergeant Bird looked suitably sympathetic, and noticed that the other, who had initially quaffed his tea in wild gulps, was now taking delicate sips.

'Did Dr Bradshaw advise you on your stock?' he asked.

'Yes. He knew a reputable dealer. Some are cowboys, you know. They don't give the fish the proper time and, er, conditions to acclimatize when they come from abroad. It weakens them; they go into shock and die soon after they've been sold. Gil knew a good man in Ilkeston. I decided to have a second tank, so we went along and chose what was needed.'

'I used to keep tropical fish myself,' said Sergeant Bird amiably, seeing no point in withholding his card any longer. 'My favourites were the angel fish – beautiful and graceful. There are so many types now; I had veil-tail and marbled.'

Barnaby's eyes lit up with enthusiasm. 'Isn't that amazing! I like the angels, too. But you can't have a lot of fish that size in a tank. I've gone in for smaller ones – tiger barbs, platies, zebras and, er, neon tetras. The catfish in the other tank are quite large. I wanted some dwarf gouramis, but Becka wasn't keen on the shape.'

'Too blunt, perhaps.'

'Yes. She even suggested that they weren't aesthetic – and I hadn't shown her those really strange fish, with beards and all kinds of projections . . .'

'Were you invited to see Dr Bradshaw's own stock?'

'Not at first. He said he was decorating, and the house was a mess. But just recently I went out there to pick up some fish he'd offered me from his breeding tank. Nice zebras – really fast swimmers. He had a false bottom in the tank. I couldn't think why, until he told me. They eat their eggs. Imagine!'

The zebras were not alone in this tendency, but Sergeant Bird resisted the temptation to cap Barnaby's story with his own.

'When did you make this visit?' he asked mildly.

'I'm not sure.' Barnaby's face grew suddenly slack, his voice vague. 'Three weeks ago . . . maybe four.'

'Perhaps you can relate it to another incident that week. Do you recollect the actual day?'

'I – er . . . Becka will know. Or there's my diary . . .' He fumbled in one of his capacious white pockets and drew out a slim leather-covered book. 'Let's see . . . Monday – no, it wouldn't have been a Monday. Hmm. These are mainly medical reminders. It can't have been a Tuesday or a Thursday during the last week in August. I was on call then. It was definitely an evening, though, and not a weekend. Maybe – wait a minute . . . it could have been the Thursday of the following week. I can't say.'

A variety of helpful hints failed to elicit the necessary information, so Sergeant Bird shelved the question pending words with Rebecca Fletcher. Still in a friendly, conversational tone, he asked:

'What was your impression of the house when you saw it?'

'I didn't really notice. Becka says I'm not very observant. He was still decorating. He had a comfortable den upstairs. There was one fish-tank in there, but the others were all round the walls of the lounge.'

'Had you heard any – rumours about his financial status?'

Barnaby looked taken aback. 'Rumours? No, I don't recall any.'

'Did people find it odd that he lived in such an expensive area yet wore an old anorak to work?'

'Nobody said so to me. He was probably fond of the anorak.'

'Was there any kind of gossip about Gilbert at the hospital?'

'What do you mean?'

'Oh, just stories. I gather hospitals are rife with one sort of tale or another.'

'I don't know any.'

'Fair enough. How was he when you went to see him?'

'Do you mean his back?'

'No – his demeanour: happy, sad, boisterous, quiet . . . ?'

Barnaby considered. 'Just normal,' he said. 'If anything, slightly better.'

'Better than what?' Sergeant Bird suppressed his eagerness; this sounded promising.

'Oh, than before. He had been edgy, moody . . . not quite his normal self. I think his back had been playing him up again. He missed a few days of work around that time.'

'Are we talking about a month ago?'

'More like two months.'

'Did the back trouble depress him?'

'I imagine it must have. It spoiled his chances in surgery. But I never heard him complain.'

'Dr Fletcher . . . I'd like you to think carefully before you answer this next question. You know that your friend Gilbert was found at the bottom of the stairs, his neck broken. Can you think of any reason to suppose that he did it himself?'

Again the young doctor's face sagged, and the mournful eyes behind thick spectacles fleetingly signalled his loss.

'Suicide,' he said quietly. 'That's what you're suggesting, isn't it? Well I say no. Never. Suicide is for the weak, and Gil was a fighter. People here didn't take the trouble to get to know him. Life was easy for them – they hadn't suffered as he had.'

'Even so – perhaps an accumulation of depressing events . . . ?'

'No, Sergeant Bird. I *know* he didn't commit suicide. There's one good reason. He didn't make any provision for his fish.'

'May I ask what makes you say that?'

The rosy cheeks became a shade rosier. 'Milton told me. In confidence, of course. No note, and ravenous fish . . . I knew then it was an accident.'

'Maybe there was no one sufficiently close to warrant a note. Maybe his mind was disturbed at the time and he simply forgot the fish.'

'Never! You must understand, Sergeant – he loved those fish. He would never have abandoned them like that. They were his friends.'

Coral clumped wearily up the gloomy stairway to her flat, sticky, tousled and ready for a bath. Her arms, taut bell-ropes with a carrier bag at the end of each, felt elongated, gorilla-like.

Fighting Joe and Mrs Public *en masse* in seething supermarkets was not her favourite way of spending an evening, but she had to be fair. Maureen had done most of their shopping of late, tabulating items on the 'tick-list' in her small, neat handwriting with shy reluctance. It was all too easy to exploit her good nature, and something to guard against.

The outer door was unlocked, but the handle still had to be turned. She made a shambling entrance, staggered to the kitchen, and plonked her burdens on to the table with relief. Directly across the short, linoleum-covered corridor behind her was the bathroom. Its door was ajar; damp, scented plumes of vapour issued from the opening, auguring her own pleasures to come. She heard the clunk of bottles being replaced on the glass shelf over the washbasin.

'Hi, Maureen,' she called. 'I've made it at last. Is the immersion still on?'

'Yes.' The disembodied voice mingled with the steam. 'The water should be hot for you. How was your day?'

'Oh, hectic as usual. Nancy was off sick, and we'd promised to take a group of schoolgirls round the ward and show them something of a nurse's work. They were late, which didn't help. An involved story about a puncture in a minibus . . . Their arrival coincided with the patients' lunches, and for the third time this week the kitchens didn't send the diabetic choices we'd asked for. Then poor old Mrs Fenner died just when the girls were crowded round her bed. You remember – the hemiplegic lady I told you about? It was all rather embarrassing. We tried to pretend she was asleep, but I don't think they were fooled in the least. The only bright spot was David – he's got a sleeper-out on our ward. A nice young girl with asthma. He came to see her this afternoon . . .'

As she chattered unremittingly, bodily fatigue in no way diminishing her conversational energy, Coral knelt and stretched, stowing tins and packages in the various kitchen cupboards. Maureen emerged from her tropical cocoon and flitted wraith-like down the corridor, a blur of pale pink towelling bathrobe. Soon the hum of the hairdryer put a temporary stop to their shouted exchanges. Coral made herself a cup of tea, carried it through to the living-room, then slumped down in the worn armchair, still wearing her bright orange raincoat.

She picked up a local paper which Maureen had presumably bought, and idly leafed through its pages. The click of the wardrobe door in the bedroom was followed by the scrape of a drawer, and five minutes later she heard Maureen cross the corridor.

'I'm afraid it'll have to be fish fingers tonight,' said Coral, without looking up. 'Our finances are a bit dicky again, but I've managed to get a chicken for Sunday. It was on an offer – we can have the rest with salad on Monday.'

'Er, thank you, Coral, but I won't be eating tonight. I'm going out.'

Coral froze in mid-paragraph and gaped at her flatmate. This was unprecedented. Maureen's social life was inextricably linked with her own, and now, suddenly, without a scrap of warning, she was acting independently.

Her gaze took in Maureen's white dress – new, surely – her

'best' navy blue jacket, the shining hair and careful make-up. Something in the blue smudges of eye-shadow and her defensive expression made Coral's stomach twist unpleasantly. She forced a laugh. 'This is rather unilateral of you. Am I permitted to know anything about this exciting date?'

Maureen looked uncomfortable. 'It's not a date. It's something serious. A discussion.'

'Really! What sort of discussion?'

'I'm sorry, Coral. I can't tell you. It's secret ... someone's reputation is at stake.'

Once again Coral's eyes raked Maureen's small, heart-shaped face. Behind the half-fearful determination there was suppressed excitement, a glow, anticipation ... with a jolt of utter certainty Coral knew she was going to meet a man. The new dress was neither here nor there; the popular myth that women only dress up for men was just that, a myth. If anything, one's toilette required excessive care if it was likely to receive the eagle-eyed scrutiny of another woman, someone who knew all the tricks and short-cuts.

No, the clothes said nothing, but Maureen's face was a banner proclaiming turbulent emotions within. Coral felt increasingly uneasy.

'Just tell me who you're meeting, then. I'm dying to know!'

Maureen knitted her fingers together and sighed. 'I can't. I'd like to ... Perhaps later, much later, when all this is over.'

'All what?' Coral sat up sharply, her eyes narrow slits of suspicion. 'Mo, what is going on? I don't like the sound of this at all. You're up to something very odd. Don't you think it would be – safer to tell me, then I know where you are and who you're with?'

'Oh, Coral! Don't be so dramatic. I'll be perfectly safe. I'm going to meet someone who's already proved himself trustworthy, so there's nothing for you to worry about.'

'No? Only the fact that you don't trust *me*. All the things we've shared, and suddenly you turn secretive. I wouldn't do that to *you*.'

'That's not fair.' Maureen was distressed. 'It's not only you. I haven't told *anyone* – it wouldn't be right. Please believe me.'

'I know,' said Coral bitterly, 'you don't think I'd be discreet. You imagine I'd gossip.' She waited for the hasty rebuttal, but Maureen stood wordless. Stung, she spat: 'Thank you very much. Keep your precious little mystery, if that's what you want.' Gripping the newspaper in furious fingers, she read the same line of print three times.

Maureen hovered nearby, unhappy at the prospect of leaving under a storm-cloud. She cleared her throat.

'There's a mention of Dr Bradshaw in the paper,' she said hesitantly. 'His solicitor is advertising for relatives. Isn't it sad – he doesn't seem to have had any family.'

'Very sad.' Coral's reply was cool.

'I – I'd better be going. I hope – you have a nice evening.'

'No doubt you will.'

As her friend's footsteps retreated into the bowels of the building, Coral compressed her lips and savagely ransacked the paper. At the foot of a page headed *'Births, Marriages and Deaths'* Mr Pendle's communication primly invited response among other legal notices. She read it rapidly, a faint snakish hiss escaping her mouth as she whispered to herself:

'*"The kin of the above-named are requested to apply to Pendle, Rathbone and Blair, Solicitors and Commissioners for Oaths, of Barstock House, 12 Castle Terrace, Nottingham ..."*'

Breathing audibly, she stared at the notice for another minute before thrusting the paper on to the floor, striding rapidly across the flat and peering out into the encroaching darkness. She still wore her orange raincoat.

10

'It's true,' laughed Philippa. 'I can drink whatever I fancy. Well, within reason.'

'That's marvellous news.' David pulled his chair closer to the bed. 'When did your kidneys start working again?'

'Thursday night – with a vengeance. It was like Niagara, but short and sharp. The flow's back to normal now, although the nurses are still charting every drop. It seems that damage to the renal tubules wasn't fully established after all. The surgeons are delighted.'

'They're not the only ones,' he said.

There was such sincerity in his tone that Philippa was touched. She held out her hand to him in a friendly manner, and it was gently clasped.

'Thanks for visiting me so often,' she said. 'It really makes a difference. You could go quite mad in one of these rooms with no distractions except for medical or nursing matters.'

'Just say the word and I'll bring you some books – thrillers, detective novels, dull haematology tomes – anything you like.'

She smiled. 'I'm afraid my concentration span for reading is still pathetic. It hasn't stopped me thinking about other things, though . . . You know, it's funny – being here in bed, dependent, has changed some of my attitudes. I used to think it was wrong for doctors to be put on pedestals by their patients, encouraged to act like minor deities, distributing wisdom, never admitting to their mistakes. I thought patients should be more involved in their own treatment, ask for information, make it a two-way process; I hated to see them practically salaam in front of some consultants who were already puffed up with over-inflated egos. The deference, the submission, the abasement: I didn't like it when my patients had that in their eyes. But now . . . I realize that if you're very ill, you don't want responsibility. You don't want a choice. You *need* someone to make the decision, to tell you what to do, someone to look up to, and – have faith in. It's vital. Without it – you lose hope.'

'The power of the mind,' agreed David. 'A kind of placebo effect. Witch doctors have known about it for centuries.'

He continued to hold her hand, and to Philippa it felt warm and natural. They chatted quietly until shuffling footsteps approached the door; when she tried to pull the hand away, he tightened his grasp.

'Oh – hello.'

Stewart Bridges nodded to David, uninterested, unsurprised.

'How are you?' he asked Philippa.

'Fine, thank you. Shouldn't you be off this weekend?'

'I swapped it.' He consulted a chart and entered a few hieroglyphics into his notebook. 'Friend's wedding next Saturday,' he added.

'Ah. What's Neil up to today?'

'Need anyone ask? Getting that deathtrap of his ready for tomorrow's race, and doing his qualifying round. He's bonkers.'

'A not unreasonable point of view,' murmured David when

Stewart had gone. 'I was talking with Neil yesterday at lunch-time. He's not satisfied with sports-car races now – what he really wants is Formula One!'

'Lunacy!' she gasped. 'He's my age. Far too old for that kind of thing.'

'Today's drivers don't see it that way. And Neil certainly doesn't, as far as actual driving skill is concerned. He's deter-mined, Pippa, believe me.'

There was a scratching at the door which might have repre-sented a knock, and it swung open. Instead of the expected figure of Stewart, or a nurse, Audrey stepped inside, a defiant look on her well-powdered face.

'Hello,' she said to Philippa. 'I was just in the area, and I thought I'd see how you were getting on.'

'That was kind of you.' Philippa hoped it wouldn't become too much of a habit; at least David now had his hand back. 'Things are going very well. I'm only mad that I can't move about yet.'

'You'll have to read books . . . Can you manage books?'

'A page or so. Then I seem to get tired.'

'Well . . . ' Audrey scanned the room nervously. 'These are nice,' she said at length, pointing to a startling array of canary-yellow chrysanthemums crammed awkwardly in a tall glass vase. 'Are they from your family?'

'A friend brought them,' answered Philippa with a small remi-niscent smile.

Audrey busied herself with a much-needed rearrangement. 'Some should be shorter,' she murmured. 'And a bit of greenery would give more interest, pad it out . . . '

Philippa dared not speak. Surely Audrey would realize that these garish, unwieldy flowers were a man's gift, a man with no artistic leanings of his own who nevertheless was not afraid to expression his affection. On her left, David sat serenely, his face in repose. Audrey finished her task, patting the new creation with fingers which were red-tipped and outwardly confident. Then she swung round to David, a question in her eyes.

A light rat-tat jolted the tableau before the wax had time to set. Nurse Benson, a third-year student, crept into the room.

'I'm sorry to interrupt,' she said diffidently. 'Dr Tate is on the ward phone for you, Dr Stannard. He knows you're not on duty, but thought you might be here. He's having trouble with a patient you both admitted yesterday . . . he wonders if he could have a word.'

'Of course,' David stood up smoothly and walked to the door. 'Won't be long,' he informed his two stricken companions.

Nurse Benson noticed nothing amiss. 'Can I get you anything?' she asked Philippa.

'Please – if it's not inconvenient, I'd love a drink. This jug's run out.'

'Will do.'

'Let *me* help! I'm sure you must be busy.' Audrey rocketed wildly from the room leaving Philippa struggling against an incongruous feeling of hysteria.

David and Audrey were gone for more than ten minutes and returned together, Audrey carefully balancing a clear plastic beaker of lemon squash which she placed on the locker top next to the flowers.

'Thank you,' said Philippa, and drank part of the liquid.

'Your jug's coming later. They're washing it out.'

'Thank you.' There seemed to be nothing more to say. Let David shoulder the burden of conversation if he so desired. New gambits were beyond her. She was pleased to be improving, but still felt tired, lethargic. She didn't want to fence with Audrey, now or at any other time. The problem, if there was one, was David's.

The door flew open yet again. Philippa's first gut reaction of irritation turned to shock at the sight of Coral, pale, dishevelled, desperate, her neat staff nurse's uniform at odds with trembling lips and clenching fists.

'Please – have any of you seen Maureen?' Her voice was gravelly; tears threatened.

'What is it, Coral?' Philippa had never seen her friend so agitated. 'She hasn't been in here today.'

'You're sure? . . . David?'

'No, sorry. I haven't – look out!'

Coral had blundered in a blind progress to the locker, which swayed alarmingly as she leaned on it. The chrysanthemums, with their high centre of gravity, had no chance; the tall vase toppled in slow majesty to the floor, where it splintered deafeningly into a spray of malevolent shards. The tiny onyx horse, helpless before the juggernaut, was also swept from his perch to

110

lie dismembered among the winking glass and sodden yellow globes.

Coral put her hands to her temples and hunched, frozen, over the devastation.

'I'm so sorry . . . I didn't mean . . . Oh, I *am* sorry.'

David was with her in an instant and seized her shaking forearms.

'Don't worry, Coral. Everything's all right. It was just an accident; we can deal with it. What's all this about Maureen?'

Coral gave a small sob, her eyes flooding with tears. 'She's gone, David. She went out last night – and didn't come back. I waited up for hours. We – we had a bit of a row because she wouldn't tell me where she was going. Oh David, I'm sure something's happened to her!'

His brows drew together in concern. 'Did she say who she was going to meet, or when she might be back?'

'No. It was a man, that's all I know. Someone she said she trusted.'

Audrey, carefully extracting splinters of glass from her fifteen denier tights, pursed her lips judiciously.

'There's your answer, surely. She stopped over with him.'

'No!' The monosyllable burst from Coral like the flat blast of a shotgun. 'She would never have done that, not Maureen. And she would have rung if she'd missed the bus and needed collecting. Or have come home by taxi. She's meant to be on duty today. Nobody's seen her! I've been asking all round the hospital.'

David gripped her shoulder. 'Listen, Coral. We'll just clear up this mess, then we can help you. She'll be all right, I'm sure. Probably got drunk last night and is still sleeping it off.'

Coral brightened a little, before looking unconvinced.

'I hadn't thought of that. But she hardly drinks: one cocktail's her limit. And she's never . . . She doesn't stay out at night.'

'Always a first time – even for Maureen. If she's not a drinker, it would have gone straight to her head.'

'Well . . . maybe.' She dropped down on flexed knees and began to scrabble among the debris at the base of the locker, picking out the larger chunks of glass.

'Leave that,' said David. 'We'll see to it.'

'No . . . please. It was my fault.'

'I'll fetch a brush and dustpan,' announced Audrey, and did so. With poorly simulated regret, she dumped the drooping chrysanthemums in the waste-paper basket, and brushed importantly at the remaining crystalline fragments, while David covered the sullen pool with paper towels.

When the bustle had subsided, Coral approached the bed, eyes downcast, pieces of onyx held within her cupped hands like an offering.

'I'm sorry about the horse, Pippa. I'll buy you another one.'

'Nonsense! He's special. I'm sure I can mend him when I'm out of this wretched plaster. Don't give it another thought.' She cast a shrewd glance at Coral's pink-blotched face. 'Go to Maureen's ward with David and see if there's any news yet. She might have rung in by now. Then let him make you a cup of tea on Byron. You can decide together whether any further action is necessary.'

Audrey hesitated. 'Is there anything I can do? Then – I'd better be getting along. Good-bye, Philippa. I, er, hope your recovery, er, proceeds.' She looked beseechingly at David. 'What about tonight?'

'I'll give you a ring,' he promised.

'Right . . . Fine.' She inclined her cheek for his absently bestowed kiss, and clicked out of the room. Coral seemed quite oblivious of the scene. Her expression was glazed, faraway, shock and incomprehension locked together in a deadly embrace, as if she had already received bad news.

'Please let me know,' said Philippa in a low voice.

'Of course.' David steered Coral out of the room and she was left alone.

At first, there was little chance to brood on Maureen's disappearance. Physical needs had reached the point of insistence. Not only had she a raging thirst, but it felt as if Niagara was threatening once again. She drained the lemon squash with three enormous gulps, and was saved from ringing the bell by the fortuitous appearance of an auxiliary nurse, who assisted with the other problem, exclaiming in wonder over the volume passed.

It was later that she began to feel light-headed and dizzy. What goes out must be replaced, she thought. Nurse Benson still hadn't returned with the water jug. Philippa glanced around the room, looking for something else to drink; there was nothing.

How quiet the corridor seemed now all the Saturday visitors had gone! Perhaps the nurses were in the office, writing their reports, or in the kitchen, enjoying a well-deserved cup of tea.

Should she wait until someone came by? No – she was feeling more unwell by the minute. The room was swimming, surreal. She would have to ring the bell.

Her hand groped for the 'Nurse-Call' device which normally rested on the locker top. It had gone – damn! It must have been knocked off in the confusion with the flowers. She leaned over as far as her unwieldy arm would allow, and saw it lying beneath the bed, attached to its flex.

Must reach it . . . A tight ache was developing once again in her pelvis; another litre of fluid, no doubt. In different circumstances there would be a funny side, but just now she was frightened. Her ears began to ring. She stretched down into the gap between the locker and the bed, her questing fingers tremulous and unresponsive. She could feel her heart hammering, and although the faintness receded for a moment as she pressed her cheek into the mattress, her limbs still felt like those of a robot.

Clumsily, she explored with her fingertips . . . they brushed only smooth, cold linoleum. She craned her neck to see down the narrow canyon, and caught a glimpse of the control unit just out of reach against the wall. Her energy was almost spent. She felt sick. One more try . . . A veil of lassitude shimmered at the edge of her vision, waiting to slither across and engulf her in deep, airless folds.

At last. Now working by touch alone, she could discern the hard edge of the box. With an involuntary grunt of effort, Philippa leaned over a fraction more. Too far . . . Her body began to roll off the edge, slowly at first, then with increasing momentum. The locker slid away; there was nothing to grasp . . . With a dull splattering thud, then a crack, she sprawled on the floor, and darkness swooped in.

In the large outer office he shared with Jackson and four others, Sergeant Bird was typing up a report. Progress was slow, as usual; despite the benefit of three consecutive courses, one on touch-typing, another explaining the mysteries of the word-processor, and a third optimistically entitled 'Computer Literacy', he remained cautious with keyboards. They were alien aids to a man who communicated through his pen, whose notebooks carried philosophy as well as fact, who relished the aesthetic value and tangible permanence of books.

The office was quiet except for the stuttering clack-clack of his machine. It was a Saturday afternoon, and while the forces of law and order were well represented elsewhere in the building, his immediate colleagues were all off duty, as he should have been. But William Bird was content. He had finished his shopping and caught up with his paperwork; the remainder of the weekend promised untrammelled pleasures such as the Montgomerys' picnic. He was looking forward to that, and sincerely hoped young Mark would manage not to injure himself.

He sighed and stretched, replaced the cover on the typewriter and eased his bulk out of the chair. Mentally debating whether to leave by the back stairs or exchange a friendly word with the desk sergeant on duty, he chose the latter. As he approached the desk, he saw that Sergeant Tomlinson was deeply engaged with a slender, flame-haired young girl.

'But he didn't take me seriously!' she was shouting. 'He said that consenting adults often stayed out all night – or words to that effect. He came up with all sorts of platitudes which I found downright *offensive!'*

The small body vibrated with vehemence.

'Well, a lot of youngsters simply don't think of the worry they cause their friends and family. They turn up in the end, though, and I'm sure it'll be the same with Maureen.'

'Oh, won't *anybody* listen? She's *not like that*. She wouldn't have let the other nurses down on the ward, and there is no *circumstance* in which she wouldn't have rung me to tell me that she was all right.'

'Didn't you mention a quarrel?'

'A minor tiff. I'm sorry I said that, everyone distorts it. Look – *please* help me. I want to report her missing. Something is wrong. I've brought her photograph – here.'

As the girl tugged a brightly coloured envelope from the bag slung over her shoulder, the sharp little profile Sergeant Bird had been watching became a three-quarter view. He sucked in his cheeks. Surely he had seen her before – or someone very much like her. His careful mind checked through all its available compartments and concluded that the acquaintance had been both slight and recent. Where . . . ? Who? He hung back while Sergeant Tomlinson took details of the absent friend or relative.

'Right,' he said at length. 'And your name is Coral Chapman.'

'Yes.'

'Of the same address.'

'Yes.'

'Excuse me,' Sergeant Bird intervened. 'Sorry to butt in, but I believe this young lady knows Inspector Montgomery.' He looked at her directly. 'I'm Sergeant Bird, one of his colleagues.'

'Oh . . . Oh, good.' Her eyes, twin amber traffic lights, widened in wonder before her features registered relief. 'Perhaps you can do something. I'm so afraid . . . '

When Coral had told her story, Sergeant Bird assumed his most avuncular and reassuring mantle. He promised diligent enquiries, and immediate notice of any news which might emerge. He stressed the number of 'missing' people who returned safe and well. He drove her to the Sherwood flat, accepted her offer of tea, covertly observed all he could, and left with a photograph of Coral and Maureen together at a party. He was deeply worried.

'But how could that happen?' Anne Markham questioned her staff nurse in angry amazement as the report of the previous day's ward events was read out to her.

Susan Fellowes looked uncomfortable. 'I don't know. Philippa said she felt faint, and the Nurse-Call unit was out of reach on the floor. She tried to pick it up, and overbalanced.'

'It was my fault.' Nurse Benson's voice from the corner was low and apologetic. 'We were a bit busy, and I forgot to replace her jug of water. She did say she was thirsty. I'm sorry . . . '

Anne frowned, perplexed. 'That may have contributed a little, but I'd be surprised if it was the actual cause . . . Let me see the charts.' She scrutinized them carefully. 'Yes – the fluid through-put was absolutely normal until that point. Why did she suddenly pass so much more that she collapsed? Tell me again what you found, Susan.'

'Well – Janet and I were on our way to the clinical room when we heard a kind of double thump. We dashed in, and Philippa was lying on her back by the side of the bed. For a minute, she didn't respond; the first blood pressure we got was eighty over forty. Then it started to rise, and she began to come round. We'd just managed to roll her over and get a bowl when she was sick.

'She asked for the commode and passed over a litre of fluid – it's all recorded there – then we helped her back to bed, cleaned her up and called Stewart. Here are the doctor's notes. He did listen to what we said about the fluid, but he seemed to be more worried in case she'd had a pulmonary embolus. He did an ECG and arranged for a chest X-ray; they didn't show any evidence of a PE.'

'Was there any respiratory arrest when you first saw Philippa?'

'No. Nor cardiac. The pulse was thready, but just palpable.'

'Hmm . . . I think –' Anne Markham was interrupted by a sharp knock on the door.

'Come in!'

Kath, a strident member of the domestic staff, stood belligerently on the threshold in a typical fishwife pose, her plain face below badly bleached hair pulled into an expression of grievance which Anne had come to recognize.

'I want a word!' she boomed ominously.

'We're just reading the report, Kath. It won't take much longer.'

'It's 'appened again and I'm not standing for it!' The woman advanced into the room.

Anne smiled pleasantly. 'I'll come and discuss the problem as soon as we've finished here. Will you be in the kitchen?'

'Aye.'

'Right, then.' She stood up and held the door, an unmistakable gesture. Under the quiet force of her personality, Kath subsided into the corridor. The thin end of a dangerous wedge was not yet established.

'Tell me what the trouble is,' invited Anne ten minutes later.

Kath held out an empty glass ampoule, rolling it between a nicotine-stained finger and thumb. 'It's these agin. I thought we'd gor over this trouble with the last lorrer nurses. It were in the basket wi' the paper 'and towels. *And* there were these, an' all!' She whipped her other hand out from her pocket like a magician. A 10 ml syringe, with a standard needle attached, gleamed in the morning sunshine.

'We aren't 'avin' it, Sister. There could be anythin' on this needle. Think if one or us 'adder got pricked. We might end up wi' AIDS. Not much good suin' th'ospital then!'

'There's no blood on this needle,' said Anne firmly. 'But you're

116

quite right to be upset. I can't imagine how it happened; all the nurses are well aware that there's a special disposal drum for the "sharps".'

'Well, *someone* did it!'

'Yes . . . I'll make full enquiries, Kath. Please accept my apologies; it won't happen again.'

'I didn't think we had anyone *on* frusemide,' said Susan Fellowes when she was told of the incident and shown the ampoule.

'Me neither.' Anne's face mirrored her bafflement. 'Let's check the Drug Kardex.'

No evidence of a patient requiring the diuretic drug was unearthed. Nurses were questioned; all denied knowledge.

'Perhaps it was Stewart,' suggested Susan. 'He might have been carrying the syringe around on another ward and got rid of it carelessly here.'

'Even Stewart knows better than that, but I'll ask him just for completion.'

The houseman, when he arrived to clerk the new surgical admissions, defended himself vigorously.

'Not guilty,' he insisted. 'None of my patients needs frusemide, and besides, I'm the one who lets you know when the sharps drum is getting full. You can't be cavalier with needles and glass.'

Anne got no further with her enquiry, but the discovery of the vial so close on the heels of the story of Philippa's collapse linked them in her mind. Frusemide would explain the pattern of events so well. But who on earth would give a girl in her situation a drug which was well known to be a powerful stimulant of urine flow? It was crazy. Could Stewart have made another of his gaffes, and be afraid to own up? Unlikely. Many would contend that he was impatient and casual, but this action represented either brute ignorance, or much, much worse . . .

Giving her head a brief shake, she went in to see Philippa.

'I've been hearing about yesterday,' she said bluntly.

Her patient looked shamefaced, but otherwise well. 'I'm sorry, Anne. I feel such a fool. I should never have leaned out of bed the way I did. I deserved to fall.'

'We'll have to put the cot sides up if you go on like that.'

'Oh, *please* don't. I'll be good. I was only trying to reach the bell-push; it's back on the locker now.'

Anne straightened the pillows and bedclothes, then paused. 'Philippa – did anyone give you anything unusual yesterday? An injection you weren't expecting, perhaps?' She found Philippa's innocent gaze difficult to meet with her own.

'No. All the drugs came at the proper time, and there were no extra ones. Why do you ask?'

'Oh, nothing to worry about. We were just trying to fathom out why you felt faint in the first place. It's a bit of a mystery.'

She chatted for a few more minutes, then left the room, still uneasy. The whole episode was odd, and inconclusive. She couldn't decide whether or not to take it to a higher quarter. Maybe some further enquiries would be in order . . .

11

'Remember,' said Carole Montgomery, 'you've promised to leave work behind today.'

'I know.' Montgomery halted the car at Donington Park's main entrance and paid for his party of three, ignoring protests from Sergeant Bird.

'Look at all these people!' Carole was astonished. 'I thought we were early.'

'Where now?' Montgomery asked her.

'Oh – according to the plan you turn left, then park as near to the Paddock as you can. Mark said to meet him there if we had time.'

They jolted along an inner road, and finally came to rest on a churned-up belt of grass.

'There seems to be a special road leading to the Paddock,' mused Carole, her dark head still bent over the circuit plan. 'We missed it. We turned off the A453 too soon.'

'Never mind. We'd have had to park here anyway.' They climbed out of the car. 'Can you carry the rug? I'll take the hamper. Will has mysterious bags of his own. All set? Good.'

Montgomery locked the car and walked over to the nearest attendant to buy passes for the Paddock, and a programme.

'Keep these,' he was advised. 'You'll need to show them again if you move out of the area.'

Inside was a mêlée of activity as cars lumbered across the grass, reversed cautiously from trailers or revved engines in their chosen spot. Porsches rubbed wings with humble Fiestas. Figures in overalls attended them dotingly, checking, adjusting, even polishing. The air was thick with fumes, a rancid mingling of diesel, petrol and sausages from the adjacent cafeteria, but the crackle of excitement reminded Montgomery of the fifth of November.

'Isn't this fun!' exclaimed Carole, raising her voice slightly in order to compete with the general hubbub. 'I don't know if we'll find Mark, though.'

'What colour is his Fiesta?'

'Pale blue. Look for the Friday foot: he says there's one painted on the side.' Friday Footwear was her uncle's family firm, the motif of a naked foot illustrating one of their slogans, *'Next best thing to Nature'*. The firm sponsored Mark, giving him no choice about the car's adornments.

'What's a Friday foot?' asked Sergeant Bird, craning his neck in all directions.

'Man Friday,' supplied Montgomery.

'Ah.'

They tramped on across the field, periodically accosted by attractive girls offering promotional leaflets and badges. Eventually, Montgomery spotted Carole's young cousin in the corner, leaning against the bonnet of a distinctive blue Fiesta XR2, wiping his hands on a rag.

'Mark!' Carole waved delightedly.

He looked up from beneath a rakish black fringe and grinned at them.

'Carole! I'm really glad you could make it. Richard ... Will. This is great!'

'Someone has to keep an eye on you,' she said darkly. 'Where are Stan and Judith this weekend?'

'Edinburgh. They've been up there since Thursday on a business trip. Now it's pleasure ... Come and meet my mechanic. This is Rob, and Tina here is giving out Friday foot badges and key-rings. I see the opposition's got to you already. You might as well have one of ours. There are some tee-shirts, too, somewhere ... Tina, are they in that bucket? Sorry, we've only large ones left. You will wear it, though, won't you, Caro?'

She held up the voluminous white tee-shirt with a fluorescent orange foot blazoned across the front.

'Discreet little number,' she said. 'You'd better win.'

'I hope so. I need the points. I'm fifteenth at present – but there are over forty entrants,' he added hastily.

'You qualified for the main race, then?' said Montgomery.

'Yes, thank God. Those who didn't will be sharing the track with the Class D Porsches.'

'Staggered start?'

'Yes. They call it a "consolation race", but I don't think it'd be much consolation to have a Porsche 924 roaring up your – um – exhaust pipe after a couple of laps.'

'Where do you suggest we sit?' asked Carole.

He considered. 'You could go up the Honda stand near the Lucas tower – that's right by the starting line – but Redgate corner is better. It's an awkward bend after a straight stretch, and you're bound to get someone spinning off.'

'We haven't come to be *ghoulish*,' she protested.

'I know. Try Redgate, anyway. You can eat your picnic on the bank and watch from the stand. It's just round there, past the bar.'

'Thanks . . . good luck, Mark.' She kissed his cheek. 'We'll be yelling for you.'

They left him discussing the engine-tuning with Rob, and carried their iron rations to the Redgate Lodge Bar.

'Just a minute,' murmured Carole, and disappeared into the Ladies' Room. She emerged shortly afterwards sporting the enormous Friday foot.

'What do you think?' she asked defiantly.

Montgomery stroked his chin. 'Do you want the truth, or would you prefer tact?'

'So much for loyalty . . . Will?'

Sergeant Bird smiled. 'We won't lose you in the crowd, that's a fact.'

The grass bank at Redgate corner was filling up quickly as Montgomery shook out their travelling rug and staked a claim. The first race was still forty minutes ahead. He studied the programme while Carole and William Bird unpacked the hamper with much laughter and chatter. Touring cars were due to start; Mark's race was one of the later ones.

Someone thrust a plate on to his lap.

'Coo-ee, we're eating,' said Carole. 'What would you like: chicken, cheese, or some of these prawns?' She unscrewed the top of a wide-necked flask to reveal a generous quantity of prawns nestling lusciously in Marie Rose sauce. There was salad in a nearby box. Montgomery took his time as he considered the offerings.

'Opportune, the seafood,' stated William Bird, delving in a carrier-bag to produce two flasks of his own. He handed them to Carole. 'This one's Muscadet, for you good people. The other's an alcohol-free wine for me. I'll drive us back.'

He was insistent, so they accepted with good grace, knowing that since he would be staying with them for supper, Montgomery could drive him home eventually.

'Spendidly chilled!' said Carole, sipping from a sturdy wine glass which Sergeant Bird had also provided. Montgomery drank very sparingly; on a murder case, even when off duty, he was always ascetic.

By the time they finished their picnic, the loudspeakers had begun to crackle with preliminary commentary. The crowd glowed with an aura of expectation. Montgomery looked behind their bank at the large grandstand; there were still some vacant seats near the top.

'Let's go up there,' he said suddenly. 'We'll get a better view.'

They scrambled to their feet, packed away the last few items, climbed the steps and settled in the hard plastic seats.

Carole surveyed the scene eagerly. 'It's nearly all country round here,' she said, 'except for that power station. It must be Ratcliffe on Soar. Pity we can't see *all* the track. I don't suppose there's any point where that's possible . . . oh, Richard! They're coming out!'

A disparate collection of touring cars was filtering on to the track and droning towards them in a leisurely manner. As they swung round the Redgate bend, their various sponsorship logos presented themselves to Montgomery and his companions.

'Nothing as distinctive as the Friday foot,' he said.

Carole's eyebrows were drawn together in puzzlement. 'They're going rather *slowly*, aren't they? It's not like a Grand Prix.'

'I believe they do a warm-up lap first,' said William Bird.

'Oh, that explains it. But how can an MG Metro compete with a Rover Vitesse?'

'Different classes,' explained Montgomery, who was monopolizing the programme. 'But they all go round at the same time.'

'That's confusing.'

'Just watch the numbers. Then you'll know who's leading his class.'

The three-minute klaxon sounded in the distance as the cars found their places on the grid. The commentator was spilling out details of the drivers and their vehicles, including non-starters who had failed at the scrutineering stage, or had come to grief during the practice session. An anticipatory buzz arose from the spectators. People leaned forward, alert. Marshals walked to designated positions with fire extinguishers. Two minutes. Someone called Andy Gregson had lost his third gear. Bad luck. One minute. The muted idling of the engines rose to a roar as they were revved in readiness for the flag . . .

The cars leapt forward at the given signal and raged towards the corner, jockeying for position, seemingly inches apart. Tyres screamed as they hurled themselves into the bend, and the rear end of an Alpha Romeo swung out ominously as the driver fought for control. The skid took him straight across the grass at the periphery of the track and into the sandy stretch beyond, where a huge fantail of grit was sprayed into the air. Waggling like a tom-cat about to strike, the car finally regained its direction and lurched back on to the track, to chase determinedly after the tail-runners ahead.

'Richard!' breathed Carole, shocked. 'This is *dangerous*.'

By three-thirty there was only one race left before Mark's, that of the Class A Porsches. Although a cool breeze had sprung up, the three were enjoying themselves enormously, fortified by cups of coffee and jam tarts. The cares of work seemed a world away.

'What's next?' asked Sergeant Bird, munching contentedly.

Montgomery opened the programme again. 'Porsches. Mainly Carreras. Ten laps – that's just under twenty miles.' He glanced idly at the list of drivers, then stopped as one particular name aroused his interest. 'Number 3 – Neil Thornton,' he read out. 'Like that medico chap . . . must be coincidence.' He noticed that Carole's face had assumed a wary expression, and kept the rest of his speculations to himself. He had promised to leave work behind and have a proper break. So often their rare weekends had been spoiled. Still . . .

He looked again, this time more covertly. Listed under 'Entrant' were various companies or teams, but in many cases the simple description 'Driver' was given. Neil Thornton was one of these. There was no more information to be found.

The nearest loudspeaker spluttered as the commentator resumed his friendly monologue. The rising wind was making it difficult to hear, but Montgomery directed all his concentration towards it. Could this possibly be the Neil Thornton he had met? Unlikely. Doctors didn't drive racing cars; they wouldn't have the time.

He caught the name when the Porsches were half-way round their warm-up lap. Number 3 was the only silver car among a plethora of black, white and red; all looked lean and mean. 'Neil Thornton and Chris Baker are neck and neck in the points,' the man with the microphone was enthusing. 'At ten rounds they've got sixty-five apiece, only two behind Jeff Saunders, who lost pole position yesterday to Neil Thornton. The silver Porsche is the one to watch . . . '

Montgomery sat back to do just that.

Neil Thornton tensed himself, and waited. The padded helmet deadened a fraction of the roar of twenty-two engines reaching their ideal state of readiness, but the vibrations transmitted up through his spine reassured him that his Porsche was going to respond, to fly, to conquer, and that this time no one would stop him.

A few feet away from the bonnet a girl in tight jeans and a skimpy top was holding up a yellow placard with a huge figure '1' on it. Another dolly-bird would be on hand to give out the prizes. Garlands with ribbons in them . . . That was how Vanda had come into his life. Yet these elements were gratuitous, irrelevant – sops to the crowd. He would forfeit them all without a backward glance, if required. He cared only for the race, pitting mind, body and machine against his rivals. He had total confidence in his own superiority. He intended to win.

Ahead, the bare track seemed to stretch to infinity. He swung his gaze left to the Lucas lights. A red glow . . . The roar around him reached a deafening crescendo. He clutched the wheel and gear lever in gauntleted hands, every muscle taut, straining like a racehorse at the starting gate. When – green lights! With a rush of primordial exultation, he slammed his right foot down.

It was proving to be a good race, thought Montgomery, as the

Porsches snarled past for the seventh time. They were now well strung out, but the leading bunch of three were contesting every bend at extraordinary speeds. Number 3 had led initially, but number 5 had cut in dangerously during the fourth lap and been allowed to pass. He was unable to savour his triumph unchallenged, however; Thornton was hanging on with an implacable air of vendetta, and just behind lurked the streamlined black Porsche of Jeff Saunders, the Championship's current leader.

Down near the wire-netting fence stood a tall blonde girl in a vivid cyclamen boiler suit, who appeared to be checking a stopwatch. Certainly the race was a fast one; the drivers probably had their eyes on the day's lap record, which conferred an extra point.

Montgomery squinted up the hill towards Maclean's corner. He could discern the leaders as vague shapes before they vanished, to reappear shortly afterwards beyond the control tower. Thornton was harrying his opponent mercilessly, threatening to overtake at any moment. Saunders had dropped back. All three hurtled along the straight stretch to Redgate. Number 5 braked late for the bend, swung out and lost his optimum line; in a second, Thornton was through. People danced and shouted above the din of the engines.

The rest of the race seemed like a foregone conclusion. In a formidable display of power, the driver of the silver Porsche pressed forward to achieve and maintain a three-second lead over his dispirited opponent. When he took the chequered flag, applause broke out in the stands.

The man Thornton acknowledged the crowd's approbation coolly during his lap of honour. Montgomery was struck by the contrast between him and some of the earlier winners who had waved wildly in all directions. It would be interesting to hear what he had to say during the mandatory interview which was to follow.

In the event, it was not the words, but the voice which registered forcefully in Montgomery's brain. The usual rambling statements, heavy with regional accent, were absent. This man gave brief, intelligent, slightly ironic replies in clipped tones – tones that Montgomery had last heard in a hospital interview-room.

He met William Bird's eye for a moment behind Carole's back and nodded. His sergeant didn't miss a trick. Here was a doctor with an expensive habit . . . The murder enquiry was now once more at the forefront of both their minds.

124

Carole sat rigidly between them. She had been silent during the Porsche race, and Montgomery thought he knew why. It had been particularly competitive, a stark reminder of the lengths people were willing to go to when they wanted to win. Mark's tenacity and determination were not so far reflected in his position in the Championship; at least it was only his first season. For all his genial manner, the lad could be very obstinate, and deep down they knew he might be tempted to take unnecessary risks.

A noise like a far-off chainsaw reached their ears, and the first cluster of Fiestas pulled on to the track for their warm-up lap. The rest followed in a thin stream. In the middle they could see Mark's car, the number 24 painted just behind the front wheel-arch in order to make room for the huge orange Friday foot splayed across the side.

'Good luck!' Carole shouted at his oblivious, helmeted profile, then stiffened once more into a brittle, angular attitude, watching the car as it swung round the distant part of the curve, a toy now, tiny against the trees.

'At least it hasn't rained,' Montgomery said casually, as the commentator's voice came at them in fitful bursts, discussing the chances of the leading contenders.

'Yes,' agreed William Bird. 'The track won't be unduly slippery.'

She rewarded their efforts with a hint of a smile, but did not speak. They all felt obscurely responsible for twenty-two-year-old Mark.

When the Fiestas finally set off all together from the grid, they carried their own wall of sound with them, a noise like a horde of furious wasps. The vehicles swarmed up the straight in a state of seething homogeneity, defying Montgomery's attempts to identify the blue Friday Footwear car. At the bend, they fought each other for the few available gaps in the formation, and as the front-runners whined past, Mark's car appeared half-way down the field near the outer edge of the track.

Montgomery was never quite sure what happened next. A red Fiesta tucked just inside the blue one seemed suddenly to lose traction and slide into its neighbour with a tap which went unheard in the all-pervading clamour of forty engines. The result was catastrophic. Friday Footwear, already at the limit of its own road-holding capacity, careened helplessly off the track to roll over and over in a series of jolting, shuddering impacts before slamming into the tyre-barrier like a hammer bursting fruit.

Montgomery's limbs felt paralysed as Carole gave an anguished cry of 'Mark!' and struggled to her feet. White as death, she groped her way to the nearest gangway and clattered clumsily down the steps. The two men followed with more caution, hollowly aware that as spectators on the wrong side of a wire-netting fence, they could do little to influence the outcome.

Below, marshals were converging on the scene, some wielding fire extinguishers. Only part of the Fiesta was visible behind the wall, but there was no sign of smoke or flame. For a moment, Montgomery allowed himself to hope, before images of shattered vertebrae flooded his mind. He called out to Carole, but she was still ahead of him, running across the grassy bank where they had enjoyed their picnic, her breath coming in staccato gasps.

Now a figure was emerging gingerly from the wreck, assisted by red-clad marshals. It slowly raised both gloved hands and eased off the crash helmet. Then it turned to look at the car.

Montgomery caught up with Carole as she stood panting by the fence, her fingers hooked in the mesh, her attention riveted on the trackside. Only yards away, Mark appeared to be writhing in agony, his fists clenched and his feet executing a strange kind of shuffle-step. It was several seconds before they realized that he was, in fact, dancing with rage.

The Paddock was still bustling as Mark dolefully pulled on the tow-rope which attached his battered Fiesta to Rob's old Audi. He had been examined by the Chief Medical Officer, narrowly avoiding the clutches of a bunch of eager St John Ambulance cadets, and pronounced a very lucky man, having escaped almost entirely unscathed. The racing journals would doubtless have clever comments to make the next week – 'Mark put his Foot in it', or some such witticism. Not exactly the kind of publicity his father was hoping for. He had been lukewarm about the whole idea anyway, and only Mark's own bubbling enthusiasm had persuaded him to act as sponsor.

His cousin was leaning over, watching him with dark eyes which were always direct, interested, concerned. Her glossy black hair curved down past her chin, and her face was still a little pinched.

'I thought your car would be crushed,' she said frankly, 'and you in it.'

'Oh, no danger.' He made his voice cheerful and confident. 'It has a roll-cage.'

'Where, inside?'

'That's right. It strengthens the section the driver sits in.'

Carole peered through the window. 'Oh, yes. I can see it now. I wish I'd known. On television the accidents are so remote, so two-dimensional, but here . . . ' She gave her head a little shake. 'I thought that red car was to blame.'

'Responsible, let's say. He understeered and lost it on the bend. There's no margin for error with so many cars at the start of a race.'

'You don't have to be philosophical just for me, you know. I'd be spitting mad.'

He grinned, feeling better. 'I was . . . I am. I feel like letting all his tyres down. Or throwing his steering-wheel in the Trent.'

'I doubt whether he got any points.' The race had continued regardless, since Mark had had the decency to crash well off the track.

Sergeant Bird appeared, holding out a plastic cup of coffee. Then Montgomery. Mark eyed the latter's lean face reflectively. His warm, attractive cousin had been married to this man for over sixteen years now, almost as long as he could remember. She was thirty-eight. And Richard? Fortyish. Perhaps forty-one. Yet despite all this time he had never felt as if he really knew Richard.

Carole was linked with his best memories of growing up. She had often visited his parents during her student days, and had taken care to spend time with him. She would bring presents – a model aeroplane, or a book full of colourful pictures. Later, after her marriage, when Richard was working an unsociable shift or trying to catch up on his sleep, she would bring their own young children, a boy and a girl in whom Mark had no interest at all at that stage. But instead of neglecting him, she would play cricket and hide-and-seek while the children received the cooing attention of his mother Judith. As an English teacher, she had sent him little notes about the most exciting boys' adventure books, classic and modern. These he had read avidly, always visualizing himself in the role of hero, convinced that one day he would single-handedly save Carole – or even his whole family – from some gruesome fate.

Reality turned out to be much more prosaic for both of them. Carole's school closed and no one else seemed to need another English teacher. Computer sciences were the new order. Now she worked as a part-time librarian; he suspected she found the job tame, and felt as caged as he did in his administrative position at Friday Footwear.

Yes, Carole he understood. Her open, honest nature appealed to his, and not entirely because of the genes they shared. Richard was different – more thoughtful, introspective. That he did a demanding job well was thanks to a combination of both physical and mental toughness, unexpected by the observer who only dwelt on his fine-boned face and pleasant voice. His eyes gave the game away. They were a particularly cold shade of blue, grey in some lights, eyes which made even the innocent feel distinctly uneasy.

'Have you a minute, Mark?' Montgomery had already commiserated in sincere but economical sentences.

'Sure.' He fell into step, still holding his coffee, as Montgomery walked casually away from the group to the edge of the Paddock.

'Do you know anything about the Porsche drivers?'

'A certain amount. Their meetings sometimes coincide with ours – and they're well covered in the journals, of course. Did you have someone specific in mind?'

'Neil Thornton.'

'Oh, the doctor! He's good. This is his third – no, maybe his fourth – season, and I think he's going to win the championship this time. He's been pipped twice. He'd be leading now if it wasn't for Frank Hodgkin, who T-boned him at Snetterton. He's got a fantastic girlfriend, tall and blonde. She's here today – a real cracker.'

'What does he get for this afternoon's win?'

Mark shrugged. 'Nothing to cover his expenses. A trophy, I think. We get a garland and a few pounds. It's more for the love of racing – and the prestige of the sponsors.'

Montgomery gave a slow nod. 'Thanks, Mark.'

'Is that what you wanted to know?' he asked, puzzled.

'Yes.'

As he shepherded his party out of the Paddock fifteen minutes later, Montgomery's eye was caught by a flash of cyclamen near the long snout of a silver Porsche. It was the girl he had earlier watched at Redgate Corner. She had tied her hair back now, and was laughing with a darkish man whose profile was very reminiscent of the crisp surgeon Montgomery had met at the District Hospital. He didn't want them to spot him, and to that end took shelter behind the useful bulwark of William Bird as his group walked past, a matter of feet away.

Snatches of the couple's conversation reached him above the whine of departing cars. At first, the girl's voice sounded pure Home Counties, like Thornton's but then she laughed again. Montgomery cringed. It was an affront to the ear, a gross, uninhibited cachinnation, and when she subsided, relaxed and off her guard, he noticed that a disconcerting vanguard of East London vowel sounds had crept into her carefully manicured pattern of speech.

How disappointing, he thought. This happened so often with pretty faces. Then he put it to the back of his mind.

Harold Warburton, engineer, felt at peace with the world as he strode along the Trent towpath at Beeston with his son Martin, his empty lunchbox, an impressive array of fishing tackle – and the catch. It had been a good day, yielding two decent perch and an eighteen-inch chub which he was looking forward to sliding nonchalantly on to his wife's kitchen scales when he got home.

There had been bream again, bottle tops which he had thrown back, but no full-sized ones today. He mused over the changes in the river during the nineteen years he had been fishing it. Once bream had been relatively rare; now he encountered them every time. Barbels, however, seemed to be on the decline this year, and some blamed pollution for this. Harold reserved his own judgement. Whatever anyone claimed, the bank of the Trent was a fine place to spend a Sunday.

A mischievous breeze had blown the afternoon into coolness, but people were still tramping the towpath and watching as a succession of gaily painted cabin cruisers chugged past, staying well upstream of the weir. As Harold drew level with the marina, the distant roar of water could be heard.

His hatchback was parked alongside the Beeston canal, a pleasant waterway which by-passed the weir via the Beeston lock.

Martin, close to entanglement with the landing net, was already hauling on his arm and demanding to watch the boats in the lock. Harold had no objection. Britain's waterways were his passion. He admired the simple logic of the locks, their sturdy Victorian engineering, the sense of timelessness they engendered.

Martin scampered up the small flight of concrete steps at the end of the towpath, and leaned over the great black beam of the lock gate.

'Look, Dad!' he cried. 'A narrowboat!'

This particular cruiser had passed them earlier, scything serenely through the grey-green river waters as they packed away their tackle. Now it lurked in the deep chamber of the lock, the gates closing it off from the river, waiting to sink even deeper from the sight of men before emerging into light and the Beeston canal.

The crew were amateurs – holidaymakers, probably, and the lock-keeper was helping them to operate the sluice.

'Don't fall in,' said Harold tersely as Martin trotted to the very edge and peered over. He relieved his son of some of their fishing gear and stood with him watching the lock-wheeling process, the trickle of water spouting into the canal almost drowned by the powerful rushing sound from the nearby weir.

It was dark below, obscurely primeval. The gunmetal afternoon sky reflected dully from the ebbing viscid pool, as if from a dirty mirror. An anxious-looking woman in a red jumper stood by the tiller of the cruiser. Children's faces peeped from the saloon windows. The menfolk were on the lock-side, one doubtfully eyeing the rope which attached the bows of the narrowboat to a nearby bollard, wondering perhaps if he had left enough slack.

At last the water pressures were equal, the heavy gates were opened with relative ease, and the tranquillity of the Beeston canal beckoned. The men cast off their ropes and leapt aboard with studied bravado. A cough, a splutter – then the rhythmic thrumming of the engine gave confidence to vessel and crew alike as she forged majestically forwards, filling the lock behind with agitated little ripples.

Harold idly looked down at the mild turbulence in the cruiser's wake. Something was there under the water, a vague white lucency wallowing in amniotic darkness, a ghost in a fluvial graveyard. He pursed his lips. People could be very careless with

130

the rags they used to wipe their dip-sticks. It was always someone else's prop which would eventually be fouled.

The white thing stirred, and seemed to unfold. There was dark
blue, as well. Harold paused, rigid, unbreathing. Surely that
wasn't . . . Appalled, he strained his eyes to penetrate the waters,
a terrible suspicion gripping his mind.

Slowly, very slowly, a hand floated into view.

12

'It's always hard to estimate in a case of immersion.' Frobisher,
Nottingham's Home Office pathologist, frowned at the attentive
group of detectives over the top of his half-moon spectacles. 'So
many variables . . . I would say the body was submerged between
forty and forty-eight hours. No longer.'

'Friday night,' murmured Sergeant Bird.

Montgomery was waiting patiently for the cause of death. A
six-page, neatly typed post-mortem report lay on the desk in
front of him by consent of the coroner, but since Frobisher had
taken the trouble to deliver it personally, it made sense to avail
himself of the horse's mouth.

'Yes, Friday night,' said Frobisher. He paused. 'I'm afraid the
PM findings are essentially negative.'

'Meaning?'

'No signs of violence. No evidence of disease which may
have brought about a natural death. *Virgo intacta*. No alcohol or
drugs . . . '

Montgomery felt the sinking pull of disappointment. 'What are
we to conclude from that?'

'Well . . . She was found in water. You might reasonably ask:
"Did she drown?" The answer, as you know from some of those
bodies disgorged by the Trent over the last few decades, is by no
means a straightforward one. Classic signs of drowning only
occur in a minority of such deaths. I refer to criteria like "frothing
at the mouth", over-distention of the lungs, water in the air
passages or stomach . . . These signs were absent from Maureen
O'Donnell, but as I've said, that proves nothing. In a freshwater
drowning, large volumes of water cross the lung membranes and

enter the bloodstream; the heart cannot cope with the increased circulatory volume, and cardiac arrest ensues. The red blood cells leak potassium, a cardiac poison, which also brings about this effect.'

'I thought people asphyxiated when they drowned,' objected Jackson.

'Yes,' said Frobisher, 'but that element is much more prominent in a seawater drowning. Cardiac failure is now known to be the major mechanism of death where fresh water is concerned.'

'Doesn't it show at your post-mortem?'

Frobisher smiled gently. 'Regrettably, no. If the heart stops in an acute situation, because of a sudden arrhythmia, perhaps, there's very little to see. Conversely, if there has been chronic disease leading up to the death, such as hypertension, then the pathology is often clear. The muscular walls of the heart are found to be thickened; a coronary artery may be blocked. There is something to visualize and measure.

'In some drownings the failing heart gives rise to pulmonary oedema – that frothing at the mouth and nose which everyone seems to know about – but there's no sign of it here.' He looked round at their mournful faces. 'There is an alternative, a condition some pathologists describe as "vagal inhibition". The vagus nerve to the heart can reflexly stop it beating under extreme circumstances – profound shock, for instance. It happens very quickly. In this case, it might have been triggered by abrupt immersion in cold water combined with a highly emotional state on the part of the victim.'

Jackson snapped his fingers. 'I get it – like abortions,' he said.

'Precisely. A tense woman, an instrumentation which has often barely begun . . . and suddenly there is a corpse.'

Montgomery sat impassively at the desk. He was remembering a case, an old case mainly concerning the West Mercia Force, but which had spread its tentacles to involve them all . . . It had started with the mysterious 'brace and bit' robberies, graduated to the shotgun murders of three innocent subpostmasters, and ended with a young girl hanging in a drainage shaft. 'Vagal inhibition' . . .

'You don't think the body was simply dumped in the lock?' he asked at last.

'It's very unlikely, but that's more your field than mine. I wouldn't care to speculate on the cause of death. You'll see in my report that although the lungs were clear, there was a little water in the nasopharynx. That in itself can provoke a reflex cardiac arrest.'

'Mm . . . It would seem to be the kindest way to go.'

'Yes. There are some results pending from our supplementary blood tests – I'll let you have them as soon as possible. We're also analysing tissue for diatoms, but I don't expect much will come of it. Have your men turned up anything helpful?'

'No witnesses; that would be too easy. Nobody has found a suicide note. She was fully clothed – suicides often place their jackets and shoes neatly on the bank. No motive so far, although we've still a lot of interviewing to do . . . '

'You don't have to be coy with me, Montgomery. It's less than a week since I autopsied a certain Dr Bradshaw from the same hospital. The inquest's in ten days – it'll be opened and adjourned.'

'I hadn't finished,' said Montgomery, unruffled. 'She may, of course, have nurtured a secret passion for Gilbert Bradshaw and been overcome by grief after his death. No one has even hinted at this, but young girls do have their secrets. If it wasn't suicide, though, what are we left with? Another accident? You know all about Philippa Rowe; we haven't stinted on the publicity. That would be three accidents occurring among a fairly close-knit group of hospital workers. At least one too many. So if it wasn't an accident . . . '

'That's what I thought.' Frobisher nodded sagely. 'Murder.'

When Frobisher had left, the seminar atmosphere was dispelled, and the detectives shuffled and scratched their heads.

'All right,' said Montgomery, holding up his hand. 'We've a lot of work to do, so let's channel it as efficiently as we can. For those of you who've just come in on this case, there's a summary here for you to read. The dead girl's flat-mate, Coral Chapman, is very upset, but she has given us one vital clue. Maureen was going out to meet a man who was previously known to her. She had described him as "someone who had already proved himself trustworthy", whatever that means. She was a shy girl whose social life depended mainly on Coral, so again this would indicate an acquaintance she felt safe with. We've got to find this man, even if only for elimination. He must be encouraged to come forward.' He turned to Sergeant Bird. 'Will?'

'Sir . . . we're making enquiries in all public houses and restaurants between Sherwood and Beeston, which includes the town centre. Maureen didn't have a car, and she wasn't picked up at the flat, so teams are working through the bus crews and taxi firms. We have some decent photographs, and there'll be posters available tomorrow.'

'Good. If you need more men, let me know, and I'll see what I can do. I suggest you check whether anyone noticed an unfamiliar car parked in the streets near the marina, especially after dark. This man must have got her to the lock on the pretext of a walk, and the most obvious access is from those streets; the towpath on the other side would have been pitch black and dangerous. Once there, she was either killed in some mysterious manner and dumped, or she was pushed in alive. A bit of a gamble, I'd have thought, but the push gets my vote. I gather she was a non-swimmer.'

'If she was dead beforehand, it would have been much easier to heave her into the Trent itself at a quieter spot,' Jackson observed cogently.

'True. Now – we're faced with exhaustive enquiries at the hospital again. A large number of people will have known Bradshaw and O'Donnell superficially, because of their theatre link, but fewer will also have known Philippa Rowe. We want accounts of those people's movements on *both* Fridays, and whether they have a car; both incidents have taken place in relatively isolated areas away from public transport routes. Check how long each person has been working at the hospital; junior doctors are curiously itinerant. Let's see if we can knock this one on the head before anything else happens.'

'Sir – '

'Yes, Will.' They were temporarily alone in Montgomery's office after drawing up a massive flow-chart of hospital personnel.

'Do you think Philippa Rowe is in danger?'

'I've been trying to work that one out. She's been in hospital for eleven days, in a serious condition but gradually getting better. If our unknown assailant *is* a hospital worker, surely he's had ample opportunity to silence her. She's under the care of three different specialties – no, four; her own haematology colleagues were called in to help with a blood-coagulation problem. That's a lot of people wandering in and out, all with a *bona fide* reason for doing so. Is he simply blasé, or very cool, or could it be that even if Philippa regains her memory she wouldn't be able to identify him? It's all "ifs" and "buts".'

'If it's an insider, there's not a lot of virtue in giving her a police guard. Someone could kill her right under our noses!'

'Yes. I don't think we're entirely helpless, though. I'll speak to Sister Markham and ensure that the ward staff are vigilant. We'll keep WPC Winger in the picture, as well. They're used to seeing her around, so there won't be much comment.'

He circled a few names on his chart. 'These people I want to interview myself. Since we're on to alibis, I might need you later. But first, I've a special job for you: find out from Coral who else might have known that Maureen was a non-swimmer. You've met her twice now; I'm sure she'll be more forthcoming with you than with me. See if there's any hint of Maureen's carrying a torch for Gilbert Bradshaw. It's not very likely, but let's be sure. Oh, and ask Coral if *she* has a car.'

'I've seen it, sir. A battered old Fiat that she parks outside the flat.'

'Battered? How battered?'

'Just general rust. No specific knocks.'

'Cars . . . something niggles with me about cars. Ah, well. I suppose it'll come.'

When William Bird stepped into Coral's flat, the atmosphere of desolation was palpable. Boxes and suitcases were stacked in the middle of the sitting-room, surrounded by pieces of tissue paper, while the chairs were covered with items in the process of being packed. He was reminded of a church hall jumble sale, where possessions invested with years of nostalgic value could only be assessed by strictly utilitarian criteria, and even then marked down. These things were Maureen's. Only she would know that the pink jumper was special because her father had chosen it himself, as was the tiny silver locket he had bought on the day she passed her nursing finals – but not the copy of *Dr Jekyll and Mr Hyde*, which always upset her because she felt so sorry for the anti-hero . . .

Now they were simply objects, and their significance to

Maureen would never be fully appreciated by others, however close. People would share out her belongings by their own yard-sticks, as *their* memories dictated ... well-meaning, sincere – inaccurate.

Coral picked up a floppy fur-fabric rabbit from a chair seat, hovered irresolutely, then put it down again.

'Three of Maureen's sisters are here,' she said. 'Bridget, Mary and Shelagh. Perhaps I should introduce you before we talk? They came over yesterday.'

She fetched the girls from the kitchen, and they stood in a shy line, their faces small and pale and dignified, uncannily resembling pictures Sergeant Bird had seen of Maureen. He said a few words of condolence, and they thanked him in a soft Irish brogue. One of them had a rosary: Bridget.

'Their parents have gone to the coroner's office,' Coral explained once they reached the privacy of her bedroom, the only place she seemed willing to talk. 'They want to take Maureen back to Ballyvaughan as soon as possible. I told them that wouldn't be allowed just yet, but they can't accept it. They need to feel they're *doing* something – it's the only way they can cope.'

'And you, Coral? How are you managing?'

'I don't matter,' she said. 'I wasn't family. It's *them* ... her sisters ... I know they look calm, but inside they're ripped apart. You wouldn't think it would have such an effect, somehow, when there are seven of them, all alike. You wouldn't think one death could wreck so many lives ... ' She shivered. 'How am I? Numb. I don't believe that she's not about to walk in through that door. It's all wrong, isn't it? You're meant to be numb first, and cry later. But I've already cried. God, I've cried. I was cruel to Maureen on the very last night of her life, and now I can't say "sorry".'

'Tell me about it.'

'There's nothing to say. I was petty – cross because she wouldn't tell me where she was going.'

'Who were Maureen's other friends? Were there any young men whose company she appeared to enjoy?'

Coral bunched the skirt of her dress into angry ridges. 'I don't know. That's what stung. She was going to meet someone special; she looked flushed, excited. She'd dressed very carefully. But she wouldn't say who it was. She insisted it wasn't a date as

such. It was going to be a discussion – something about someone's reputation.'

'Did she say whose?'

Coral shook her head wearily. 'No. I was avid for details, but
Mo was unexpectedly stubborn. She was always keen to do what
was right, especially where principles like honour and justice
were at stake. She despised idle gossip . . . I'm afraid I'm not the
most discreet of people.'

'Did she ever evince a particular fondness for Dr Bradshaw?'

Her golden eyes met his for a second, and flickered away. He
was reminded of a nervous cat.

'No . . . that is, I don't know. She didn't see him socially, but
earlier in the summer they spent a lot of time in the same oper-
ating theatre.'

'How did she react to his death?'

'Shock, horror . . . just like everyone else.'

'Did her mood or demeanour change at all?'

'Umm . . . yes, it did,' she said wonderingly. 'She went quiet
. . . thoughtful. I suppose I should say even quieter than usual.'

'Sad?'

'Not especially. Just – ruminative.'

'I see. What was Maureen actually doing on the night that he
died?'

'The same as me – working. We were both on a "late", so it was
after nine when we finally left the hospital. We walked back to the
flat together. It isn't far – less than a mile. I only use the car at
weekends. Maureen wanted an early night, so she stayed in, but I
had a quick wash and change, then went to join the District
crowd at the Mortar and Pestle.'

'What sort of time would this be?'

She shrugged. 'Around ten. I like to feel I've done something
with a day as well as work. It's a bit of a ritual on Fridays for those
who aren't on duty or away for the weekend.'

'Who did you drink with?'

'David Stannard. We're old friends.' Something in his expression must have changed, because she went on defensively.
'It's only a hospital crowd, Sergeant Bird. Just a group of pals.
Their girlfriends are for Saturday night, but on Fridays you can
actually *talk* to the men.'

The moment of raw insight was not lost on Sergeant Bird; he
filed it away for future use.

'Did you see him arrive?'

'No, he was already there.'

'Who was he with?'

'No one specific. They were all standing by the bar. It was packed.'

'Tell me who else you saw, then.'

'I'm not sure. I might be confusing the occasion – we go there quite a lot. I think Tony Spitz was there. He's in surgery. Not Mr Crowland's team; another one. Gemma Tolbury and some of the Raleigh Ward staff. Oh – don't write this down! I can't swear to it.'

'Not to worry,' said Sergeant Bird easily. 'This is only to point me in the right direction. What did you do after closing time?'

'David walked me back to the flat. He's very good about things like that. I would have made him a coffee, but we decided not to disturb Maureen. I went to bed myself shortly after.'

'Are you sure Maureen was in her room?'

Coral looked surprised. 'Well, there was nothing to indicate that she wasn't. She was certainly there the next morning. I'm quite a light sleeper; I'd have heard if she'd come in during the night. Anyway, the idea's ridiculous – she didn't stay out at nights. That's why I knew – ' A shadow passed over her face, leaving a lonely, defeated look.

'Yes. Indeed. Could Maureen drive?'

'No.'

'And you told me she couldn't swim.'

'That's true. She was afraid of water. I was going to teach her . . . ' A fat, oily tear welled up in her right eye and shimmered on the point of the lower lashes before she brushed it away. 'Please, Sergeant. I know I shouldn't ask, but – did she drown? The newspapers say she did. I keep imagining her . . . dark, cold, slimy water . . . panicking – no air. Her sisters seem to think that it was somehow beautiful and saintly. They've visualized her death as a peaceful one; I hear them talking about it. But drowning's not like that, is it? It's struggling and thrashing and terror before everything finally sinks like lead . . . '

Yes, thought Sergeant Bird. Ophelia's romantic image was nothing but a con.

He made a quick decision. 'Not always,' he said quietly. 'We think the cold water stopped her heart straight away.' And the panic.

'Then . . . ' Her voice was tremulous. 'She didn't – suffer?'

138

'No.'

'Please – excuse me.' Coral struggled to her feet and rushed from the room.

She was gone for ten minutes, returning pale and pink-eyed, but composed.

'I'm sorry,' she said. 'Please go on with your questions. I want to be helpful. I want you to know everything. Then you can find out – why.'

Sergeant Bird nodded, and spoke in brisk tones. 'We were discussing the fact that Maureen couldn't swim. Who knew about this, apart from her family and yourself?'

'Just one or two friends.'

'Who in particular?'

'Well . . . no one special. A few people at the hospital. Anne Markham, David, of course . . . Pippa.' She stopped. 'It's ironic – we were only talking about this the other day.'

A faint excitement stirred inside Sergeant Bird.

'Where were you talking?' he asked levelly.

'In Pippa's room. It was last Thursday evening.'

'Tell me exactly who was there.'

Coral looked puzzled, but complied. 'Pippa and David,' she said slowly, 'that wretched Audrey, and Barnaby. Maybe Stewart Bridges – I can't quite remember. No – he came in later with Neil Thornton. We were asking them to participate in the sponsored swim.'

'No one else?'

She thought hard. 'No.'

'Thank you. I don't suppose Maureen kept a diary, did she?'

Coral's second 'No' was crisp and emphatic.

'You seem very sure,' probed Sergeant Bird gently. He had already drawn his own conclusions, but waited to hear Coral's explanation.

'I am,' she said. 'You can't live with someone for two years and not know whether or not they keep a diary. Diarists are – *compulsive*. And besides, we've packed all her clothes and papers. There was nothing like a notebook or diary.'

'Pity. It might have given us a clue as to the man she met.' He looked her full in the face. 'What will you do now, Coral?'

'I – how do you mean?'

'The flat.'

'Oh. Yes. I'm not really sure. It's far too expensive for one

139

person, but I don't want to share with a stranger. I suppose I could go back to the Nurses' Home, but I couldn't *stand* it there before. You can't imagine what it's like, all those women together. No . . . there must be some other way. Perhaps something will turn up.'

Sergeant Bird's smile was tinged with compassion. 'Perhaps.'

When he had left the girls to their task and passed down the narrow wooden staircase, William Bird left the building, spent five minutes round the corner, then entered it again. Montgomery was expecting him at the hospital shortly, but there were things he wanted to check first. The entrance hall was cool and dim. He paused outside one of the ground-floor flats, then rapped softly on the door.

'Neil, I want to ask you a favour.'

'Mm?'

'It's to do with Philippa . . . ' Anne Markham fiddled with her watch. 'I hate to say this, but I don't trust Stewart's management. He made that stupid mistake over the antibiotics, and I don't think his sterile technique is as it should be. He seems to forget that her resistance to pathogens is low . . . I wondered – would you keep a closer eye on her, and perhaps take any samples we need?'

'Anne, that's not very practical. You know I'm in theatre or clinic most of the time. And besides, what do I tell Stewart when I barge in and assume his duties?' He looked at her closely. 'Stewart's always been careless; it's nothing new. Is there some other reason you're not happy with him?'

Dumbly, she nodded.

13

'Hello! Have you come to see Pippa?'

Anne Markham smiled cheerfully at Montgomery as he stood outside her office door, but his professional eyes noted the underlying look of strain on her face. Maureen's loss had been a bad blow to everyone.

'Not just yet,' he answered. 'In fact, I'd like a word with you.'

'Me?' She glanced around assessingly. 'It's not very private in here. I'm afraid it'll have to be the interview room again. Please take over, Staff.'

Ensconced in the stuffy little room, Montgomery came straight to the point. 'We can't ignore the possibility of a link between these incidents involving hospital personnel,' he said. 'Nothing is proven either way at present, but your assistance would be very valuable as we gather our evidence.'

'Tell me what you need; I'll do my best.'

He leaned forward. 'Philippa Rowe . . . has her progress been as you would have expected?'

Her brow puckered as she tried to work out the hidden nuances in his question. 'Well – er – in general terms, yes.'

Montgomery gazed calmly at her crisp uniform and neatly swept back hair. A reply of guillotine-like precision should have come from those narrow lips. Someone had tickled up the waters in Anne Markham's private pool.

'But there have been one or two small hiccups,' he stated.

'You – you could say that.' Now she was clearly embarrassed. 'A couple of incidents have occurred – carelessness, really.'

'Can you describe them?'

She told him, in layman's terms, about the antibiotics and the diuretic drug.

'Let me get this straight,' said Montgomery. 'Stewart Bridges wrote up these antibiotics on the drug treatment card?'

'Yes.'

'The consultant spotted the error, and Stewart didn't deny it was his?'

'Yes.'

'Had he ever done anything like this before – with another patient?'

'Not entirely the same, but he's often thoughtless in minor ways. He itches to be in theatre instead of working on the wards. All his notes are hastily scrawled – bordering on illegible. Also – ' She lowered her eyes.

'Go on.'

'He won't accept that he has anything to learn on the ward. He's got an arrogant streak. We can all learn from other people.'

'Very true. I gather this young man only qualified in the summer?'

'Yes.'

'Hmm. Do you think he gave the frusemide injection?'

'He denies it absolutely. No, I don't think even Stewart would do anything so stupid. And besides, Philippa is certain that no extra injections were given that afternoon.'

'Dr Bridges would know how to dispose of a needle properly, I suppose?'

'Oh yes.'

'May I see the syringe your domestic found?'

Once again, she looked uncomfortable.

'I'm afraid not, Inspector,' she said slowly. 'It's gone. It was just a mystery we couldn't solve, and eventually someone threw the pieces away. I'm sorry.'

'It may not be of any moment,' said Montgomery, 'But if a similar incident occurs – '

'We'll be alert,' she promised.

'Good. Now, how many doctors and nurses have a genuine professional reason for visiting Philippa?'

'Heavens! Well over twenty doctors; she's under the care of four teams at present. And her friends are medics, of course.'

'How often do they come?'

Anne Markham explained the elaborate system of consultant ward rounds, and the relative autonomy of the junior doctors.

'I'll get the notes,' she offered. 'They usually write something, even just a line.'

Montgomery browsed through the thick folder, wishing he could retain the services of an interpreter for twenty-four hours. All professions had their jargon but rarely were the terms so incomprehensible. The file itself was a veritable labyrinth, with ward and operation notes flanked by baffling laboratory forms.

'What does NAD mean?' he asked.

'No Abnormality Detected,' she supplied, then twinkled at him. 'In Stewart's case, it's interpreted as Not Actually Done.'

Montgomery's mouth tugged into an answering smile. 'And these initials at the end of each entry? Are they the individual doctor concerned?'

'Yes.'

'BF' appeared almost as regularly as 'SB'; the initials seemed appropriate in view of everything Montgomery had heard about the neurology SHO.

'How do I find out who is on duty at any particular time, Sister?'

'Well, for the nurses there's the Off Duty rota. It's in the office – I can show you. The doctors all have different rotas, depending on their seniority and whether or not they work for a busy team. Switchboard has a kind of master copy.'

'Thank you. By the way, did you know Gilbert Bradshaw well?'

'I barely knew him at all, Inspector. I sometimes came across him assessing patients for anaesthetic; he might comment on the pre-med, or suggest an ECG. No more.'

She was quietly emphatic.

Sergeant Bird had joined him by the time Montgomery was putting the same questions to Neil Thornton. The tall registrar was busy, as usual, but had that knack of a good GP of listening thoughtfully and appearing to have all the time in the world. No neurotic streak like Jackson and himself, thought Montgomery wryly; he had more in common with Sergeant Bird. William Bird's compassion, however, was missing; this man was cool and clinical.

'Yes, Sister told me about the frusemide on Monday. It's quite extraordinary. None of our patients requires it at present.'

'Can it only be administered intravenously?'

'Oh, no. You can give an intramuscular injection – rather painful and best avoided if possible – or it can be taken orally as tablets.'

'Would the liquid from a vial be active orally?'

Neil cocked a mildly quizzical eyebrow but made no comment. 'Yes.'

'And has this drug any place at all in the treatment of renal failure?'

The young surgeon sighed. 'I don't want to confuse you, Inspector. The answer's a straight "no" for a person who is recovering, like Philippa. Diuretic drugs – that is, agents increasing the flow of urine – are not needed because she's now passing fluids normally. But right at the start, some people do use them to try to stimulate the kidneys and improve the outcome. We did that ourselves using mannitol, a different diuretic which works osmotically, but it seemed to have no effect.'

143

'I think I understand,' said Montgomery doubtfully. 'At the beginning, it may help; later, it doesn't. Is there any way of telling if the drug was given to Philippa?'

'Not by now. Its elimination half-life is very short – less than two hours. There'll be nothing left to measure. But in any case, from what I've heard, Philippa's collapse was very non-specific. I mean, *why* should anyone want to give her frusemide?'

His puzzlement was genuine, in Montgomery's estimation.

'That's what we're trying to find out. Mr Thornton . . . suppose for a moment that someone was out to harm Philippa – kill her, even. Would you consider frusemide an effective agent to attain that end?'

Something unreadable flashed into the deep blue eyes, but he answered readily enough.

'It's an odd choice. I can't decide if it's very subtle or totally brainless. You would have to assume that no nurse was going to look in on Philippa for hours, and even then, there'd be no guarantee of serious consequences . . . With respect, the idea sounds quite cockeyed.'

'How do you account for the ampoule and syringe?'

'I don't have to account for them. I wasn't there. But when I first heard the story I assumed someone from another ward had simply dumped them in our clinical room *en passant*.'

'What's your opinion of Stewart Bridges as a doctor?'

'Do I have to answer that?' Neil began to smile with unexpected charm. 'I prefer to say good things about members of my own team.'

'Stretch a point. Tell me the truth.'

'We all have our crosses to bear, Inspector. Stewart just happens to be mine. I only hope I'll never be called on to give him a reference! In a nutshell, he wants the jam but not the bread and butter, the exotic but not the mundane. He's slapdash in his ward work so that he can spend as much time as possible in theatre. There, he's selectively keen. If it's interesting, he'll stay, but if we're just closing up, for instance, he has a tendency to wander off and drink coffee. Most other housemen I've known jump at the chance to practise their blanket stitch.'

'I see . . . Does he often work two weekends in succession?'

'No. He only started the job two months ago. Before that, he was a medical student. I'm pretty sure this is the first time he's swapped his duty . . . something about a wedding.'

'Did he instigate the alteration?'

'I imagine so. It was for his benefit. You'd better ask him.'

'I shall. You may have gathered from your friends that we're routinely questioning anyone with the slightest connection with Dr Bradshaw and Nurse O'Donnell. Would you mind telling me what you were doing on the evening of Friday the sixteenth, and also Friday the twenty-third of this month?'

Neil was unperturbed. 'I'll admit I was expecting you to ask. I'm only sorry that my answer's not going to be entirely satisfactory. Take the first Friday. I wasn't on duty. I have sporadic second-on responsibilities between the days we admit emergencies. My girlfriend Vanda, who's a model based in London, was busy on an assignment, so I stayed late at the hospital writing up a paper for the BJS – sorry, *British Journal of Surgery*.'

'Can you describe the evening?'

'Yes – pretty dull. I went to the library just before five; it's in the Postgraduate Centre, which occupies a wing away from the main part of the hospital. The librarian was about to leave, and she gave me the key. That's standard practice. I worked till about six-thirty, had some glop in the canteen, then carried on till maybe nine. I then locked my briefcase in the boot of the car and drifted across to the Mess. I got a glass of beer from the bar and watched television until midnight. It was *Bullitt* – I enjoyed the car chase.'

'And after that?'

'Back to the flat. We were due to be on "take" the next morning.'

'Fine. Thank you, Mr Thornton. Who else did you see in the library?'

He grimaced. 'No one. It was Friday. You know – POETS day. I wouldn't have been there myself if Vanda had been in Nottingham. One thing I can tell you – if I'd had the least idea of what was going to happen in Sylvia Vale that night, I'd have talked to anyone and everyone in the hospital. As it is, I know my story's a bit weak.'

Montgomery made no comment. 'What car do you drive?'

'A Vauxhall Cavalier.'

'And you race a Porsche?'

'Yes.'

'Expensive.'

'I win. But you're right, it is expensive. I'm in debt to my bank manager, but fortunately he takes a long-term view.'

'Where do you keep the cars?'

'I drive to work in the Cavalier; my flat's in West Bridgford. The Porsche stays in Arthur Wright's garage – he's my mechanic.'

'And where do you park the Cavalier?'

'Wherever I can find a space. Usually the front car-park, where the porter's kiosk is.'

Montgomery nodded. 'Think carefully, Mr Thornton ... Was there *anyone* you met and spoke to that night?'

'Well, as I said, the library was empty. I wasn't long in the canteen – didn't see any of my colleagues, so I had a table to myself. Let's see – oh, yes. Albert was on duty when I locked my briefcase away. We exchanged a few words.'

'Is that the porter?'

'Yes. He lurks in that little kiosk adjoining the main building, ostensibly to give out information, but also to make sure that visitors don't park in the area reserved for medical staff. He's slowly going out of his skull with boredom. There's a chance he might remember me.'

'And your film?'

Neil's face cleared. 'I'm on a better footing there. Mike Whiting watched the whole thing.' He turned to Sergeant Bird, who was taking immaculate longhand notes. 'He's in the ENT department.'

'Very good,' the sergeant replied.

'Doesn't the Mortar and Pestle hold any attractions for you?' asked Montgomery. 'We've been hearing how it's a favourite among hospital personnel, especially on Friday nights.'

'A migration of lemmings,' said Neil, his narrow upper lip curling with faint scorn. 'I don't run with the crowd. Each to his own. Personally, I didn't feel that *Bullitt* had any competition worth considering.' He glanced at his watch. 'Inspector, I'm afraid I really have to go soon.'

'Of course. We appreciate your co-operation. Briefly, then – what were your movements last Friday night?'

The blue eyes gleamed reminiscently. 'I was at home. In the flat. With Vanda.'

'Ah. All night?'

'All night.'

A model, Neil had said. Yes, it figured. In his mind's eye,

Montgomery could see the tall girl with the good bone structure standing by the track at Donington Park, blonde hair whipping across her face, stopwatch in hand. He remembered the carefully controlled accent which nevertheless failed to hide her East London origins, and wondered about their relationship. It seemed incongruous. Was she attracted to his racing persona, and all the superficial glamour that engendered, or was it the serious surgeon who had caught her eye? Respectability . . . That could be a powerful magnet if her background was as he suspected. And what of Neil himself? Vanda was fine mistress material, but presumably he envisaged nothing more. As the wife of a potential consultant, she would constantly let him down.

The handsome face watched Mongomery calmly. This man pulled for Number One; he had virtually said as much. Team efforts were not his *métier*. Girlfriends would be considered expendable . . . Look out, Vanda.

'Bridges? You want to know about Bridges? Can't imagine why.'

Vernon Crowland had just returned to his office from the private wing to find unexpected visitors.

'General enquiries,' said Montgomery smoothly.

'Like the last time,' sighed the consultant. 'You might as well sit down. Bridges . . . not living up to his promise. Most of his student surgery was done at the Victoria – they said he was keen. In a way he is, but he's no good as a houseman. Resents the ward work – cuts corners. Then he'll willingly spend hours assisting in theatre while I fix an aortic aneurysm. If he sticks with surgery, he'll be disappointed: the bulk of the workload consists of varicose veins, hernias and haemorrhoids – oh, and vasectomies. I did nine this morning. Scintillating. The only way to survive the tedium was to run through 'The Lark Ascending' in my head. Must admit, though, it pays well. Professional men don't like their wives to be on the Pill.'

'If you had to give Stewart Bridges a reference, what would you say?' asked Montgomery, remembering Neil Thornton's comment.

'What? Bridges? Hah! There's no "if" about it: I shall have to one day. I suppose I'll fall back on that time-honoured line: "You will be very lucky to get this young man to work for you".'

Sergeant Bird gave an involuntary snicker, and the consultant beamed expansively.

Montgomery pressed on. 'You said Dr Bridges trained at the Victoria. When he came here, was Nurse O'Donnell still working in the theatre?'

The beam vanished as if someone had pulled a lightswitch. 'Little Maureen O'Donnell,' he rasped in a bleak voice. 'No, she had gone back to the wards by then.' His eyes snapped upwards to hold Montgomery's in a powerful lock. 'Find the bastard,' he commanded. 'Find the person who killed a decent girl. If money's any problem, I'll put up a reward.'

'Thank you. It's not certain yet that she was killed, but – '

'Don't give me that! You must think we're blind around here. Something very unpleasant is going on, isn't it? I know you've been talking to the junior doctors and nursing staff. I don't think you'll get much joy there. The porters are an odd bunch; I suggest you interview them. And that pharmacy storeman – he's definitely a psycho. You need to look at faces, Inspector. They'll tell you all you need to know.'

'Er, yes. We do try. At present, we're in the business of exclusion. With that in mind, would you be kind enough to outline for us your own movements last Friday evening?'

'Gladly. I was at home. Dinner-party. Ten people.'

'And the Friday before?'

'Ah, an excellent concert. The Czech Philharmonic Orchestra – a selection of Dvořák works. Tell that to the people who think culture begins and ends in London!'

'Who were you with?'

The air of bonhomie was returning; Mr Crowland leaned back in his chair. 'My wife, son, daughter-in-law, Jones, Mrs Jones and two of our neighbours. Have you met Jones yet, Inspector?'

'Not personally, but I intend to.'

'Hah! You should.' He wagged a didactic finger in Montgomery's direction. 'Jones is a dry stick,' he said. 'A dry stick.'

'Phew!' Montgomery's feet carried him ever more rapidly towards the exit to the building. The 'dry stick' had taken an hour to unburden himself of assorted minor grievances, ill-founded opinions and two watertight alibis.

He turned to Sergeant Bird, who was wheezing at his elbow. 'Will – if I ever end up like those two, you will tell me, won't you?'

'Would I still have a job if I did?'

'Probably not – but think of the satisfaction.'

He thought. 'You've got something there, sir.'

Narrowed eyes in a lugubrious face watched them as they crossed the car-park and climbed into Montgomery's Metro, taken from the station pool. Albert was in residence, ready to wield his small quota of power if any visitor was unlucky enough to choose the wrong parking-spot.

'Should we have a word?' asked Sergeant Bird reluctantly. 'He's part of Thornton's alibi.'

Montgomery shook his head and stifled a yawn. Between them, the consultants had reduced him to a state of mental torpor. 'Tomorrow,' he said. 'Let's get all the stories first. Jackson and Smythe can check up on the details.' He let in the clutch, and steered the car carefully round the kiosk. Sergeant Bird gave a friendly wave as they drove past; he received a penetrating glower in return.

For once, Jackson felt enthusiastic about his work. 'Do you mean *the* Vanda?' he demanded of Montgomery, almost slopping his morning coffee into its saucer. 'The Coco Palm Soap Girl? The one who strips off on a tropical island and washes herself?'

'I always knew there was a gap in my education,' said Montgomery. 'This girl is tall and blonde.'

'That's her! She's on the box every now and then. What's she doing in Nottingham?'

'She doesn't live here. I understand she has a flat in London, but stays with Neil Thornton in between major engagements. Her full name is Vanda Pitts.'

'Oh!'

'You can see why she prefers her Christian name,' said Sergeant Bird. 'I wonder if that part's genuine.'

'Check it out, Brian,' instructed Montgomery.

'Yes, sir!' Jackson practically stood to attention. After a moment, he swung round to eye up Smythe, the young detective constable who frequently partnered him during enquiries. 'You'd better let me do all the talking,' he said.

Smythe blinked. He had a lean, impassive face into which people read whatever expression they wanted. His eyes were

149

brown with a perpetual liquid sheen, and the hair above them was impossibly short. He looked like a poet who had wandered into the army by mistake.

'And you a married man,' he chided.

'Better than being a bender.' Jackson knew it wasn't true; Smythe was merely between girlfriends.

They set off amicably for West Bridgford, a wealthy suburb on the south bank of the Trent, and found that Neil Thornton's home was one of a modern block of flats skilfully camouflaged to blend in with the large mature houses surrounding it.

'Leave it all to me,' Jackson repeated airily as they approached the deserted entrance hall. 'You can look and learn.'

'She might be out.'

'You really must try to curb your optimism.'

He rang the bell marked 'Thornton' and was quickly rewarded by the buzz and crackle of the intercom.

'Who is it?' The female voice, though distorted, had an exciting husky quality.

'Police, ma'am. Just a routine enquiry.'

'I'm afraid Mr Thornton isn't here. He's at the hospital.'

'That's all right. We'd like to see you, if it's convenient.'

'Well . . . I'm not actually dressed yet.' She made it sound like a question.

Jackson leaned towards the microphone. 'We have broad minds, ma'am.'

There was a faint chuckle. 'Come on up.'

Jackson and Smythe exchanged glances before the door lock was released with a loud click, allowing them to step into a lobby smelling of new carpets. On their way up the silent stairs there was much smoothing of garments and, in Jackson's case, combing of hair.

The door of Flat Four opened before they reached it. Vanda Pitts leaned in a fluid pose against the lintel wearing a gentian silk housecoat which hid nothing and accentuated plenty. Her hair was loose and casually tousled – almost certainly permed that way. The face, bare of make-up, was a little pale in the thin morning light, but otherwise held its own; the finely-chiselled nose was straight and short, the full lower lip held just the right degree of pout. Only the eyes gave Jackson a jolt. They were of a hard, glacial blue which reminded him uncomfortably of Montgomery's.

150

'Come in, boys,' she invited. 'Anyone's welcome except the tax man.'

Jackson strutted across the threshold, mildy irritated to notice that Smythe had decided to play the gawky schoolboy. Vanda closed the door behind them, and motioned them to a black leather-covered settee.

'Sit down. Can I get you a drink?'

There was a small bar in the corner of the room, which was as wide and soulless as a spaceship in a bad science-fiction film. The carpet was black and unremittingly plain. The pure white ceiling and walls gained little relief from anchored spotlights and the occasional art-deco mirror. Furniture was functional. The only human interest was represented by a huge poster of Vanda, bikini-clad, reclining against the bonnet of a silver Porsche Carrera.

She followed the line of Jackson's gaze. 'I made him put that up,' she said. 'He tolerates it because of the car. Now about that drink – '

'No thanks, we're on duty.'

'I promise I won't tell.' She pursed her lips and pressed the side of her forefinger against them.

Jackson shook his head; Smythe couldn't be trusted to keep quiet. 'No. You ought to take a look at this, though, before you entertain so blithely. I'm Sergeant Jackson. This is Smythe.' He held out his warrant card, and Smythe followed suit.

Her inspection was cursory. 'No need. You've both got "cop" stamped all over you. What is it you want?'

'We'd like a description of your movements last Friday. Everyone you met, what they did, what they said.'

She arched her eyebrows. 'Is that all? May I ask why?'

Jackson smiled. 'You can ask. We're investigating a serious crime.'

Vanda shrugged, and lowered herself into a chair with studied grace. 'Have it your way. I can guess. It's in every paper, and Neil's told me a few bits and pieces. Those people from the hospital . . . I've only actually met Philippa. All right, then. Friday . . . I was in Knightsbridge in the morning. I saw my agent, Teri Golding, and discussed a bit of show modelling work she's laid on for me for next week. It's a low-key, provincial assignment, the type I used to do in my teens. It's just a fill-in, really, while I think about an offer I've had from Milan. My face has become too familiar over here, so I'm taking a break from editorial and advertising work and having a bit of a holiday – my first for months.

'Back to Friday. I drove up the M1 after lunch, and reached the flat here at four-thirty. I unpacked, had a bath and mooched around with magazines. Neil got in at six-thirty. He was tired, and I'm no cook, so we went and bought a take-away Chinese meal. After that, we listened to records and went to bed.'

'What time was this?'

'Nine-ish.'

'Bit early, wouldn't you say?'

She rolled her eyes. 'I didn't say we went to *sleep*.'

'Beg pardon. I thought you indicated that he was tired.'

She crossed one slender leg over the other, and swayed the foot gently. She was wearing light, white canvas pumps and no stockings. 'Sergeant Jackson, are you always as obtuse as this? Show me the man, barring eunuchs, who will let a little minor fatigue deprive him of his – opportunities. He'd had a busy week. We drank champagne – that's quite usual – and liaised. End of story.'

'Not quite,' said Jackson gruffly. 'Did he leave your company for any reason at all after six-thirty?'

'No.'

'When did you go to sleep?'

'Eleven.'

'How do you know he didn't leave the flat after eleven?'

Vanda made an exasperated sound. 'Because I'm not deaf. And anyway, why on earth should he do that?'

Jackson ignored her question, and continued with his own.

'How long have you known him, Miss Pitts?'

'Please call me Vanda. I'd rather you did.' She swung her head round to look at the poster on the wall. 'It's been two years. I met him at Brands Hatch, where he'd just won a race in the Porsche.' The corners of her mouth crept upwards; Smythe was captivated. 'He's different, you know; I saw that straight away. He has *depth*. People don't appreciate that because on the surface he's all cool professionalism. But underneath – there's warmth and life and drive and humour. Ambition shouldn't be a dirty word. It is in this country, but in America it would be admired, applauded. He knows where he's going, and those who don't are jealous of him. He's man enough to be proud of my work instead of seeing it as a threat to his ego. He doesn't want a "little woman" type bustling around him; he wants a partner.'

It was a long answer to a short question. Jackson was not the most perceptive of men, but his detective's instinct had long been sharpened on the whetstone of human nature; he thought he could recognize a trace of wishful thinking in her panegyric.

'Are you going to get hitched, then?' he asked cheerfully.

'Probably – one day. There's no hurry. We've both got some travelling to do first.'

'I dare say ... What has he said to you about these deaths among his colleagues?'

Her face became serious. 'We're human, Sergeant. And curious. Obviously we've discussed it, but Neil doesn't have any particular inside knowledge. The papers appear to know more than we do. He was upset about that nurse; he worked with her in theatre for some months. He's also very concerned about Philippa. Normally he's a bit of an automaton with respect to his patients, but he seems to be taking all her ups and downs personally. I think he's afraid she'll die of some preventable complication.' She shivered. 'The whole thing's horrible. Have the police any ideas?'

'The odd lead,' said Jackson, getting to his feet and meandering round the periphery of the room. 'I thought medics had lots of books and journals. Where does Neil keep his?'

'He's got a study – the door over there.' She pointed. 'Would you like to see?'

'Don't mind if I do. These are large flats, aren't they? It's deceptive from the outside ... Thank you.'

The neatly extracted conducted tour yielded nothing but brief impressions: a study/library stuffed with medical and mechanical literature in almost equal quantities, a spotless, impersonal kitchen gleaming with white appliances, and a spacious bedroom in which at last a touch of feminine influence was apparent. The thick wool carpet and velvet draperies were a rich apricot colour, as was the rumpled counterpane on the bed. The sheets, however, were dark brown and lustrous. There was nothing improper to be seen in the room, except a black stocking thrown negligently across a dralon-padded stool, yet the atmosphere was sharply erotic.

Vanda was on the point of escorting them back to the lounge when the belt of her housecoat subtly disengaged itself, and the facings slid apart. Jackson didn't know where to look; he was torn between decorum and fascination with the firm, honey-tanned flesh so suddenly revealed. Directly opposite the bedroom door hung a gilt-framed mirror. He could see his face reflected – stiff, speechless. As he hastened to control his breathing, Vanda unhurriedly retied the belt, looking over his shoulder as she did so. Jackson turned to his colleague suspiciously. Smythe's brown eyes shone more moistly than ever; they seemed to ripple. He was staring at the smooth projection of Vanda's hipbone under its flimsy silken covering.

She opened her mouth to speak. 'That's it, apart from the bathroom.'

'Nice place,' said Jackson flatly. He felt weak at the knees. 'Thanks for showing us round. I've just one more question . . . Is your name really Vanda Pitts?'

She laughed, displaying even white teeth in excellent condition.

'Unfortunately, yes. My mother couldn't do much about the surname, but she was determined to have a daughter on the stage, or in some kind of limelight, so she chose Vanda. At least it beats Ethel.'

'And do you really use Coco Palm soap?' The soft, hungry voice was Smythe's.

'No – I can't stand the stuff! Sorry. Sergeant – do I have to write anything down? Sign anything?'

'Not at this stage. We'll let you know if that should be necessary.'

'Fine. Come and see me again if you need any more. I'm already bored with leisure. I'd go mad without my work.'

She addressed Jackson, but her eyes moved to include Smythe in the invitation. He was whisked out of the flat before the colour could recede from his poetic cheekbones.

14

'You pick your times, don't you,' said David Stannard testily, scowling at Montgomery over an enormous pile of notes. 'This is Outpatients. As you can see, I'm up to my eyeballs.' He gave a brief laugh as if to rob the words of offence, but Montgomery sensed a hostility which had not been present at their previous meeting.

'I'm sorry. We've all got a job to do.' He planted himself squarely in front of the desk in the small clinical room the registrar occupied.

'That's just it; I don't see much evidence of your results. Someone round here's *killing* people. Oh, hell. Look . . . I'm busy. Can't you come back later?'

'We'd like you to make a statement as soon as possible, Dr Stannard. It's imperative that this person doesn't strike again.'

'I'd agree with you there. Tell you what . . . I'll come to your station at lunch time. I don't want to give the nosy parkers here a field day. It may be well after one if this clinic overruns, but I will come. Is that good enough?'

'That would be fine.'

Barnaby Fletcher was more available, though clearly nervous at the sight of two plain-clothed officers. His coat was askew, as usual, and his hair looked as if he had suffered from an accidental brush with a Van de Graaff generator.

'Where was I?' he repeated stupidly. 'Oh dear – I never imagined anyone would want to know *that*. I mean – I didn't write it down, or anything. Gosh!'

'Just think of the events one by one,' said Sergeant Bird soothingly. 'Let's take the first Friday. Were you on duty?'

'No, but I stayed at the hospital. It's Becka's mother, you see . . . she comes to the house every Friday afternoon, and stays well into the evening. I – we . . . it's difficult. Polite conversation, I mean. And she *drools* all over Paul. I'm sure it's bad for him. Do you want to see his picture? Here. Anyway, I try to be late on Fridays. And it does give them a chance to gossip.'

Montgomery could sympathize with the sentiments expressed. 'That's most understandable,' he said. 'Tell us what you actually did.'

'I stayed on the ward until six. Then I had some plaice and chips in the canteen. Then I went to the library to read, but it was locked. I think – yes, I went to the "quiet room" in the Mess, the one without a television, and read a bit of *King Solomon's Mines*. I should have been studying, but on a Friday night you don't feel like it. I went home a little bit after nine. Becka knew I wouldn't want dinner.'

'Who did you talk to during the evening?'

He gaped. 'I didn't really notice. I don't think there was anyone. The canteen was very quiet . . . Just a few nurses. I suppose – oh, wait! I saw Neil coming away from the car-park. He was getting rather wet. We crossed on the path as I was leaving the Mess. I can't remember if we spoke.'

'Where was he going?' asked Montgomery.

'Into the Mess.'

'Are you sure of the time?'

'Give or take fifteen minutes . . . or maybe twenty.'

'Thank you, Dr Fletcher. Now, can we turn to the second Friday, a week later?'

'Last Friday?'

'Yes.'

'Er . . . yes. I was on duty. We have an interesting rota – I can explain it if you like. Ah. Well . . . I pottered around, really. There wasn't a lot going on. Neurology's not exactly an acute specialty. I can be on call from home – my house is just a couple of miles from the hospital. I don't carry a cardiac-arrest bleep, you see, so it doesn't matter if I'm not actually on the premises. But Becka's mother – '

'Quite. Where did you "potter", Dr Fletcher?'

'Oh, the ward, the Mess. I saw some relatives at seven . . .'

'And when did you arrive home?'

'Ten o'clock.'

Montgomery painstakingly ascertained possible witnesses to Barnaby's peregrinations on the night in question. The process was so tiring that he almost neglected a key point. Sergeant Bird caught his eye and intervened.

'Dr Fletcher – do you have a car?'

'Yes.'

'And do you drive to work, or walk?'

'I drive. I should walk, I know. Healthier.'

'What make is your car?'

Barnaby's face was as ingenuous as a nun's. 'It's a Citroën,' he said happily. 'A bright yellow 2CV.'

'Let me reiterate.' Montgomery steepled his fingers and regarded

David Stannard across the cluttered surface of his desk. 'You spent the early part of last Friday evening in the biochemistry lab on the hospital campus, working on some blood samples you had taken from volunteer patients. At seven forty-five you had a canteen meal, and by eight forty-five you were walking to the Mortar and Pestle, where you passed the rest of the night in a moderately uninhibited state until closing time.'

'Spot on.'

'Most of your friends joined you later, some time around nine-thirty, having been at a "drug do" sponsored by Poole and Endicott. This took the form of a slide show and a buffet meal. You say you were unaware of the event.'

'Of course. I wouldn't have wasted my money in the canteen if I'd known. I might have heard about it earlier, and forgotten – I've got a diary, but I don't use it very much.'

'What did you do when the pub closed?'

'We all went off to a party in one of the hospital flats. I left about one and went to bed.'

'Did you see Nurse Chapman at all that night?'

'No.'

'Didn't that surprise you? I thought she was one of the set who haunted the Mortar and Pestle on a regular basis.'

'Not always. Coral had had a tiring week, and I assumed she was having an evening in.'

'Did you leave the party on your own?'

David's jaw tightened. 'Yes.'

'You've got a girlfriend, haven't you? I believe you made reference to "the devoted Audrey" once.'

'That was a mistake,' said David tersely. 'She doesn't deserve that description, and I had no right to express it. It isn't Audrey's fault that I don't feel towards her as she would like me to. We'll have to work it out, but just now is a bad time.'

'How often do you see her?'

'Once or twice a week.'

'You didn't take her to the party on Friday?'

'No. It was a spontaneous decision to go.'

'You feel quite free to go out in Audrey's absence?'

'Yes. She doesn't own me.'

'Do you know what Audrey was doing on Friday night?'

A faint expression of guilt flitted across David Stannard's features before he straightened his back defiantly.

'I haven't a clue.'

'What about Maureen O'Donnell?'

'Yes, what about Maureen?'

'Did you see her on Friday?'

'Briefly in the corridor at lunch-time.'

'Was that the last time you saw her?'

'Yes.'

'Has she ever confided in you?'

'Confided?' He looked perplexed.

'Yes. Shared secrets.'

'You mean without Coral's knowledge?'

Montgomery nodded.

'No . . . I can't recall that ever happening.'

'Did she discuss Gilbert Bradshaw with you at any time?'

'No. We were more concerned with Pippa.'

'You're sure?'

'Of course I'm sure!' David exploded crossly. He blinked for a moment, then slumped dejectedly in the chair. 'I'm sorry, Inspector. I'm not helping you, am I? I keep thinking of Maureen . . . Was there some way we could have prevented her death? I – I have to say this . . .' He raised his head and looked at Montgomery levelly. '. . . I've been wondering if you were doing enough. Are you taking it seriously? Do you expect results, or are you just going through the motions?'

'We expect results.' Montgomery's voice was cool, unruffled. He held back for a thoughtful pause before speaking again. 'Dr Stannard . . . I imagine you find in medicine that the messenger is often confused with the message. You may have merely diagnosed, but the patients or their relatives behave as if you have actually created the condition, and the treatment is somehow all for *your* benefit. Yes? . . . Well, think about it: there are many parallels between medicine and police work. I'd prefer you not to fall into the same trap. We're doing our best.'

'I accept that. I'm sorry.'

'Right, let's move on. What car do you drive?'

'A Ford XR3i.' He gave the number.

'Where is it normally parked?'

'In the residents' car-park, near to my flat.'

'When do you use it?'

'Evenings and weekends.'

'Tell me about bamboo rats.'

David was startled. 'What?'

'Bamboo rats. Little furry creatures. You saw a television programme all about them.'

'Oh – yes. Let's see . . . They're a sort of mole rat from Asia. Spend most of their time underground. They don't have any necks, and their eyes are small and piggy. That's it – they look more like guinea pigs than rats, except that their ears are tiny and they've got tails. They dig a lot, as you'd expect, not only with their claws and foretoes, but also with their incisor teeth. They can close their lips behind the teeth to stop their mouths filling with soil . . . Is that enough?'

'What do they eat?' asked Montgomery.

'Bamboo.' David's tone was pitying.

When the registrar had signed his formal statement and left, Sergeant Bird sighed.

'Guilt,' he said.

'Who, Stannard?' Montgomery was already wading through a sheaf of notes.

'Those relatives you spoke about. In hospitals, in police stations. Their attitude stems from guilt. Their own. But Stannard? I don't know.'

'Neither do I, Will. Neither do I.'

'Pow-wow time,' muttered Brian Jackson, easing himself out of his chair and meandering over to join the huddle of detectives who were stretching the capacity of Montgomery's office to its limits.

Sergeant Bird capped his fountain pen and stowed it away in a pocket. He had been drawing a plan of the hospital from memory, and something didn't seem to be quite right. Reservations were many with this case, anyway; Montgomery was uneasy about aspects of the hit-and-run car, and the alibis of some of the medical staff were as leaky as a colander. He was glad to have the opportunity to try to rationalize their findings.

He sat down in the corner as Montgomery made a few preliminary remarks.

'So we've looked closely at seven particular people. The two consultants, Mr Crowland and Dr Jones, have impeccable alibis:

159

we can rule them out without the least compunction. Similarly, Milton Gale. He was unlucky enough to be the one to find Bradshaw's body, but that is his sole connection with the case. His alibis for both Friday nights are faultless.

'Stewart Bridges presents a more difficult problem. Like Dr Gale, he has only been working at the District Hospital since the beginning of August, a time during which Maureen O'Donnell was no longer a member of the theatre staff. By all accounts, their paths have rarely crossed either professionally or socially. He saw a lot of Bradshaw, however.

'On the night of Bradshaw's death he was on duty. I understand it was an ordinary night on call, not an emergency "take" like the following day. The workload is very variable on such nights, and a houseman has responsibilities in different parts of the hospital. Haslam and Grange – ' he nodded towards two burly detective constables ' – have checked on his account of his movements, and apart from a rather unsatisfactory period around nine o'clock, there are good and sufficient witnesses to back up his story. The hiatus of fifty minutes would barely give him time to drive to Sylvia Vale and commit a double atrocity.

'A week later, when Maureen O'Donnell died, Bridges was off duty on the Friday night but not the Saturday. He had swapped part of the weekend with a colleague in order to have the following Saturday free to attend a wedding. At first, I thought that was suspicious, but it turns out to be common practice. The medical rota in the switchboard room is nearly illegible because of all the crossings-out. So . . . on the Friday he was off duty and claims he had a very early night. Eight o'clock. There's no one to verify this, so we have to leave a question mark against Bridges for that second Friday.'

'Isn't he the one who overdosed Philippa Rowe? Gave her too many antibiotics?' Smythe had a pile of papers on his knee and was riffling through them industriously.

'Yes . . . I'm not sure how much weight to place on that incident. Or the other one I told you about. Bridges has a reputation for being slapdash, so it was in character, and Anne Markham felt that the mistake would have come to light pretty quickly anyway. His name was written on the Drug Kardex; if the results had been serious, we'd have traced the perpetrator with no trouble at all.

'One more thing – he's living in at the hospital at present and doesn't have a car. That's not to say that he didn't borrow one, but it's a point worth considering.

'Next, I'd like us to turn to David Stannard. He had strong links with Philippa Rowe and Maureen O'Donnell, but any special connection with Bradshaw so far eludes us. He claims he spent the first Friday watching television and drinking in the Mortar and Pestle. The only corroborating witness I know of so far is Coral Chapman, Maureen's flatmate, who says she met him in the pub.'

'At ten o'clock,' put in Sergeant Bird.

'That's right. At ten. So – what other witnesses have we? Who's been making the enquiries?'

'Sir.' Colin Haslam raised his hand a few inches. 'I've spoken to a whole crowd of medical students and a Dr Allsopp from the Casualty Department. They can't swear to his presence in the pub on that particular night. They were tight, and some of them don't know him very well.'

'A Dr Spitz was mentioned?'

'I'm afraid he's gone on holiday.'

'Wonderful. Stewart Bridges was equally vague about Stannard's presence in the Mess. He nipped in there himself to read the papers.' He paused. 'Effectively, then, Stannard has no alibi until ten o'clock. He runs a Ford XR3i – a new one – so he'd have had no trouble driving out to Sylvia Vale and back.

'His movements a week later aren't terribly satisfactory, either. He spent the early part of the evening alone in a biochemistry laboratory – that's in the pathology complex. Have you got the plan, Will? Thanks . . . Here, next to microbiology . . . He then ate in the canteen, unseen by any of his colleagues who were enjoying a drug company-sponsored buffet meal. After that, he walked to the Mortar and Pestle where again he was alone until those selfsame colleagues appeared around nine-thirty. He stayed in their company until one a.m.

'Maureen O'Donnell set out for her rendezvous at seven. She may have met someone in the hospital grounds, which are within walking distance of the Sherwood flat, or she may have caught a bus into the centre of town.'

'A gentleman would have picked her up, if she didn't have a car,' observed Smythe.

'A gentleman wouldn't have murdered her,' retorted Jackson crushingly.

'You don't suppose', said Smythe to Montgomery, 'that this young girl was stood up, or humiliated in some way, so she walked along the river bank in order to kill time before facing Coral in the flat, and she . . . somehow, slipped?'

'No,' said Montgomery.

'Moving on to Neil Thornton,' he continued, 'we've got a chap who is a respected surgeon, destined for great things according to his colleagues, yet who has an unexpected side to his character, in that he is equally dedicated to whirling round racing-circuits in a lethal machine. He worked closely with both Bradshaw and Maureen O'Donnell, but he appears to have known Philippa Rowe only superficially.

'The night of Bradshaw's death, he was working in the library – diligent lot, aren't they! – until nine, apart from a short break in the canteen around six-thirty. After that, he watched television in the Mess until midnight. He drives a Vauxhall Cavalier to and from work, but at weekends he races a silver Porsche which I understand is housed in a lock-up garage belonging to his mechanic, Arthur Wright. There are a smattering of possible witnesses for that Friday – Colin?'

Haslam hastily referred to his notebook. 'We talked to Sunny Jim again,' he said, 'alias Albert the porter. He was on a late shift that night and was stationed at the enquiry desk inside the main entrance. There's a little sitting room behind the desk which projects out to form the car-park kiosk; during the day he doubles as a car-park attendant.

'By eight-thirty, all the visitors had gone, and he had nothing much to do. He remembers speaking to Thornton just before nine. Thornton had come from the direction of the library, and was stowing his briefcase away in the Vauxhall before taking a small path to the side door which leads to the Mess. He saw someone else coming the opposite way along the same path, and is fairly certain that it was Dr Fletcher. As for the car, he is adamant that it was standing there all afternoon and evening; it was parked right in front of his kiosk.

'We then questioned Dr Michael Whiting, a registrar in the Ear, Nose and Throat Department. He was in the Mess from a quarter to nine onwards, and confirms that Mr Thornton watched the whole of *Bullitt* and part of another programme. They both left around midnight.'

'Thank you,' said Montgomery. 'He's in the clear after nine, then, but not before. If Albert is right about the car, that's another point in his favour. His alibi for the Friday when Maureen O'Donnell disappeared is more straightforward. He claims he was at home with his girlfriend, the model Vanda Pitts. Brian and Graham drew the short straw there – ' the others laughed a trifle enviously, ' – so we await their report with bated breath.'

Smythe opened his mouth to speak, then thought better of it and glanced at Jackson.

'We saw Miss Pitts,' said that worthy, 'in the flat. Mr Thornton was not present. She stated that he came home at six-thirty and was with her for the rest of the evening.'

'Did you believe her?'

'On balance, yes. She's obviously fond of him, but I think she has a tough streak of self-interest. I've been reading up some old magazine articles which profile her; she's very career-orientated. I can't see her deliberately mixing herself up with something which would jeopardize that. A professional model's work depends on reputation and goodwill.'

'True. And is her name really Vanda Pitts?'

'Yes. I contacted her agent and Somerset House.'

'Good. Anything to add, Graham?'

Smythe shook his head, a faraway look in his eyes.

'No good asking *him*,' said Jackson abrasively. 'He's starstruck. Another ten minutes in that flat and she'd have vamped him!'

'Does she use Coco Palm soap?' grinned Colin Haslam.

'No.' Smythe's voice was soft and sad.

'Another bubble burst,' mocked Jackson. 'Another myth dispelled. The boy will go into a decline.'

'So shall we all, if we don't get on,' cut in Montgomery sharply. 'I want us to concentrate now on Barnaby Fletcher. As you know, he's the sort of doctor who is guaranteed to bring on a heart attack if by some mischance you're his patient. He's clumsy, he's absent-minded . . . and it's just possible that he exaggerates it for our benefit. A few gentle enquiries among his immediate colleagues should clarify that one.

'He knew Gilbert Bradshaw better than anyone else in the hospital, which isn't saying much, and actually visited him at home two weeks before his death. That is an approximation; he's not sure himself.

'On the first Friday he went to the canteen at six, tried the library afterwards but found it locked, then settled in the "quiet room" in the Doctors' Mess where he read alone until nine o'clock. He then went home.

'The evening of the second Friday, he was on call, and says he "pottered" around the hospital until ten before going home. The only point of reference he was able to give was an interview with the brother and sister-in-law of one of his patients at seven o'clock. Someone was going to follow that up – you, Will?'

'Yes, sir. I went to the neurology ward last night and spoke to the staff nurse on duty. She saw Dr Fletcher herself; apparently he spent twenty minutes with the couple. He recorded the gist of the interview in the medical notes, with a prefix of "19.00 hrs", then left shortly afterwards.'

'So he could still have met Maureen O'Donnell somewhere at, say, seven-thirty,' mused Montgomery.

'He wasn't at the sponsored buffet,' said Sergeant Bird. 'I asked around. Perhaps he was unaware of it, or perhaps he simply forgot.'

'Hmm. No other witnesses?'

'Not for that night. We've yet to see his wife and check when he arrived home.'

'There's a bit of cross-pollination in the stories of our possible suspects, as well,' said Montgomery. 'Going back to the night Bradshaw died, Fletcher said he tried the library door at six-thirty, but couldn't get in because it was locked. Now, Thornton had just left the library to go to the canteen, and its security was temporarily his responsibility, so he locked up behind him. If Fletcher was lying, he ran a risk that one or more people were actually in there working, who would contradict his statement. That strikes me as an unnecessary risk, so he probably spoke the truth.'

'Why didn't they meet?' Grange's bass voice was alert and interested.

'A good point. One was going to the library from the canteen, and the other one was reversing those destinations. Can we have the drawing again, Will?'

There was a muted crackling sound. 'I should have used the blackboard,' said Sergeant Bird. 'I'll transfer it later. But here we are . . . I think I've worked out what happened. It's been puzzling me.' He tapped the paper with a stubby finger. 'This is the Postgraduate Centre, which houses the library. It projects from the main part of the hospital because it was built more recently.

164

To get to the canteen, you can stay indoors by taking *this* route, or leave by this side door into the grounds. Anyone labouring away in the library would probably be glad of a breath of air; it's my guess that Thornton took the outdoor way, especially since the rain hadn't started then.'

'Something else to be checked,' said Montgomery. 'Our other link is Albert, who seems to have no particular axe to grind apart from general malevolence towards the world at large. He spotted both Thornton and Fletcher outside around nine o'clock, and Fletcher independently recalls seeing Thornton on the path. I think we can assume that they were there at that time. Now – any questions or points?'

Smythe caught his eye. 'Sir – how long would it take to drive out to Sylvia Vale and commit the two possible crimes we were initially considering?'

'Your estimate's as good as mine. Say twenty minutes of fast driving, twenty minutes for the separate attacks, including setting the locks, then the return trip. An hour . . . that's the absolute minimum. I feel increasingly convinced that our assailant was expected, and so he may well have spent the time in conversation to allay suspicion.'

'He or she,' murmured Sergeant Bird.

'Yes. He or she. But Maureen O'Donnell's murder was almost certainly the work of a man. No one has come forward yet for exclusion.'

'Might be afraid to.'

'True enough. Anything else?'

'I've been studying the statements,' said Haslam, 'and all three doctors who claimed to eat in the canteen that first evening say they did so alone, because it was Friday and none of their friends was around. But dinners are only served from six o'clock onwards, so you've got Stannard, Fletcher and Thornton all eating between six and seven o'clock, and none of them meeting each other. I find that rum.'

'Twenty minutes each,' offered Jackson.

'*I* wouldn't like to compress the consumption of an evening meal into twenty minutes,' stated Sergeant Bird emphatically. 'You'd end up with ulcers.'

'Doctors have ulcers anyway,' said Montgomery. 'They must be used to snatched breaks. But I take your point. Any other observations?'

'We haven't discussed motives yet,' said a young detective constable.

'That's because there isn't a glaringly obvious one to date. Thornton admits to being in some financial difficulties, and Stannard confesses he's still in love with Philippa Rowe. I don't know if you can make something out of that; the revelations were freely given. If the money was significant, then the fact has to be faced that Gilbert Bradshaw was worth much more dead than alive, but only to the legal beneficiaries, and we've no news of their identity yet, have we, Brian?'

'No. I'm still waiting for Mr Pendle to call.'

'Let me know when he does. We're lucky that Pendle's involved; he's one of only a handful of solicitors prepared to co-operate with us. In the meantime, we must continue our enquiries in the usual painstaking manner. I want Maureen O'Donnell's photograph circulated in *any* pub or restaurant she may have been taken to that night. The post-mortem showed that she had eaten scampi shortly before her death, so that should help to narrow it down. If we haven't made progress by the end of the weekend, I'll apply for a slot on "Crimescan".'

'Shall we include the cars in the enquiry?' asked Sergeant Bird.

'Yes. See if anyone spotted a blue Ford XR3i or a yellow Citroën 2CV in a pub or restaurant car-park at the relevant time. Colin – would you check the marina area again, asking specifically about those two types of car? Good.' He paused, distracted. 'Why do I feel there's something special about this Citroën? The minute Fletcher told me the make of his car it rang a bell, but I'm damned if I know why. Did one of you make a point about a Citroën some time back?' His interrogatory gaze met with shrugs and blank faces.

'Wait a minute!' Haslam startled himself and others by shattering the silence. 'There *was* a Citroën mentioned. The first time we spoke to Albert, we asked him whether he'd noticed any damage to the Maestro and he said "no", but then went on to tell us that a Citroën had been in a bump.'

'That's it!' cried Montgomery. 'Was he more specific? Was it before or after the incident with Philippa Rowe?'

'I'm sorry – I don't know. It didn't seem relevant at the time. We were only interested in the Maestro. And he confirmed that the car had previously been intact, which seemed to clinch it.'

'This needs looking into.' Montgomery was excited, scenting a

166

more rewarding trail, a steely gleam in his blue-grey eyes. 'Our Dr Fletcher has some explaining to do.'

15

The Maestros paraded in a gleaming row of reds, blacks, and metallic blues. A young man with overalls and an irritating whistle buffed the windscreens into fierce reflectors of the overhead sun, while an angular-featured salesman in a blue shirt and matching tie approached a small group of prospective customers with a glossy brochure.

'Beautiful, aren't they?' he said by way of greeting. 'Excellent fuel economy. Feel free to sit inside. Is there anything I can help you with?'

'Thanks; we're just looking.' Montgomery made his voice sound unencouraging.

'Is it saloons you're interested in? We've some nice Rovers round the corner. Or a small car for the lady? Let her test drive a Metro; she'd love it.'

Montgomery shook his head and made a non-committal noise. The salesman refused to be deterred.

'Well, let me give you one of our brochures. Look at the new colours – picture a Shantung Gold model standing in your driveway. Or you can have two-tone paint now as a no-cost option on several of the cars. I'll leave you to decide. Plenty of time.' He retreated, casting many an affable look over his left shoulder, to a desk behind the enormous plate-glass window at the front of the garage.

'Why *are* we here?' hissed WPC Rosalind Winger, who was wearing civilian clothes.

'I want to conduct a little experiment,' replied Montgomery, 'and this garage happens to be nearer than Forensic's Vehicle Examination Area. Stand there, please, Will, then miladdo won't wonder what on earth we're up to. I'd rather this was unofficial. Now, Ros . . . are those new tights? Pity. Never mind, I'll buy you some more . . . I'd like you to stand in front of that bumper bar. Anywhere – it's the same height all the way along. Thank you.' He crouched down and made two marks on the side of her

167

leg with a felt-tipped pen. 'Now – rise on tiptoe, as if you were running.' Two further marks were lightly drawn. 'Stand against the headlight . . . good.'

Rosalind Winger was quick on the uptake. 'I understand what you're doing, but the results don't make sense . . . Philippa's right leg was broken in the middle of the shin, yet this bumper is on a level with my knee!'

'Our friend's coming back,' warned Sergeant Bird.

'No problem. Smile at him, Ros,' instructed Montgomery. 'Wave the brochure.'

They left the garage in a controlled hurry, and turned into the leafy suburban drive where Montgomery's car was parked.

'Wasn't she run over by the Maestro after all?' asked WPC Winger, agog.

'Oh, I think she was,' said Montgomery.

'But – '

'Another car knocked her down first.'

William Bird nodded slowly; the girl looked wary but willing to be convinced.

'It would explain several of the oddities we had reservations about,' Montgomery continued. 'Why did Bradshaw's assailant lose vital seconds grovelling for the keys to an unfamiliar car when he was trying to catch Philippa Rowe? It would have been easier to jump straight inside his own vehicle . . . I think he did just that. He followed her in a car with a bumper bar several inches lower than that on a Maestro, and stopped her in a singularly callous manner. Then, rather than leave more clues on his own car, he reversed back into Bradshaw's grounds, found the garage keys at leisure, and drove the Maestro over the girl to finish off the job. That's when her woollen jumper got snagged on the jacking point. Remember, the heavy rainfall obliterated all tyre tracks.'

'Forensic found no trace of him in the Maestro.'

'They wouldn't necessarily, Will, if he was careful. I assume he wore gloves, and Locard's rule doesn't always work when you want it to . . . You know about Locard, don't you, Ros?'

'Yes,' she answered. 'He was an eminent French criminologist who said that every contact leaves traces: things are brought to a scene of crime, and things are taken away – hairs, fibres, whatever.'

'That's right. Something may yet crop up on further examination, but it doesn't help us now. The concept of two cars, though, is an attractive one. It would explain the lack of cuts or glass in Philippa's leg, apart from one gash at the level of the fracture, even though the Maestro's offside headlamp was smashed.'

'But there was glass on the road,' interjected the policewoman. 'I've read all the reports. And it's been identified as coming from a Maestro.'

'Yes. I think we're dealing with someone very clever. A person with the presence of mind to crash the Maestro into a lamp-post or something well away from the scene, and scatter glass next to Philippa's body. In the dark and the rain, and after all the trauma, he'd be satisfied that she was dead.'

She shuddered. 'How *loathsome*!'

'Look at Maureen O'Donnell – a girl afraid of water. She was thrown into a lock at night . . . What do you say, Will? Any flaws?'

'Possibly one, sir. The matter of suspension. That could make a considerable difference to the height of a car's chassis, and hence the bumper bar.'

'I know, but would it make seven inches of difference? I'll grant the test was crude. We can find out more specific details by checking Philippa Rowe's measurements against Bradshaw's Maestro, seeking to prove that that particular car could not have inflicted those injuries. Who is the orthopaedic surgeon in charge, Ros?'

'A Mr Lightfoot.'

'Right. We'll take you back to the station, then Will and I must contact him as soon as we can.'

Mr Lightfoot was a long, loose man in his late forties with fair hair and a walrus-like moustache.

'I've done as you asked,' he said to Montgomery. 'Here are the new X-ray films. The radiology department taped a kind of ruler to Philippa's leg, which we can use to assess the magnification of the film, and hence the real height of the fracture above the lower part of the heel bone. We'll add on a little extra for the soft tissue of the heel pad.'

'Thank you for getting this work done so promptly,' said Montgomery. 'It could prove to be crucial evidence. How do we calculate the level of the fracture?'

169

They pored over the simple procedure as it was explained. 'Twenty-four centimetres,' stated Lightfoot. 'That's just under nine point five inches. It tallies with the estimate I made from the outside of the leg.' He noticed their fascination with the X-ray; the two halves of Philippa Rowe's tibia were held together by a long metal plate from which eight vicious-looking screws projected. 'You're right,' he laughed, in answer to their comments. 'It's pure carpentry. We use stainless steel, so that the tissues don't react.'

'May we take the films?' asked Montgomery.

'Technically, they're NHS property, but I'll arrange with the X-ray people for you to have copies.' He paused. 'You do realize, don't you, that our "exact" measurement is a gross approximation for your purposes. It all depends on the position of the foot when she was struck.'

'We'll allow for it,' said Montgomery. 'Thanks again for your help.'

They left him dictating notes on to a small machine, twirling one end of his moustache in a meditative manner.

'I don't intend to give Rebecca Fletcher any warning.' Montgomery's tone was uncompromising as he stared through the windscreen at the traffic-choked city roads while Sergeant Bird changed gear unhurriedly and slowed down for a dilapidated van which had swung out into the main stream from a side road. 'We don't want her concocting a story with Barnaby . . . Damn it, Will! What are all these drivers doing on the streets at half-past four in the afternoon? Maniacs, half of them!'

'We're out,' said his sergeant calmly.

'That's different . . . Up the road past the off-licence, then I'll direct you more precisely.'

The house was a small 1940s semi-detached, in need of improvement. From the narrow front gate led a steeply angled drive, which ended at a warped garage door painted primrose yellow.

The detectives parked in the road thirty yards away, and strode up to the glazed front door. It opened before they could ring the bell.

'Hello. Do come in . . . Oh, I'm sorry. You're not from the Gas Board, are you? I saw you through the door.' The young woman who had spoken paused expectantly. She had porcelain-smooth skin and wavy hair the colour of corn which she had twisted into a neat bun. Her eyes were serene, untroubled. An apron tied round her slender waist accentuated her perfect hour-glass figure. So this was Barnaby Fletcher's wife.

'Detective Inspector Montgomery, Notts CID. My colleague, Sergeant Bird.' He flipped open the wallet containing his warrant card.

'Oh yes!' she exclaimed, looking pleased. 'Barnaby's been helping you, hasn't he? I think it made him feel quite important. I'm awfully sorry, but he's not home yet. Would you like to wait? I'm just preparing his tea.'

'Thank you.'

They stepped through a tiny hall into the living-room, which was furnished in warm shades of yellow and cream. Almost immediately an ear-splitting yell issued from the floor above.

'Oh dear – that's Paul,' she said apologetically. 'I was expecting a new gas cooker this afternoon, so I kept him upstairs in case the confusion upset him. Please excuse me – make yourselves comfortable.'

She left the room, and shortly they heard muted clucking sounds. The wailing died down to an uncertain 'heh', then ceased altogether.

'Miraculous,' said Sergeant Bird.

'Sounds more as if she just strangled him,' muttered Montgomery, prowling the perimeter. Despite having had two of his own, he was not unduly fond of babies and young children. He stopped opposite a fish-tank at the back of the room. Golden light permeated the gently waving plant fronds and flashed from the smooth, iridescent bodies of darting fish; bubbles from the aerator gurgled softly to each other, soothing the ear.

'It's pleasant, but he hasn't quite got Bradshaw's touch,' he said.

'This one is picturesque.' Sergeant Bird was peering into another tank, closer to the window. The darkish grey hues of the artificial sandbanks were offset by plants of all shapes and sizes, some green, some russet, flanking a fairy castle with archways and turrets. A small shoal of catfish foraged placidly at the bottom of the tank.

'Drab fish,' said Montgomery. 'And why is the sand grey?'

'It's restful to the catfish. They like to stay near the bottom – see the way their mouths turn down. They're nice fish – peaceful and good-tempered.'

'Boring,' said Montgomery with a little shake of his head, and returned to the tumble and twist of tetras and tiger barbs.

The sound of footsteps on the stairs heralded Rebecca Fletcher's return.

'Sorry to leave you like that,' she said as she closed the door behind her. 'Paul's asleep now. He's a good baby; we're very fortunate.'

'We've been admiring your fish,' said Montgomery as they sat down. 'I gather Gilbert Bradshaw helped to choose some of them.'

Sadness stilled her face for a moment, but she replied readily enough. 'Yes – he did. Barnaby had got himself into a bit of a tangle the first time around, and Gil was very good about it. He came here on a Sunday and helped us with a leaking tank. A week or so later they went off to Ilkeston together and bought some more fish. I was glad, because – Barnaby doesn't often meet people who share his interests.'

'Do you like fish, as well?'

'He bought them for me,' she answered tangentially, 'which was very sweet of him.' An expression of maternal fondness lit up her satin features. 'I don't know how well you know Barnaby by now, but you'll have seen that he's rather gauche in company. He's never able to say what he means; sometimes he expresses himself better by actions. I got the feeling that Gil was like that, too . . . It's such a shame about his accident. I'm sorry not only for him, but for Barnaby. He lost a friend.'

'You think it was an accident, even now?'

'Oh yes. Barnaby's convinced it wasn't suicide, and any other explanation would be quite incredible. I mean, who would want to harm Gil?'

'A good question. Did you ever visit him in Sylvia Vale?'

'No. I was invited, but there was Paul to consider. In any case, I thought it would be more enjoyable for Barnaby if there were just the two of them, talking fish.'

'Did he go often?'

'Only once. A few weeks ago.'

'Can you recall the actual date?'

'It'll be on the kitchen calendar.' She sprang up from the chair and left the room, returning within seconds holding a long, spiral-bound calendar decorated with prints of marrows, artichokes and peppers.

'Here,' she said, pointing at an entry. 'Thursday.'

It was the first week in September. Montgomery ran his eye down the other entries, but they were ordinary, engagement-diary events: 'Dentist 2p.m.', 'Mum at 4', 'Clinic 10.30', 'Cheryl's birthday'.

'Do you mind if I look at this?' he asked belatedly.

'Of course not.'

He examined every page from the beginning of the year, with especial reference to July and August, but nothing of value emerged.

'It must be difficult for you to get out, with a young baby to look after,' he remarked.

'Yes, but I expected that, and I don't mind. Actually, I'm lucky because my mother lives quite near, and she comes for tea on a regular basis.'

'That's good. Does she see much of Barnaby?'

Rebecca Fletcher gave an indulgent smile. 'He escapes whenever he can. It's not that they don't like each other, it's more that Mum has a tendency to gush, and it makes him uncomfortable. He also feels that he's interrupting a cosy session of women's gossip when he comes home.'

'So he comes late?'

'That's right. It was ten o'clock last Friday.'

'Was that unusually late?'

'A little. But he was on duty. Sometimes it's been nine. He's trying to write a paper on amnesia, although I suspect he's not getting on with it very quickly. I know that I'd be pretty loath to work on a Friday night!'

Montgomery nodded affably. 'It was bad luck about his car.'

'Yes, it was,' she agreed. 'We didn't want to mess up the No-Claims Bonus, so we paid for the repairs ourselves.' She paused, and looked at him uncertainly. 'Is – that why you've come? Did Barnaby tell you about the car, or was it someone else? Don't say we should have reported it – not when it was on our own property. No one else was involved; nobody was injured.'

'We don't have all the details,' said Montgomery. 'I'd be obliged if you'd fill us in.'

'Well – ' She spread her hands vaguely. 'There isn't much to say. He left the car on the slope while he fumbled with the garage door – it doesn't hang straight, and it's stiff. Unfortunately, he

173

hadn't put the handbrake on. The car rolled down, and smashed into the gatepost.'

'Backwards?'

'No. He reverses up the drive because otherwise it's so difficult to pull out into the main road in the mornings.'

'Did you see the accident yourself?'

'No, I was in the back bedroom putting some clothes away. But he told me immediately afterwards.'

'When was this?'

'I can't quite remember. Around two weeks ago. Nobody was hurt, Inspector.'

Montgomery shelved further questions. His sharp ears had picked up the whine of a car reversing off the main road. He stretched his neck to see out of the window; in the fading light, a yellow Citroën 2CV jolted gingerly up the drive to halt with a judder in front of the garage door. Barnaby Fletcher heaved himself out of the driver's seat, oblivious of his audience. He vanished from sight, but his movements were signalled by a series of banging sounds, followed by the screech of protesting metal, before the car was finally driven into its shelter.

The familiar ruffled head passed the window. They heard the click of a key in the lock.

'It's me! Coo-ee, I'm home!' called a voice.

Rebecca met Montgomery's eye, and he nodded assent. She slipped from the room into the hall.

'Who else would it be, silly?' she teased, then her voice dropped to a more cautious tone as she told him about their guests.

He thundered into the lounge immediately, pink-cheeked, startled, hair awry.

'Inspector Montgomery – Sergeant Bird. What a surprise! Have you been waiting long? Gosh!'

They acknowledged his greeting in a polite manner.

'Er – have you had tea? Would you like some?'

Montgomery heard the intake of Sergeant Bird's breath, preparatory to eager acceptance. 'No thank you,' he said firmly. 'We won't be stopping long. We just wanted a few details of your car accident.'

Barnaby looked amazed. 'My – car?' he repeated stupidly. 'It was only a little knock. Well, the front bumper and one headlamp. I'm afraid I was clumsy – yet again. I didn't put the handbrake on, and it rolled down the drive, straight into the gatepost. I must have driven in at a slight angle. It was so annoying.' He cocked his head on one side. 'Inspector – surely your time is valuable? Why do you want to know about my little accident?'

'Simple,' said Montgomery smoothly. 'In our efforts to trace the driver who knocked down Philippa Rowe, we are contacting garages to find out if anyone has had the front end of his car repaired during the last fortnight. Since we happened to hear about your bump, we thought it would save time in the long run to exclude you as soon as possible. Which garage did you take the Citroën to?'

'We went to Arthur Wright. That's the mechanic who goes with Neil to the races and looks after his Porsche. Oh – perhaps you don't know. That's Mr Thornton. He does sports car racing in his spare time. Anyway, Arthur Wright has a small business of his own. Neil got me a bit of a discount, which was good of him. I had the car back within two days . . .' Barnaby was garrulous in his relief.

'When was this, exactly?'

'Er – last Thursday.'

'The accident?'

'No, that was the Wednesday of the week before. We spent a day or two deciding, then we found Mr Wright was away.'

Montgomery took the address and left after a few pleasantries. As he walked crisply down the drive with Sergeant Bird at his side, they could hear Barnaby's voice as the front door swung shut.

'How's Paul?'

'The station, sir?'

'No, let's go for gold. You're game, aren't you, Will? We're getting somewhere at last; I can sense it.'

'Just say the word.'

'Words. Sylvia Vale.'

Sergeant Bird groaned. 'I had a feeling you were going to come out with that.' He negotiated a network of sideroads, and soon they were heading northwards through the city suburbs. 'Were you serious about making enquiries in every garage?'

'Absolutely. This incident of Barnaby Fletcher's isn't conclusive. He might have been telling the truth. His wife seems an honest woman, and she believes in him.'

'Yet bumping his car just then . . .'

'I know. But he didn't try to hide the fact, he parked the car for all to see – including Albert – in the main hospital car-park.'

'Why do you think nobody mentioned it to us?'

'Two reasons at least. Either the accident was well before the weekend, as he said, or no one imagines that Barnaby could possibly be linked with what's been going on. I favour the latter.' He peered out as lighted windows and Lowry-type figures flashed past in the gloom. The evening had turned clammy and close. 'Look how soon it's gone dark. Such a bright day, too. Probably one of the last this year . . . You know, Will, I've been unhappy about that Maestro right from the start, but I couldn't work out why. The Citroën has acted as a catalyst, bringing all the discrepancies to the surface – the bumper bar; the glass. And we've still got that unlocked garage door to sort out. It's funny – if Philippa Rowe had actually been a corpse, Forensic would have cottoned on immediately. As it is, it's no one's fault.'

'Apropos Barnaby Fletcher,' said Sergeant Bird, weaving dog-gedly through the homebound traffic, 'I agree with what you said. His character doesn't seem to fit.'

'Let's say the character he projects,' warned Montgomery. 'No, it doesn't. I'd sooner believe it of an impersonal type like Thorn-ton, but circumstantially he's almost ruled out. His car never left the hospital grounds that first Friday, and he was seen at nine by two people. The night Maureen O'Donnell disappeared, he was with his girlfriend, and the next day when someone *may* have administered a harmful drug to Philippa Rowe, he was at Donington Park qualifying for Sunday's race. That's easy enough to check.'

'Yes, sir. And whoever speaks to Arthur Wright can ask about the Citroën at the same time.'

'It's the imperfections that convince me,' mused Montgomery. 'If I thought for a moment that Thornton was involved, I wouldn't have him within a mile of Philippa Rowe. But a really cool, calculating individual would have come up with a better alibi for the night Bradshaw died. His is somewhat hit-and-miss: he admits as much. And make no mistake – there's a very cold brain behind that car switch.'

He turned to Sergeant Bird. 'He was angry the first time I saw him – furious about what happened to Philippa. I think it was the

176

wantonness of the damage – a healthy girl suddenly smashed almost beyond recall.'

They drove in silence for a few minutes.

'David Stannard was hostile,' remarked Sergeant Bird.

'Yes. I rather think he's regretting some of the things he told me on the previous occasion. When you open up to a stranger you don't really expect to meet that person again.'

'You believed him, then?'

'What, about Philippa Rowe?'

'Yes. You told me he said he was still in love with her.'

'He seemed sincere, but my mind is wide open. He wouldn't be the first man to take his revenge on a girlfriend who's walked out on him.'

A small shopping parade just ahead on the left sported a familiar red-and-white canopy.

'Oh look, Sir – fried chicken. Can't we stop; I'm getting terrible hunger pangs.'

'I suppose so. I hate to see a grown man cry.' Montgomery could exist for days on very little. 'Don't take too long. I'll give Carole a ring while you're in there.'

Ten minutes later, Sergeant Bird was replete. 'That's better. I can function now,' he said.

Montgomery wiped his fingers on a pocket handkerchief as the car sped away into the darkness. Three chips and a swig of ginger beer constituted his own foray into sybaritism.

'Sylvia Vale,' he murmured. 'Sounds as if a wood was there once.'

'Yes,' agreed Sergeant Bird. 'It was probably one of the lower tracts of Sherwood Forest. That used to cover an enormous acreage in medieval times and beyond.'

'Not a lot left now,' said Montgomery. 'Mainly farming land. I remember seeing a small coppice behind Bradshaw's house.'

The roads became lonelier, and soon they were turning into Beechcroft Lane. Montgomery's shirt felt sticky; he wound down the window but the air outside was sullen, pregnant with moisture. From over the hills came a low rumble of thunder. 'It's going to rain,' he said superfluously.

'Like before.'

They were both silent.

Another growl sounded from the far distance. 'Where shall I park?' asked William Bird.

177

'Outside Bradshaw's house. There's nowhere else unless we stop in the road.'

They bounced along the rutted driveway, headlamps picking out the straggling shapes of trees and untended bushes. Ahead loomed the house – black, isolated, no warmth of welcome. With a strange unspoken reluctance they parked beyond the front door.

'Right,' said Montgomery, rubbing his hands briskly to dispel the morale-sapping atmosphere. 'Our man has just run over Philippa Rowe in the Maestro. He needs to reproduce the impact damage which his own car must have sustained when it knocked her down. He can't cruise around the district for too long in case one of the residents spots her body, even though it is a filthy night. What does he do?'

'Well . . . he can assume that police will be involved sooner or later, and will search the premises and a goodly portion of the road outside. He'll look for a tree, lamp-post or telegraph pole outside those expected boundaries.'

'My thoughts exactly. He would go up towards the farm, but not so far as to bring himself into earshot of either Number Three or Number Five. That leaves any pole along the stretch of road abutting the field. Let's go and investigate.'

'On foot?' Sergeant Bird cast an uneasy glance skywards, although nothing could be seen in the impenetrable blackness.

'Of course. Have you got a torch?'

'Yes.'

'Let's be off, then.'

The darting beam lit their way, illuminating the various pot-holes of the driveway and the lush, contemptuous growth of weeds down its centre. Once, Montgomery stumbled and cursed under his breath. They passed the shrubbery, which smelt dank and faintly putrescent. Unbidden parallels swam into their minds.

A misty orange glow greeted them as they approached the gatepost. The road to the right was moderately well lit, but on the left it wound into oblivion like a dark snake.

'Not exactly generous with their lamp-posts up there,' commented Sergeant Bird. 'If I lived here, I think I'd complain.'

'They've probably all got quartz halogen headlamps.'

There was no pavement. Long-buried boy-scout instinct nagged at them to face the non-existent traffic, but they resolutely ignored it and continued to look for clues on the left-hand side of the road. The heavy airlessness was oppressive. For a supposed beauty spot, thought Montgomery, Sylvia Vale had its shortcomings that evening.

Eventually, a cluster of blurred, haloed lights shimmered ahead, soon identifiable as the front windows of Number Three. The house stood some yards from the road in sumptuously landscaped gardens – a smug, executive dwelling, oozing the money which buys privacy. A sentinel street-lamp dominated the area outside the gates.

'Can't be that one,' muttered Montgomery. 'Back we go.'

Sergeant Bird sniffed the air like a pointer. 'We're about to be soaked,' he announced.

The first drops fell with a gentle splatter when they had covered less than half the return distance to Number One. Montgomery wore a thin navy jacket while Sergeant Bird favoured a rather tattered brown tweed; neither was dressed for a deluge.

'Tree up ahead,' said Montgomery. 'Let's take stock.'

'Just as well the storm has moved on,' replied the sergeant pontifically, 'or under a tree would be the last place to choose.'

The tree, dimly discerned as a broad-leafed variety with a tangle of grasses and wild flowers at the foot of its trunk, occupied a position equidistant from the road and the barbed-wire fencing of the field behind. It offered complete shelter for the refugees, who huddled close to the bole as the soft 'pitter-pat' turned into a furious drumming and gallons of water plummeted out of the darkness.

'Fools' errand, this,' grumbled Sergeant Bird.

'You can't talk like that – I'm your boss . . . Will! Do that again . . . Shine the torch down into the grass. No – give it to me.' Montgomery's urgent tone transmitted an infectious excitement. Sergeant Bird watched eagerly as he knelt among the vegetation, carefully separating matted stems and clumps of grass. Something winked in the torchlight, something bright . . . glass.

'Clever bastard,' breathed Montgomery.

'Bit hard on your mother.'

'I'm not referring to *myself*. He did it . . . just as we'd worked it out. I'd lay heavy odds that this is from the Maestro headlamp.' He dropped the pieces into a small plastic bag and sealed it, stowing it away in an inner pocket. They then examined the bark near the base of the tree, and were rewarded by the sight of a suspicious gouge.

'We'll send Forensic out tomorrow – in daylight,' said Montgomery tersely, scanning the ground between the tree and the road with wide sweeps of the torch beam. 'With the eye of faith, there are tracks here . . . Look at these flattened grasses . . .'

His ruminations were interrupted by the sound of a powerful engine and the swish of tyres; a white Range Rover was approaching, headlamps ablaze, its wipers working at full speed against the water load. Montgomery was dazzled and threw up an arm to protect his eyes, but was still just able to make out the pale blur of a face as the vehicle swept past on the other side of the narrow road.

'Resident, or visitor, I wonder,' he said.

'Resident. It's turning into Number Five . . . No, wait – it's coming out again.'

The Range Rover geared down noisily and pulled up in a sheet of spray ten yards from where they stood.

'Do you need any help? Have you lost your way?'

The male voice through the opened window had a crisp, upper-middle-class enunciation. The engine of the Range Rover was still running.

'No; we're fine, thank you.'

'This is a cul-de-sac. Are you visiting one of the houses?' An edge of suspicion had crept into his tone.

Montgomery sighed and stepped forward into the rain. He rounded the front of the vehicle and offered his warrant card to the driver. 'Montgomery – CID,' he said.

'Oh – that's different. I thought you were prowlers.' The man switched off the engine. 'My name's Pettifer. I live at Number Five.'

'Ah, yes. You've spoken to our Sergeant Jackson.'

'That's right. Can I be of any assistance to you now? I don't see your car.'

'It's not too far away. Tell me – are you on your way home from work?'

'Yes, I am.'

'And is this your normal time?' Montgomery flashed the torch beam onto his wrist watch to discover with a sense of shock that it was only a quarter to seven. It felt like at least nine o'clock.

'Give or take a few minutes, yes.'

'You found the injured girl two weeks ago, didn't you?'

'Yes – I was out jogging. I made a statement to that effect.'

'Is there any chance you could have failed to notice her on the night before as you drove past?'

'None whatsoever. Look at this road – there's barely room for two Minis to pass. I'd have seen her all right. How is she, Inspector?'

'Slowly improving. Just one more thing – ' Montgomery was rapidly resembling a drowned rat. 'Did you have much contact with the Bradshaws while they were alive?'

'No. They were a strange family – kept very much to themselves. Look, are you sure you don't want a lift somewhere?'

Montgomery politely declined and watched as the Range Rover completed its circular trip back to base.

'What does he want with that thing?' Sergeant Bird was tramping close by his left elbow. 'He's not a farmer.'

'Status symbol, my lad,' said Montgomery. 'It's the kind of vehicle you and I only dream about.'

They reached Gilbert Bradshaw's house without further incident, and Sergeant Bird made an immediate beeline for their Metro.

'Wait,' said Montgomery. 'We don't want to have to come here again.' He pulled open the counter-weighted garage door and they retreated into its cavernous shelter. 'We know now that a third party was involved. He crashed the Maestro then brought it back to this garage. He set the front door deadlock, slammed it shut and locked the mortice from outside. Then what? Why didn't he lock the garage?'

'Forgot.'

'No, Will. This man's a perfectionist. It's a final touch that would have cost him nothing.' He slapped his palm impatiently with a clenched fist. 'We'll only find the answer here. If we leave it now, we lose it.'

Sergeant Bird found a light switch, and flooded the garage with a harsh fluorescent glare. Montgomery blinked and continued his monologue. 'The keys were made to appear as if they'd just slipped out of Bradshaw's pocket because of his fall. The only other set were in a kitchen drawer. I thought our experiment was reasonably scientific, and we couldn't throw the keys accurately to that position, so how did the killer do it? Magic?'

To his horror, Sergeant Bird suddenly beamed. 'Yes,' he said.

'Magic.' He was looking over Montgomery's shoulder, but his face wore a reminiscent expression.

'What do you mean?' demanded Montgomery.

Sergeant Bird stared for a moment longer, then transferred his gaze to his companion. 'May I tell you a story, sir, about when I was a lad?'

'If you must.' Montgomery resisted the urge to make him come to the point. William Bird was four years his senior in age, but seemed to revel in making it sound like forty. His recollections, however, had often proved to be of great value in past cases.

Sergeant Bird stood four-square and launched into his tale. 'One Christmas my grandfather gave me a magic box,' he said. 'There were lots of good tricks, but one in particular caught the family's imagination. They never did find out how it worked.

'I'd ask my cousin Kevin to put a secret mark on a sixpence while I was out of the room. Then I'd get him to hold the coin through a handkerchief in front of everyone, while I gave my auntie a small box to hold, all done up in rubber bands. After a few magic passes and incantations, I'd whip the handkerchief out of his hands, and the sixpence would have vanished. I'd then turn to my auntie, and ask her to open the drawer of the box.

'She'd undo the bands and pull the drawer open, only to find another box wrapped in bands, and inside that, another. Eventually, she'd come to a little pouch, just big enough to hold a sixpence, and there it would be – with Kevin's own secret mark on it!'

'Amazing,' said Montgomery, bemused. 'But what has all this to do with the keys?'

Sergeant Bird smiled blandly, savouring his moment. 'The first part of the trick is the only potentially awkward bit. You've already sewn a sixpence into the border of the handkerchief, so when you take Kevin's you palm it as you drape the handkerchief over your hand and give him the other one to hold through the linen. Then, while you chat away and keep everyone's attention on Kevin, you slip the *real* sixpence into the box, which is in your pocket, before offering it to Auntie Maud.'

'You said there were several boxes and a pouch.'

'There are. The nub of the trick is an ingenious little metal device called a "coin slide"; it's rather like a flattened cylinder. Before the performance, you insert one end into the pouch, and

182

secure that with a band. Then you place it in the drawer of the smallest box, close it up with the slide jutting out, and put a few more bands round the drawer as if to hold it shut. You carry on for as many boxes as you've got – the more the merrier, as long as the largest will still fit in your pocket. So later, when you've palmed your sixpence, all you have to do is feed it into the free end of the coin slide, let it travel right down into the pouch, and remove the slide from the set of boxes. It's easy to do with one hand. The elastic band round the neck of the pouch contracts down, of course, which foxes people no end when they come to it.'

'William,' said Montgomery in frustration, 'if you don't tell me what all this is in aid of within the next five seconds, there'll be some GBH around here.'

'You're tired,' soothed his sergeant, 'or you'd have seen it yourself. Behind you. Not a coin slide, but a very decent key slide.'

Montgomery whirled round to stare at the strips of wood veneer stacked against the side wall of the garage. Eight feet, ten feet long . . . yes, it was possible. It was more than possible.

'Will,' he said, 'you may continue to harbour your delusions of genius. Quickly – let's try it.'

He seized a ten-foot strip of veneer and walked out into the night, ignoring the slackening rain. 'This should be just long enough; at least I know my Pythagoras.'

Sergeant Bird followed with a small block of wood to wedge the letter-box open.

Five minutes later they were back in the car.

'Perfect,' said Montgomery, well satisfied. 'The keys will slide to any chosen point without dropping off the side. Our man has to return the strip of veneer to the garage, since he knows the police will search the whole vicinity, but he can't lock the garage because the key is now stranded in the hall.'

'Do you want the wood strips checking for fingerprints?'

'I suppose we should, but I expect he was wearing gloves.'

The car swished along roads which became progressively brighter and more populated. Sergeant Bird was very quiet; Montgomery wondered what new ferment of relevant retrospection was bubbling in his brain.

'What's on your mind now, Will?' he asked.

'Dinner.'

16

Detective Constables Haslam and Grange had just completed their final interview with Albert, whose information about damage to Barnaby Fletcher's Citroën had been released with an air of grudging largesse.

'What next?' asked Grange, swinging himself into the passenger seat of their Metro.

'The mechanic, Arthur Wright.' Colin Haslam briefly consulted a street map of Nottingham, then gave it to Grange to refold. 'It's not far. He should have records of the repair.'

Five minutes later, they pulled up opposite a back-street garage which bore Arthur Wright's name on a chipped wooden placard to the left of the judas door. From inside came a rhythmic rasping and another, lighter sound like a soda-water syphon. Haslam tapped on the judas, and on receiving no reply, pushed it open.

A scruffy young man in oil-smeared overalls took his finger off the trigger of the paint-sprayer he was holding and gave them an interrogative look.

'Yeah?'

'Are you Mr Wright?'

'Nah.' He jerked a thumb towards a figure crouched behind a rather rusty Datsun. 'That's him.'

The two detectives picked their way carefully over a floor littered with cables, cylinders and other assorted hazards, including a sizeable pit. When they reached the Datsun, the scraping stopped as the other man stood up. He was almost thirty years of age, short, but with luxuriant mid-brown hair curling unfashionably over the collar of his overalls. His expression was frank, with no trace of the shiftiness typical of the 'cowboys' of his trade.

'Hello. What can I do for you?' he asked.

Haslam introduced himself. 'Is there anywhere we can talk?'

'Yes; the office. Come through.' He led them through a side door which came out behind the counter of a small but comfortable room serving as a combined office and waiting-area. An attractive dark-haired woman paused as she typed up an account, and gave them a friendly smile.

'This is Linda, my wife,' said Arthur Wright. 'Would you prefer it if she left for a few minutes?'

'Not if she normally works here. It could be helpful.'

184

'Police', explained Wright to his wife. She raised her eyebrows, but did not look unduly perturbed.

'We're interested in any car that's come your way since the sixteenth of September with damage to the front end – anything from a bent bumper to the full works. It may have been involved in a hit-and-run.'

They exchanged startled glances. 'That Citroën,' said Linda.

Arthur Wright frowned, and began to leaf through a large desk diary whose pages were liberally stamped with grimy finger-prints. 'There was a Citroën,' he agreed as he searched. 'Bumper bar and offside headlamp . . . but it can't be the car you're after. It was a friend of a friend; doctor from the District Hospital. A Dr Fletcher . . . yes, here we are. September twenty-second.'

'How did he account for the accident?' asked Haslam.

'Said he left the handbrake off, and it rolled down an incline into his gatepost. Judging by the way he tried to leave with the handbrake *on*, I could believe it.'

'When did he say the accident happened?'

'Some time during the week I was away – that is, the week leading up to Tuesday the twentieth. He brought it in a couple of days after I got back. It didn't need a lot of work.'

'You didn't notice anything – unusual – about the headlamp, did you?'

'You mean . . . blood?'

'Yes.'

'There was nothing. Ordinary job – nice bloke, I thought.'

'Any other front-end repairs? Or resprays?'

Linda shook her head, and her husband slid the book across to Haslam. 'Have a look,' he offered.

Haslam was soon satisfied that he had drawn a blank, and turned to the other purpose of the visit.

'You're Neil Thornton's mechanic, aren't you?'

Arthur's Wright's eyes lit up with enthusiasm. 'Yes,' he said, before the brightness faded into puzzlement. 'I thought this was just a random visit.'

'Not quite. Two birds with one stone. But we *are* checking all the local garages,' Haslam reassured him.

'Okay . . . What do you want to know?'

'Where was he on Saturday the twenty-fourth?' That was the day Montgomery seemed to think that someone had adminis-tered a harmful drug to Philippa Rowe.

'Here. We were working on the Porsche. Gary out there was dealing with the rest.'

Haslam turned to Linda. 'How long was he with you, Mrs Wright?'

'Oh, virtually all day. He had his dinner with us – I mean lunch. Then he went off with Arthur to do his qualifying round at Donington. They came back at six and we all had another meal together. He left just after seven.'

'Thank you. That's very useful. Don't mind my asking, will you, but – do you make a good living from this?' He indicated the premises with a sweep of his arm.

She smiled, quite unoffended. 'We get by.'

'David!' Philippa no longer felt inclined to disguise her pleasure in his company; she had news to share with him, familiar friend and lover of the past.

His welcome was more cautious. 'Pippa . . . hello. I'd like to say you look well but you don't. Your temperature's all over the place. What's wrong?'

She sighed. 'Do you have to be so *blunt*? It's really unflattering. I washed my hair this morning – well, the nurse did.'

'It's very nice, but you look flushed,' he insisted. 'Has anyone from Crowland's team been in to see you today?'

She fluttered her fingers irritably. 'Please – forget all that, David. Of course there are ups and downs. Leave them for now – I've got something to tell you.'

'Go on, then.' He sat down with an air of reluctant acquiescence.

'I've got some of Thursday back!' This cryptic message was enough to make him stiffen perceptibly.

'You know Michael Wylie,' she went on. 'I've mentioned him before. He's one of my haemophiliacs; he comes every Thursday lunch-time for a lesson in intravenous injection.'

'The one you said wasn't too bright?'

'That's him. Well, before today I could scarcely remember anything about the last session we had. It was all hopelessly vague. But this morning – I woke up and found I could recall whole chunks of our conversation, virtually word for word. He'd got the strange idea that any white surface is sterile. That's because I used to open a sterile packet of gauze swabs for him, and put the unwrapped butterfly needle on top of those while we prepared his arm and searched for a vein. He understood that the bench was dirty, but when his turn came, he got the most *revolting* handkerchief out of his pocket and opened the butterfly pack out on to that! We had to start all over again . . . But I remember it, David! I can see his face right now, struggling to understand. Isn't that wonderful!'

'I'm pleased, Pippa,' he said woodenly.

She stared at him, suddenly apprehensive. 'You're not. You're not pleased at all . . . Why?'

By way of reply he cast a rapid glance at the door, which was closed, before leaning over the bed.

'Listen,' he instructed, his voice very low. 'This is important. Who else knows that you're getting your memory back?'

A dark nuance in his tone slid over her like the shadowy cloak of fear.

'Only Anne.'

'No one else?'

'No.'

'Promise me something, Pippa. Keep this to yourself for now. Promise!'

He gripped her fingers in his. Their strength surprised her.

'I promise.'

'Audrey? Can you check if Mrs Jelbart's notes are anywhere in the office? We need them here at the clinic, and Records say they're booked out to us. Bring them over as soon as you can . . . Thank you.'

The line was disconnected before Audrey could reply. Pursing her mouth, she stood up, and walked to the nearest set of pigeon-holes. Her consultant always took it for granted that minor administrative miracles would be performed daily by his staff. His uncertain temper provided the otherwise missing incentive for their efforts.

'Jelbart . . .' she murmured, lifting off a manageable portion from the top of a huge stack of notes.

One of the other secretaries paused in the middle of typing a letter. 'Did you say Jelbart?'

'Yes. The notes should be at the clinic, but they're not.'

'Try Dr Rashid's dictation pile. I'm sure I saw the name there.'

187

She was right. 'Thanks,' said Audrey, pleased, and bustled out of the office clutching the folder. She tapped her way downstairs and left the building by a side door; the air was sharp and fresh, a welcome contrast to the close atmosphere inside.

The quickest route to Outpatients lay round the next corner and through the main car-park. She had hardly covered five yards when two figures crossed her line of vision ahead, a man and a woman, walking slowly, engrossed in their conversation.

Audrey shrank back against the towering wall of the Department of Medicine, the response purely reflex. David and Coral were oblivious of her presence. The tall, white-coated registrar had his arm tightly locked round the elfin girl's shoulders, and his head was bent down to hers. Comfort for distress? Friendly advice? . . . Or was it something quite different?

As they vanished from sight, Audrey leaned against the rough brickwork, her body trembling. She felt cold and insecure. Philippa Rowe was a rival she could fight against, someone tangible, with a known identity. But how could she defend her position against these other, unknown adversaries, people she had never considered in that light before?

I should have challenged them, she chided herself angrily. I should have carried on walking, and spoken. At least then I would have seen her face . . .

A faint swill of nausea made her swallow. Above, the tapping of typewriters through an open window recalled her to the mission in hand. Perhaps she was being watched. Clumsily, she opened the folder she was carrying, and pretended to examine the contents. But her mind thrust its way down that path she had always managed to seal off before. The fact could no longer be ignored; David was slipping away from her.

'Neil, I'm not at all happy about Philippa.'

Anne Markham beckoned the surgeon into Cavendish Ward's kitchen, where it was easier to have a private word.

'Neither am I,' Neil admitted frankly. He looked tired after a long session in theatre, and after a moment's hesitation, sat down on one of the hard wooden chairs, an uncharacteristic action for him.

'She's got the *look* of someone with an infection,' went on Anne, 'yet all the culture reports are coming back negative.

You've already put her on broad-spectrum antibiotics again. I don't know what else we should be doing. What do you think?'

'I agree with your instinct,' said Neil. 'I've always had a gut feeling that Philippa was going to fare badly, even when things were apparently looking up. But there's nothing definite for us to treat. We've swabbed every conceivable area. The urine's clear. Those blood cultures I sent off just now were the fourth set in thirty-six hours. Clinically, her chest, leg and abdomen are fine. We can't assess the arm, but it's not giving her particular discomfort. There's only the temperature chart telling us something is amiss, and that's non-specific.'

'I know,' sighed Anne. 'I just feel that Philippa needs all our skills, and we're failing her in some way.' She sank down on one of the chairs herself, and looked at the floor. 'Neil . . . don't think I've gone loopy, please, but I do wonder if someone is sabotaging our treatment.'

'Really, Anne!'

'I know . . . it's crazy. But that frusemide was never explained, and remember, she's only here because some person ran over her in a car.'

She lifted her eyes to his and saw that their deep blue was thoughtful.

'Anyone else but you, Anne,' he said slowly, 'and I *would* be ringing for the little yellow van. As it is, what you're suggesting seems incredible.' He grimaced. 'It's not that the idea's new to me; Inspector Montgomery came out with a similar proposal on Tuesday. I just thought he was indulging in undue extrapolation from one small mysterious incident. People are always leaving syringes lying around; they shouldn't, but they do. But now *you're* taking it seriously, as well . . . that's different.'

'So you think it's possible?'

'Possible, yes. Probable, no.'

'We must prove it!' she said decisively.

'I shall ponder ways and means,' he promised, rising to his feet, 'but for now, duty calls. There's a chap with suspected renal calculus in Casualty. I'd better not keep him waiting.'

'Are you on tonight?'

'For my sins, yes.'

'You look as if you could do with some sleep. Since you can't have that, let me give you one of our special biscuits.'

'I don't eat biscuits.'

'You haven't seen these.' She opened a cupboard at the back of the kitchen and extracted an enamelled tin from the darkest corner. It contained a high-quality assortment of Continental spiced biscuits, each of them covered in rich plain chocolate. '*Now* do you eat biscuits?'

'My arm could definitely be twisted,' he laughed, and accepted two. 'Thanks,' he said, then strode out of the door, his concentration already directed towards the unfortunate patient in Casualty.

Anne felt a momentary twinge of envy for Vanda Pitts. Smiling at her foolishness, she pressed the lid down on the biscuit tin.

'So you think Arthur Wright is honest,' said Montgomery.

Haslam and Grange both nodded emphatic agreement. Once more at the station, the detectives were comparing the fruits of their investigations. Definitive evidence seemed as far away as ever.

'Not well-off, but decent,' stated Colin Haslam. 'No hint of a criminal record, and nothing shady in the garage.'

'He was quite open about Fletcher's car,' added Grange.

Montgomery gave a grim smile. 'Fletcher's car ... it hasn't been the lead we hoped for, has it? The timing of the repair was perfect, but you say Albert saw that it was damaged during the week before Bradshaw's death. Is he certain of that?'

'Ninety per cent,' said Haslam.

'Hm. You've heard about the tests on the Maestro, haven't you? The forensic staff conclude that Philippa Rowe's impact injuries couldn't possibly have been caused by that type of car, unless she was standing on some raised object like a stone! The Citroën would have been an ideal candidate, with its low bumper bar. What a pity ... Did you check into Fletcher's background, Will?'

'Yes, Sir. I've spoken to three people who knew him at medical school, and he does seem to be as advertised. He failed several exams, and only just scraped through the rest. He managed to destroy a vital centrifuge costing thousands of pounds. It makes you wonder who's responsible for his being out on the wards at this very minute! Overall, his colleagues look upon him as a kind of bumbling innocent. They have no recollections of malice or viciousness ... Oh, one more thing; I had a quick word with

Thornton. He did leave the Postgraduate Centre by the side door on that first Friday, so that could be the reason he didn't meet Fletcher when he went for his meal.'

'Another loose end tied up, at least,' ceded Montgomery. 'I wonder – ' He broke off and stared through the open doorway into the outer office, where Jackson had been sitting at his desk sorting through papers.

The sergeant was taking a telephone call. His habitual round-shouldered sag had pulled itself into a ramrod, military bearing. His eyes, not usually features of note, gleamed like metal discs, and an involuntary smile was slowly blossoming over his lower face. The pen in his right hand danced across a note-pad as if it had a life of its own.

' . . . Thank you,' he said.

He put down the receiver, tore off the top sheet of paper and bounded into Montgomery's office.

'You look like the Cheshire Cat,' observed Sergeant Bird.

'I *am* the Cheshire Cat,' said Jackson.

'He disappeared. Nothing was left but the grin.'

'Out with it, Brian.' Impatience, rarely far away, was clawing at Montgomery.

Jackson turned to him. 'That was Pendle – Bradshaw's solicitor. He's had a reply to his advertisement from someone who used to know Mrs Bradshaw before she died. There was a younger sister, who married a miner and caused a family rift which never healed. His name was Chapman . . . and they had a daughter called Coral.'

17

'Why didn't you tell us that Gilbert Bradshaw was your cousin?' Montgomery asked bluntly.

'My – cousin?' Coral swallowed nervously. It was her afternoon off. She had been home from work for two hours, and wore a soft turquoise knitted dress: her aureate eyes were enormous, windows to the disordered thoughts beyond. They had caught her completely unprepared.

'Yes, cousin. You're aware of that, of course.'

191

'I –'

Montgomery watched her, tight-lipped. He knew now why he had felt that strange, elusive tug of memory on first meeting this girl. That picture at Bradshaw's house . . . his mother had just the same chin as her niece. The same sharp, feline features, too. Had Bradshaw ever noticed it?

Coral twisted on the chair. 'I – yes. I can explain, but – you won't understand.'

'Try us.'

'I *know* you won't! That's why I didn't say anything before.'

'I think it's greatly in your interest to do so now.'

She looked to Sergeant Bird for support, but his kindly, grave face only underlined her situation.

'We've been having a chat with your neighbour downstairs,' went on Montgomery. 'He's pleased that you're keeping on the flat. He says he doesn't want another family of black people moving in – not his exact words. He was keen to impress us with the rent he has to pay. It's a lot, isn't it?'

She stared at him, her fear beginning to harden into anger.

'Will you be sharing again, Coral?'

There was a further pause, but when she answered, her voice was granite.

'You're the people who've been poking and prying. Find out for yourselves. I think you're contemptible.'

'If witnesses would come clean in the first place, we'd have a lot less "poking and prying" to do,' said Montgomery coolly. 'It wastes our time – and allows tragedies to occur.'

'You *can't* blame me for Maureen's death! You *can't*!' Her composure cracked, and tears gushed out of her eyes. She brushed them away with the back of her hand, which trembled, then laced her fingers together so tightly that the knuckles glared ivory beneath the skin.

'Did Maureen know that Gilbert was your cousin?'

'No! She never knew. Nobody did – not even Gilbert.'

'Why don't you tell us about it?'

'About what? A family feud that's nearly thirty years old? I wasn't around then, I only saw the result. My mother, working when she was ill, to keep food on our table. She died before I could repay her . . . another stable-door.'

'Can you explain a bit more, Coral?' asked Sergeant Bird. 'Was the quarrel between your mother and her sister?'

'No – not initially. My mother came from what was known as a "good family"; still is, I suppose. Her parents were well satisfied when her sister Marion became a Bradshaw, because they were equally respectable. But my mother, who was fourteen years younger than Marion, disappointed them when her time came by choosing a coal-miner. A lot of harsh words were said, so I'm told. They cut her off completely. Marion sided with her parents at first, but when my father was killed in a mining accident, she offered some Bradshaw money. It was too late. My mother had her pride, and turned her down flat. Aunt Marion was offended . . . they were never in contact again.'

A dull fury shone in her eyes like glowing coals. Coral was a girl of quick passions and quick recoveries. 'It was all so stupid. Year after year – estrangement for the want of a few conciliatory words. When I started at the hospital, it didn't take long for gossip about Gil to reach me. Nurses are interested in any unmarried doctor, especially a rich one . . . but they pronounced him dull, and weak, and not worth bothering with. I did think of introducing myself to him as his cousin, but there didn't seem to be any point. He wasn't my type, I could see that. My name meant nothing to him. His parents had probably protected him from the whole affair!' She looked up challengingly. 'Now they're all dead, after wasting their lives being lonely and proud. It's a *crime!*'

'Have you any other relatives?' asked Montgomery quietly.

'No.'

'Who do you think might benefit from Gilbert's will, then?'

'I don't know. A charity, perhaps . . . or does it go to the Crown?' Her voice was just a little too innocent.

'You've never considered the question before?'

'Oh, no.'

'Tell me how you intend to keep on the flat.'

'I'll have to share again. It seems the lesser of the two evils.'

'You have someone in mind?'

'No specific person.'

'You've advertised, then?'

'Yes.'

'Where? The *Recorder*?'

'Yes . . . No. Not yet. I'm just about to.'

'Ah, I see.' He created a more comfortable position in the chair.

'Let's go over a few recent events again, Coral. Starting on September sixteenth . . . '

Sergeant Bird fastened his seat-belt and turned to Montgomery.

'It's funny, sir. The first time I saw Nurse Chapman I felt she looked familiar, but I couldn't place it.'

'*Now* you tell me.'

'I made one or two enquiries, though, on the strength of the instinct. Particularly the other downstairs neighbour. I asked him if Coral had gone out on the night that Maureen disappeared. He couldn't be sure, but he did notice that her car was in its place outside the flats when he left at nine for some fish and chips, and when he returned at twenty-past.'

Montgomery nodded. 'You realize, don't you, Will, that we only have *Coral*'s word for this story of Maureen meeting a man. That's been one of our major leads. A man – and probably a hospital man. Now I don't know what to believe.'

They arrived back at the station to find Jackson still grinning.

'More news,' he announced with relish. 'Smythe went down to The Boatman pub this lunch-time with Maureen O'Donnell's photograph. It's less than a mile from the Beeston marina, and it's been canvassed twice already: there was a poster, but it had been covered up by a darts schedule. Anyway, a man there, an unemployed labourer, thought he recognized her. He described what she was wearing when last seen – white dress, dark blue jacket – and says she was sitting at a corner table around nine o'clock with a dark-haired man. She was facing him, but he remembers nothing of the man except that he was tall and dark. He insists an identity parade would be useless.'

'What were they doing?' asked Montgomery.

'He thinks they had a bar snack. The couple who run the pub can't confirm it because Fridays and Saturdays are their busiest nights.'

'Why did they catch his eye?'

'He was waiting for a friend, and killing time. He said the girl looked a bit self-conscious, as if she wasn't used to being in a pub, or was on a first date, or something. His words.'

'Have you seen the friend?'

'Not yet but he sat with his back to them, so he's unlikely to come up with anything more on the man. "Tall and dark", sir . . . this is our breakthrough!'

Montgomery made his approbation clear. 'Good work, Brian. Tell Graham he gets two house points.' Rapidly he digested the implications. 'This doesn't preclude involvement on Coral Chapman's part: if anything, it strengthens the possibility. She's a close friend of David Stannard's, and their alibis for the latter end of Friday the sixteenth are mutually dependent. No one else is sure exactly if or when they were in the Mortar and Pestle that night. At the risk of sounding sexist, I'd say that business with the cars in Sylvia Vale was a distinctly male touch, whereas a feminine mind probably suggested Stannard should create an air of conspiracy with Maureen, which would be sure to hook her – especially if she was also attracted to him. Coral may well have been speaking the truth there.'

'You think she's an accessory, then?' Brian Jackson's eyes were eager.

'Yes. But I also think it was her idea. We've found no feasible motive for Bradshaw's murder except the old favourite – gain. She knew she was likely to be his heir. She had scraped by all her life while he was sitting on a potential fortune in property. She hadn't allowed any ties of affection to develop between them – in fact, he represented a branch of the family her mother had quarrelled with bitterly. Coral might have felt that his money was her due.'

'Shall we bring her in?'

Montgomery held up a cautionary hand. 'Hold your horses. It's all surmise at present; there's not an iota of proof. We need to examine the fabric of their alibis – Stannard's in particular – find the holes, and tear them to shreds. If we fail, and this theory is correct, you can imagine what will follow. Coral Chapman will inherit the house in Sylvia Vale, sell it and live happily ever after with David Stannard. There won't be a damn thing we can do to stop them.'

'Did anyone uncover the movements of the blue XR3i on either of the nights in question?' asked William Bird.

'No. Every resident in a hospital room or flat has now been interviewed. No one recalls seeing damage, but that's not saying much; they don't recall seeing the car that night, either. Those spending the weekend away tend to leave as soon as they decently can, while the rest are either socializing or working their socks off on the wards.' He paused, assessing, introspective. 'We'd better keep plugging away at those garages. We need tangible proof, if only to persuade Philippa. As things stand, she won't believe it. And yet . . . her memory may turn out to be the only evidence we'll ever have.'

Stewart Bridges threw down the latest batch of reports from the microbiology lab. 'Blood cultures still negative,' he growled.

Neil perched on the edge of Sister's desk and craned his neck to look at the forms.

'Philippa's, I presume?'

'Yes. But haematology are making comments like ''toxic neutrophilia'' on *their* reports. And her temperature chart's like a set of crocodile's teeth.'

Together they frowned at the small slips of paper, as if trying to make sense of the contradictory results.

'It must be a localized abscess,' said Neil. 'Perhaps something's brewing up in the retroperitoneum?'

A faint rustling noise heralded the approach of Nurse Benson. She cleared her throat and waited for their attention.

'Excuse me, Dr Bridges. Mrs Cutler is having a rigor. Staff nurse thinks it may be a transfusion reaction . . . Please could you come?'

As Stewart left the office, Anne Markham quietly entered it.

'You've seen the lab results?' she asked Neil.

'Yes.'

'I just can't believe that they're growing nothing from the samples. Philippa's got all the hallmarks of a septicaemia.'

'Has she had rigors, too?'

'She did have, about four o'clock. They've stopped now. Neil . . . what happens to the specimens when they get to the lab? Is there any way that they could be – tampered with?'

Neil unhurriedly closed the door and motioned Anne to her chair, resuming his own uncomfortable position on the desk. He needed a moment to think. The idea was appalling, unlikely though it sounded, and he had a lot of respect for Sister Markham.

When he spoke, it was in his usual measured tones.

'The blood culture bottles are kept in an incubator so that the

196

bacteria can multiply,' he answered. 'Then they're plated out on to a solid medium, a kind of nutrient gel, where the colonies grow to a visible size. Individual ones are then picked off and studied in detail. If you're talking about material from swabs, though, it's plated out directly.'

'Do the lab technicians do all this?'

'Usually. But there may be some junior doctors in training for pathology.'

'What about medical students?'

'No. They learn their microbiology down at the University.'

'So someone who didn't belong to the lab would be obvious?'

He smiled at her, because her face had become tense and grim.

'No less obvious than if he went through the door wearing a red nose and banging cymbals.'

She gave him a tentative smile in return. 'Let's forget the daytime, then. Who has access at night?'

'The technician on call.'

'No one else?'

'Well, anyone entitled to the key. Security, of course, and the relevant medical staff.'

She shook her head, dissatisfied. 'We hardly know them. They don't come to the wards like other doctors unless there's a really special case. I think it's someone who has actually visited Philippa.'

'That frusemide?'

'Exactly.'

Neil stood up. 'You're half-way to convincing me, Anne. It would be possible for a person with the right key to interfere with the samples in the lab. They could change the labels, bring in false specimens, substitute one Petri dish or its lid for another . . . but who, and why?'

'If we knew that, we wouldn't be too worried about "how".'

A clumping sound in the corridor warned them that their brief period of privacy was over.

'We'll arrange an abdominal film,' said Neil in normal tones as Stewart entered the room, Nurse Benson in tow. 'Ah – how's Mrs Cutler?'

'She's got a blotchy rash now. We've slowed the drip and given her hydrocortisone and chlorpheniramine.'

'Good. She does need the blood. Have we any more patients coming in?'

'No, but the medics want to transfer one of theirs to us. They're on "take", too. It's a lady with a perforated duodenal ulcer, who was initially diagnosed as having a myocardial infarction. Dave Stannard's going to ring you – oh, here he comes.'

'Hi, Dave,' said Neil as the tall physician squeezed his way into the tiny office. 'We don't really need extra custom, you know.'

'Got to keep you on your toes,' said David affably. 'Has Stewart told you about our lady?'

'In broad terms.'

They discussed the details, then Stewart slunk out to the clinical room, relieving the congestion in the office. David lingered to exchange pleasantries with Anne Markham.

Under cover of writing a brief memo in his notebook, Neil watched his medical friend, seeing him with new eyes. He recalled that David had spent six months in the pathology department, three of them in microbiology, before switching to general medicine. He would have had a key; perhaps he never returned it. Certainly the Doctors' Residence keys were forever going missing, scattered about the country in a miscellany of pockets as their owners scrabbled for the next rung on the career ladder. Reluctantly he saw there was only one way to find out.

He picked up the discarded pathology forms and gave an exasperated cluck.

'Half our results aren't back from microbiology,' he said to Anne. 'The porters must have forgotten to collect the last batch.'

'Cultures can take days,' said David casually.

'I know, but there are some we phoned up about, which were definitely going to be ready. I bet they're just sitting in the "Out" tray.' He feigned a start of realization. 'Dave – you've done a microbiology SHO job, haven't you? I don't suppose you still have the key? We could go and take a quick look.' Over David's shoulder, Anne's face was suddenly alert. In the corner, Nurse Benson hummed softly as she penned a report in her rounded, childish handwriting.

David dug a bunch of keys from an inner pocket, glanced at them and promptly replaced them.

'Sorry,' he said. 'If I've still got one, it isn't here. There might be one in my flat; I really don't remember.'

Anne had gone pale, but she forced a laugh. 'I thought microbiology attachments were renowned for their lack of out-of-hours

198

commitment, for the medics at least. Did they actually give you a key in the first place?'

'Oh, yes. I was in on some Saturday mornings . . . Do you want me to nip to the flat, Neil? I can't promise anything.'

'No, it's okay. The results aren't so urgent. We can manage.' He adroitly steered the conversation along other lines, and even chuckled at one of David's jokes, but a portion of his mind was acutely aware of Anne, her horrified insight and deep dismay.

Montgomery pulled down the blind on his kitchen window. Behind him, Carole was boiling a kettle for her last cup of tea of the night; the caffeine content never seemed to affect her sleep. Ten minutes earlier their two teenaged children, homework done, had finally gone to bed.

As she baptized the tea-bag, drained it and plopped its turgid weight into the kitchen waste-bin, he leaned abstractedly against the sink, sighing with irritation at intervals.

'You know what they say,' she offered idly when no signs of communication were forthcoming. 'Two heads are better than one.'

'Usually,' he granted, 'but I can't rationalize my thoughts enough to put a case to you.'

'No problem. I don't mind disjointed fragments. Use me as a sounding-board.'

'All right,' he said slowly. 'You asked for it.' He took a sip of her tea. 'How would you feel if you were knocked down by a Citroën?'

'What sort of Citroën?'

'A 2CV.'

'Unimpressed.'

'Why?'

'Well – it's just a hairdryer on wheels. It would be – ignomini-ous. Like being knocked down by a bicycle or an ambulance.'

'How about a Ford XR3i?'

'Ah. Much more respectable.'

'A better image?'

'Yes.'

'I agree. The image fits with both the man and the machine. The difficulty is this: the XR3i is undamaged while the Citroën re-cently had a front-end garage repair. More important still, the bumper bar on the XR3i is the wrong height to have inflicted the injuries found on the pedestrian, while that on the Citroën is perfectly positioned.'

'When was the repair? Does it tie in?'

'The repair does, yes. But we've one witness, a hospital porter, who states that the car was damaged during the week *before* the hit-and-run accident. Also we haven't the slightest glimmer of a motive for that particular driver, beyond the fact that he knew the victim superficially. We're much more suspicious of the other chap.'

'Perhaps he borrowed the Citroën,' suggested Carole musingly.

'I did wonder, but borrowing a damaged car would pre-suppose that he knew he was going to have to chase someone and knock her down, which is ridiculous. That part couldn't have been planned.'

'I wasn't thinking along those lines. I simply meant that if he was driving off to do something shady, he might have temporarily acquired another person's car so that his own wouldn't be spotted near the scene. In that context, the damage would have been quite incidental. Are Citroëns easy to break into?'

'He may not have needed to,' said Montgomery. 'The owner of the 2CV is renowned for his general absent-mindedness; perhaps that car wasn't even locked.'

'The other man ... what about his alibi for the night in question?'

'We're still checking it – exhaustively.' He looked across at her for a moment, head tilted, considering. 'You know, there is an area where you could help me, because of your work in the library. The man we're investigating is a doctor called David Stannard. He claims he was watching a nature programme the night Gilbert Bradshaw was killed, and gave me a very glib description of the appearance and habits of the bamboo rat. If he didn't, in fact, see the programme, he must have read it up somewhere; they don't have a video recorder in the Doctors' Mess, and the television guides gave no specific details. Would your library have any record?'

She frowned doubtfully. 'We're only a small branch library, Richard. And we're not fully computerized . . . I can certainly find out if he's a member, whether with us or Nottingham Central. If he still has the book out, there's a chance – but not if he's returned it. What does he look like?'

'Unremarkable – no scars or humps. Caucasian, six feet tall, 155 pounds, clean shaven, dark-brown hair, unparted, brown eyes with very clear whites. Good skin. Pleasant manner when he wants it to be.'

'I'm sorry – apart from the eyes that could be anyone.'

'I'd agree with you.' He thought again. 'It's just possible that a friend may have picked it up for him. A small, slender sprite of a girl with a face like a kitten and a great puffball of red hair – natural red. Her name's Coral Chapman.'

'I know.'

'What do you mean?' he demanded sharply. 'How do you know? I haven't mentioned her before.'

'No; you've been very circumspect about this whole case. The newspapers haven't, though. They referred to her when Maureen O'Donnell was found dead. But even before that, I'd seen her. She came into the library about a week ago when I was on duty at the desk.'

'You're sure?'

'Yes. Only a blind person wouldn't have noticed that hair.'

'But there are lots of redheads. How can you be certain it was *her*?'

Carole laughed. 'Honestly, Richard. You ask me a question, then you can't accept that I've actually got an answer for you! What nasty, suspicious minds policemen have. I'll tell you why I know. First of all, her Christian name. It struck me that it was almost identical with mine in terms of letters, and yet so much more exotic. It suited her. Then the surname, Chapman: it reminded me of the Lotus man. Mark is always going on about how wonderful he was. But it was the book that really lodged her in my mind, because someone else needed it urgently a couple of days after she'd borrowed it. A boy who was about to start at Law School.'

'A law student? What *was* the book, for heaven's sake?'

'*Introduction to English Law*, by Philip James.'

David Stannard yawned, and looked at his watch. Seven-thirty a.m. Time for breakfast – cardiac-arrest bleep allowing – before the long, tortuous ward round which inevitably followed a night on 'take'. He hoped the houseman had documented the locations of all their new patients; the usual bed shortage had led to 'sleepers-out' all over the hospital. They had even been forced to exile one of their fitter ladies to the ENT ward.

He walked wearily down a quiet green corridor. None of his team had got to bed the previous night; a steady stream of heart, lung and drug-overdose patients had seen to that. As a result, he felt strangely light-headed. He knew from experience that the full weight of his sleep lack would not strike until the next day.

As he came abreast of the small passageway leading to Cavendish Ward, he felt the urge to check on Philippa and see how things were progressing. While his feet slowed their soft tread, he fought to curb the compulsion. A low profile was best; it would be foolish to overplay his hand at this stage.

He turned away, then halted, reconsidering. Yes, he *would* go. It need only take a minute . . .

Noiselessly he padded to the door of Philippa's side room. Someone was in the nurses' locker-room diagonally opposite, a blur of maroon in the dimness, but he didn't pause to find out who. Without knocking, he pushed the door open and entered.

Philippa gave a low mutter. Her eyes were closed, her head to one side; lank wisps of black hair were plastered randomly across her forehead. Her rapid, shallow panting filled the room.

David slowly advanced to the bed and stared down at Philippa's face. Her cheeks had sunk into ghastly hollows, and the parted lips were ominously blue. His gaze travelled to her fingers; they, too, were blue. Cyanosis . . . circulatory failure.

The door opened without warning behind him. Anne Markham's maroon jacket was unbuttoned at the top, revealing the blue Sister's uniform; she must have only just arrived for duty. Her accusing eyes flicked to him briefly before they were transfixed by the figure in the bed. She drew in a sharp breath.

'Anne.' David's whisper was choked and alien. 'She's dying.'

Coral Chapman was angry to see Inspector Montgomery and Sergeant Bird approaching Byron Ward in a business-like manner. It was bad enough their coming to the flat, but here in front of her colleagues and patients an official encounter would be most undesirable. She was tempted to leave by the fire exit, then rejected the idea. Let them come! Her father had been a tough man, from what little she could remember. She would be a worthy daughter to him.

'Hello, Inspector,' she greeted him in syrupy tones. 'I'm afraid Sister has just gone home. Or was it me you wanted?'

'Yes,' said Montgomery. 'We would like another word.'

'What a pity. I'm in charge of the ward . . . I couldn't possibly leave my patients.'

Montgomery coolly scanned the two rows of beds and their occupants. Byron Ward was enjoying the hiatus between the bustle of the afternoon visiting hour and the clatter of the evening meal. 'The ward looks nice and quiet,' he remarked. 'We could talk in your office.'

Two of the nearest patients, both elderly ladies, began to stare at the trio in a penetrating way. Coral clenched her fist. 'The phone is always ringing. There'd be constant interruptions.'

'We'll chance it,' said Montgomery cheerfully.

They filed through to the empty office and sat down.

'We're interested in a book you took out from Sherwood Branch Library on September twenty-first,' explained Montgomery. 'It was called *Introduction to English Law*. Could you tell us why you chose this subject?'

'It was recalled. I hardly read any of it.'

'We know that. But what was the initial attraction of the book?'

'Just general knowledge. I'm always confused by references in plays and things to "The Bar" and "Benches" and 'taking silk'. I wanted to know what it all meant, and the book covered many different topics.'

'Indeed it did. Did you by chance alight on the section dealing with wills and probate?'

'No.'

'Why ever not? Weren't you curious to know what might happen to your cousin's estate? You seem to be his closest relative.'

'I've no idea what was in Gilbert's will! I told you we never communicated. He could have left it all to a charity.'

'You think he made a will, then?'

'I don't know. It's not something I've considered.'

Montgomery's face wore an expression of pained disbelief. 'Coral . . . we're all inquisitive where wills are concerned. Especially when we're a bit short of cash. There's no harm in *wondering* if we're entitled to anything.'

'Well, I didn't.'

She paused, on the brink of returning fire with a question of her own, but at the last moment her resolve failed. In the distance, someone croaked 'Nurse!'

'I must go,' she said firmly.

Montgomery smiled his assent. 'Of course. We wouldn't dream of keeping you from your duties. When do you finish your shift?'

'Around nine o'clock.'

'Are you off home then?'

'Probably.'

'Have a pleasant evening. Don't worry about us; we can see you again when it's more convenient. Perhaps tomorrow or the day after?'

'I'd hate you to put yourselves out on my account,' said Coral, holding the door for them.

'That's most thoughtful – but it's no trouble.'

'We'll let her stew awhile,' said Montgomery as the two detectives left the vicinity of Byron Ward and walked towards the surgical wing. 'In the meantime, though, we'd better keep Anne Markham in the picture, or whoever's in charge of Cavendish Ward at present. She can put a temporary ban on all visitors to Philippa, including doctors who aren't directly connected with her treatment. That way, Coral and David will be kept at arm's length while we acquire some evidence.'

'It could take too much time, sir.'

'I know. If Philippa's well enough, we must try and arrange her transfer to another hospital at the earliest opportunity. I'll discuss it with Mr Crowland tomorrow. He may have a private bed available.'

As Montgomery strode down the passageway to Cavendish Ward, his initial relief at finding Anne Markham still on duty changed to alarm when he saw how tense and disturbed she was. For a moment, he felt a dark premonition that Philippa had died.

'Inspector Montgomery . . . ' Anne faltered, taking a few hesitant steps to meet him. 'Sergeant Bird . . . I'm so glad you've come. We need to speak to you. Something awful has happened.'

'Is it Philippa? Has she . . . ?'

'No, she's not dead. Neil has saved her life – for the second time. But we think – we're almost sure – someone had deliberately tried to kill her, someone right here in the hospital!'

'Is your interview room free? Can we talk in there?'

'Yes. Just give me a minute to fetch Neil. Staff Nurse is looking after the ward; I only stayed on to do some paperwork. I'm glad I did.'

With a minimum of delay, the four settled down in the interview room, Neil and Anne facing the police officers across the low coffee table which occupied the centre. Montgomery found no reassurance in the grim demeanour of the surgeon. Thornton's obvious disquiet simply strengthened his own conviction that Philippa must be moved from the District Hospital with all speed. Anne touched Neil's arm. 'Please would you explain?'

'If you really want me to,' he replied, 'but the credit is yours. Your actions saved Philippa long before anyone else cottoned on.' He turned to address Montgomery and Bird. 'This is rather difficult to outline,' he said. 'It concerns elements of hospital procedure. But I'll do my best.

'You know that Philippa has had her ups and downs. Over the last few days, we became convinced that she had a hidden focus of infection which was making her systemically ill. Our tests and examinations showed nothing. We sent numerous swabs and blood samples to the lab, but all the results came back negative. It didn't make sense, unless the antibiotics she was already on were clouding the picture. Philippa was going downhill before our eyes.

'Yesterday, Anne shared with me her suspicion that the samples were being tampered with in some way while they were incubating in the microbiology lab. I must admit, I found the idea a shocking one, but on reflection it at least provided an explanation for our lack of results. We talked about who might have a key to the lab – ' Anne raised her head as if to speak, then subsided again ' – and what might have been done to the specimens. Then we had to leave the matter because other people came into the room.

'Anne had no chance to tell me that she had already put her theory to the test. She had taken blood from Philippa herself yesterday, and sent it to the lab under a false name. This morning, Philippa was in a terrible state. Samples we'd sent under her own name were still growing no bacteria, but the falsely named blood cultures showed overwhelming growths of MRSA, a formidable bug which is resistant to all but one of our antibiotics.'

'Neil treated her very promptly,' broke in Anne, 'and this evening she's beginning to improve.'

'Could this pattern of events have happened by chance?' asked Montgomery.

'Not when we sent so many samples,' said Anne. 'The only one with a false name showed massive growths of bacteria which the lab could positively identify. I know that Neil's reluctant to tell you this, but one of Philippa's friends used to do a microbiology job and was given a key to the lab.'

'May I ask who?'

'David Stannard.'

Sergeant Bird pursed his lips and met Montgomery's eye.

'You're sure? Mr Thornton?'

Neil nodded heavily. 'We ought to tell the medical and nursing hierarchies what we've told you, but quite frankly, I don't think they'd believe us, and their kind of enquiry would be a ponderous one. Administrators would be involved . . . the whole thing would be a mess. Anne and I feel a sense of urgency now. If someone's gunning for Philippa, perhaps she shouldn't be here at all. But she's still too ill to be moved.'

'Thank you for your candour,' said Montgomery. 'While Philippa remains here, I'd like you to instruct the relevant nursing staff that she isn't well enough for any visitors, even hospital personnel. Be emphatic; make sure there's no misunderstanding. The ban must include any friends of Dr Stannard's, such as Nurse Chapman. I'll try to send a police officer to the ward tonight as an added precaution.' If two more could be spared, he thought, Stannard and Chapman could be kept under surveillance.

'Thank you,' said Anne warmly. 'That's a load off our minds.'

'Would it be possible to see Philippa?' asked Montgomery as they prepared to leave.

'She was asleep when I last looked,' said Neil, 'but I don't see why not.' He led them to the side room and opened the door softly. Philippa slept on, pale and peaceful, oblivious of the intrusion. It seemed to Montgomery that there was piquant irony in a situation where a defenceless girl, surrounded by caring people, could nevertheless be in deadly danger.

Neil Thornton guessed his thoughts. His fine blue eyes, faintly dimmed with exhaustion, glanced at Philippa, and then at Montgomery. 'All our patients are important,' he said in a low voice, 'but Philippa is special.'

As they walked up the corridor, he stifled a yawn.

'Go home, Neil,' urged Anne. 'You've been up half the night, and Stewart went ages ago. I'll tell the nurses all they need to know.'

'Thanks,' he said, and accompanied Montgomery and Bird along the main corridor to the stairs.

Behind them, Barnaby Fletcher emerged from a lift, looked about him, then trundled off in the direction of the surgical wing.

18

'You're like a cat on hot bricks!' exclaimed Carole as Montgomery prowled around the living-room, picking things up and putting them back again. 'You hardly touched your supper. If it's the case you're worried about, I hope you solve it soon.'

Montgomery removed the circulars from his pile of mail, crushed them into a large ball, and threw it at the waste-paper basket in the corner. It bounced against the rim and fell to the floor, disintegrating into a confusion of component pieces. 'That's my case,' he said sardonically. 'Disparate parts which superficially make up a whole. Inferences and probabilities, circumstantial evidence . . . but nothing direct, nothing to glue it all together. We've got two murder scenes, an attempted murder scene and a girl with loss of memory, yet we can't nail the perpetrators because there's no real evidence.'

'You think two people were responsible?'

He grimaced. 'It's quite a handful for one.'

Moodily he gathered up the papers and thrust them into the basket. He knew he wasn't being fair to Carole. She was a lively, intelligent woman who had contributed useful ideas to many of his past cases, yet this one, which was taking over his every waking thought, was somehow sacrosanct. Beyond his query about the library books, he had studiously avoided discussing it.

Many policemen found themselves divorced for exactly that reason. Their wives felt excluded, outsiders to a world of secrets, personal danger and unique camaraderie; their place was always second to the job. For the first time in months, Montgomery wondered if he was taking Carole for granted. She was the supporting cast to his protagonist when a case became difficult; for someone with so many bright qualities of her own, perhaps it was the harder role.

'Sorry,' he muttered. 'Yes, I think it was two people. Our men have scoured the areas concerned, but they've come up with nothing to link either suspect with the crimes. One of them's a girl. I don't think she'd break under questioning, or I'd have her in. But subtle harassment isn't working, and we're very short of time.'

He went to the window and pulled the curtain to one side. It was eight-thirty in the evening, and the willow tree in his front garden hung lank and dismal, as if weighted down by the pressure of the heavy, moisture-laden air all around. Only light from the window gilded its drooping branches; the moon was hidden behind a dense black canopy of cloud.

'The weather men have predicted another wet night,' said Carole.

'They may be right this time,' he replied.

He continued to stare out into the garden. Perversely, the prospect of rain attracted him. Rain was intimately associated with his case: Philippa Rowe had lain all night under a steady downpour, and his best discoveries in Sylvia Vale had been made in the midst of a deluge.

Sylvia Vale ... Bradshaw's house, garage and grounds had now been searched to such an extent that not one ant's egg could have escaped detection. No more could be done there. Montgomery himself was as familiar with the locality as many of his officers. But the Beeston lock was different. That part of the investigation had been in other hands. He had seen it once, in daylight.

Carole was just behind him when he swung round.

'I must go to Beeston,' he said.

'Tonight?'

'Yes.'

A resigned look stole over her face. 'Don't get soaked again. If you can wait five minutes, I'll make you a flask of coffee.'

She walked abruptly into the kitchen, but he followed.

'Carole – come with me.'

She paused, one hand on the kettle.

'Are you sure?'

'Absolutely sure.'

They arrived at the Boatman pub in Montgomery's own Sierra, and conducted a brief reconnaissance before leaving for Beeston lock. The timing was right; Montgomery felt that the visit had provided a reasonably accurate assessment of the pub's occupancy on the night Maureen ate there. He was also interested in his wife's impressions.

'What did you think of it?' he asked as he steered the car along the quiet residential roads leading to the canal.

'Popular place,' said Carole. 'I thought the public bar was slightly seedy, but the lounge bar had some cosy little niches ideal for couples. Their menu was more comprehensive than I expected.'

'Did you notice the poster about Maureen?'

'No. I didn't realize there was one.'

'Just to the right of the bar. I only saw it because I was looking for it; a great hulk of a beer drinker was standing in the way, the type that puts down roots. I doubt more than ten per cent of tonight's clientele even know it's there, and that's an optimistic estimate. It's hardly surprising our feed-back has been poor.'

He parked neatly alongside the grass verge bordering the canal and saw beneath him the cabin-tops of narrowboats drawn up against the bank. Here and there lights glinted from cracks between patterned curtains.

'That pub was well chosen by Maureen's killer,' he went on. 'It's on the opposite side of Nottingham to the District Hospital, so it's not a regular haunt of the medics or nursing staff. It's very busy at weekends, yet there are private corners where you can sit and talk. Add to that its proximity to the lock, and he couldn't have done much better. Do you fancy a walk?'

'Of course, seeing as that's why we're here. I've got my umbrella; the rain can't be far away.'

Montgomery secured the car, then linked her arm through his. In the still air, the rushing sound of the weir was prominent as they strolled up the road towards the lock. Another couple passed them, meandering the other way.

'That's odd.' Montgomery stopped and frowned as the lock-keeper's cottage came into view on the opposite bank. The whole enclosure in front of his garden was illuminated by a tall sodium lamp which threw a misty orange glare across the footbridge, the great lock gates and the concrete working areas on each side of the deep watery cleft. 'It's lit up like a circus.'

'For safety, I suppose,' said Carole. 'Look – there's a lifebelt across there.'

Gingerly they approached the edge and peered over. The flat, opaque surface of the water reflected a dull orange at the canal end of the lock where the lamp was, but by the gates at the river end it was black and cryptic, decidedly sinister. The level was nine feet below them and the closest ladder yards away, set in the centre of the wall.

Carole stared, shuddered, then drew back to assess the rest of her surroundings. The street they had walked along was empty now; the other couple had vanished into the misty night. A wooden fence separated them from the nearest houses. Across the water, the drawn curtains of the lock-keeper's cottage gave it a blind appearance. The sense of isolation was very strong.

'How quiet it is,' she whispered.

'With all that row?' asked Montgomery, gesturing in the direction of the weir.

'I didn't mean degree of noise, I meant the people. Where are they all?'

Montgomery checked his watch. 'It's ten past nine now,' he said, 'so they're in pubs, cinemas, restaurants, or at home watching their television sets, as I imagine the lock-keeper is doing.' He leaned close to her and lowered his voice. 'Put yourself in Maureen O'Donnell's shoes for a moment. You're a young nurse, inexperienced in the ways of the world; you're afraid of water but you're in the company of someone you know and trust. How near to that lock-side would you go?'

'I'd be reassured by the lamp,' she said thoughtfully, 'so I'd come to this point with no particular qualms. As for the rest, it would depend how handsome the chap was. If the situation was romantic, I might be off my guard.'

'Good. My view exactly. Let's take it a step further. He steers you to the river end of the lock, holding you tightly so you feel no stirrings of alarm. At the crucial moment, with no warning, he pushes you over the edge. What would you do?'

'Scream!'

'Go on, then.'

She stared at him. 'You want me to scream? Now?'

'Yes.'

After a furtive glance over her shoulder, Carole emitted a half-hearted croak.

'I feel *silly*,' she hissed.

'I thought you wanted to help.'

'I do, but – can't you scream yourself?'

'Talk about silly.'

'What a coward!'

'My voice is too low-pitched. Yours will be much more authentic . . .'

'All right,' Carole cut in brusquely. She motioned to him to stand away, then closed her eyes. Summoning up all her powers of imagination and empathy, she took a deep breath and let out a scream of chilling anguish and fear.

They drew together again, listening, Montgomery's right ear cocked at an expectant angle. Beyond the lock-keeper's cottage the weir roared heedlessly; in the distance a car engine idled and a door slammed. Their immediate vicinity remained empty of any other pedestrians.

Montgomery placed a mollifying hand on his wife's shoulder. 'Thank you,' he said. 'It really was necessary.'

She nodded a grudging acknowledgement. 'What are we listening for now?'

'Any sign of life. Running feet, shouts – even police cars.'

They waited, but nothing changed as the minutes ticked by. Dampness seemed to sink and settle all around them. The front door of the cottage opposite remained firmly shut.

Carole slowly relaxed her position, which had been frozen in an attitude mirroring Montgomery's.

'Nobody's coming,' she said in a voice of wonder. 'They didn't hear.'

Montgomery's eyes were darting between the cottage and the nearest houses.

'Why didn't they hear?' she went on. 'Is it because of the weir?'

'Partly. But the lock-keeper's almost certainly watching something engrossing on television. If Maureen did scream, the person who could best have helped her was unaware of it. And the weir isn't the only background noise. There's a railway line just up the road from here. A heavy goods train might have been chugging past at the time.'

Carole's face was grim in the harsh orange light. Without a word, she returned to the edge of the lock, holding on the belt of Montgomery's raincoat.

'Maureen fell into the water,' she said quietly, looking down at the almost oily sheen below. 'If she saw the ladder at all, she must

211

have known it was beyond her reach. Do you think she took a long time to die?'

'No. Frobisher submitted "vagal inhibition" as the cause of death – a kind of shock.'

'Shock . . . that's interesting. I was reading one of our library books recently, a sort of history of notorious British criminals. You remember George Joseph Smith, the "brides in the bath" man? The police couldn't work out how he managed to kill all those women in the bathrooms of public boarding-houses without someone hearing a commotion. There were no undue water splashes, either. The inspector in charge of the case decided to conduct some experiments with a volunteer nurse in a bathing suit. He found he couldn't hold her under for more than a few seconds because of her vigorous struggles, so he pulled her legs sharply towards the tap end . . . The moment her head went under water, she became unconscious. They had to resuscitate her. Apparently the collapse was caused by the shock of the water rushing up her nose!'

'Yes,' agreed Montgomery, 'it can happen as suddenly as that. Maureen probably sank very quickly. We were fortunate the body wasn't damaged by propellers; the post-mortem would have been much more difficult.'

'Why was there no damage from those narrowboats?'

'Well, the chamber of the lock is deep, even though the canal isn't, and the draught of the barges is surprisingly shallow – less than three feet. The ordinary cabin cruisers don't need much more. So they missed her.'

Carole shuddered. 'A small mercy for her family, anyway,' she said.

Montgomery stood silently, hands folded, his head bowed in respect.

'We'll catch the couple who did this,' he said at last. 'They'll have made a mistake somewhere along the line . . . We'll find it.'

A thin drizzle began to fall, so light as to be scarcely perceptible.

'Have you got what you came for?' asked Carole hesitantly. 'Shall we go home?'

'I needed to get the feel of the place at night,' said Montgomery. 'In daylight, it's just a pretty spot full of bustle and colour, where the idea of a crime would be totally alien.' He tilted his face up to the vast brooding sky, enjoying the cool sheen of

212

droplets which refreshed his skin and stimulated his mind. 'Just now, though, I'm closer to the psyche of the person who brought Maureen here after sharing a meal with her.'

'I'll go back to the car if you like, then you can think in peace. But please take the umbrella; you got absolutely *saturated* that evening you went to Sylvia Vale. No one should get wet when they don't need to.'

Montgomery started as Carole's chance remark triggered an echoing chord in his memory. Surely someone else had commented on rain in similar terms . . . a gratuitous soaking connected with the night Gilbert Bradshaw died . . .

He snapped his fingers. Barnaby Fletcher! He had spoken of meeting Neil Thornton in the hospital car-park, close to Albert's kiosk.

'He was getting rather wet.'

Montgomery whirled round to Carole, alarming her. 'I'll come with you,' he said urgently. 'You've reminded me of something. It could be very important.'

As they hurried down the canal-side road, random sentences flashed into his mind like teleprint messages.

Arthur Wright is honest.

Vanda Pitts is ambitious.

Anne Markham is intelligent.

Stewart Bridges is careless.

A pattern was emerging, a suspicion forming that one individual had made full use of these people and their qualities. Someone tall and dark and plausible . . .

They scrambled into the car, Montgomery gunning the starter motor while Carole was still fumbling with her seat-belt.

'We're looking for a telephone box,' he shouted. 'Do you know Mark's number?'

'Mark? I – yes.'

'Good.'

'Mark? Richard here. Sorry I've no time to be courteous. I need to ask you something. Yes – police work. Tell me: in racing circles, what does "T-boned" mean?'

Montgomery pulled on the handbrake and stared up at the block

213

of flats rearing above the tree-lined car park. Beside him, Sergeant Bird unclipped his seat-belt and exhaled softly.

'Was Carole upset, sir, to be dumped at home without ceremony?'

'I don't think so. I hope she understood.'

'If you're right about Thornton, then we have to confront him tonight. You think he's up there?'

'His light's on. I telephoned the hospital when I'd finished speaking to Mark, and asked if they'd bleep him. There was no reply. He's not on duty; remember, we saw him leave in the Cavalier.'

'What about protection for Philippa?'

'DC Coleman has been on Cavandish Ward since seven o'clock. He's in radio contact with Haslam and Grange, who are keeping Stannard and Chapman's flats under surveillance.' He slapped the dashboard of the Sierra with the flat of his hand. 'I wish this was a car from the pool. Still, no matter. Let's have a quick word with some of the downstairs residents, then give Thornton a surprise.'

Vanda Pitts readily admitted them to the flat. As Montgomery saw the girl at close quarters for the first time, he was struck by the contrast between her eyes, which were hard and glittery like quartz, and the charming smile with which she greeted them.

'This is unexpected,' she said. 'Is there something Sergeant Jackson forgot to ask me? Do sit down.'

'Thank you, but we may not be stopping. Is Mr Thornton at home?'

'I'm afraid you've missed him. He went out about half an hour ago to see a friend.'

'When will he be back?'

She shrugged. 'Late-ish.'

'Where does this friend live?'

'I don't know.'

Montgomery kept his voice neutral. 'Tell me, Miss Pitts, why did you lie to Sergeant Jackson about your movements on the night of Friday the twenty-third?'

Her jaw began to sag before she snapped it shut and glared at him.

'That's an outrageous thing to say! I've never lied to anyone, and certainly not to the police.'

214

'Really? Perhaps you were – simply forgetful, then. You claimed you were with Mr Thornton from six-thirty p.m., but of course you couldn't have been, because you didn't arrive here until Saturday, the following day.'

'Who says so?'

'A reliable informant.'

'Your "informant" probably saw me returning from the shops,' she stated smugly.

'With a suitcase and model bag?'

She looked uncertain for a moment before trying a new tack. 'Some of the residents here are rather sheltered types,' she said in bored, deliberate tones. 'I think they're jealous of our lifestyle. One or two of them would say anything to bring us down a peg.'

Montgomery's face remained impassive. 'Let's hope your London neighbours don't entertain similar attitudes,' he remarked.

Vanda turned away abruptly, opened a white leather handbag which was lying on the settee, drew out a packet of cigarettes and proceeded to light one. She then paced the room, supporting one elbow with the other hand while she smoked in short, erratic puffs.

'Look, Inspector,' she said at last. 'I may have made a mistake. I found your officers intimidating . . . they did nothing but leer at me. It was difficult to concentrate on the questions.'

'They said you were very fond of Mr Thornton,' said Montgomery quietly. 'Do you think you're helping him by telling lies on his behalf?'

'I've just explained; it was a mistake!'

'Trying to shield him makes you an accessory,' went on Montgomery as if she hadn't spoken. 'If, as we suspect, he is a double murderer, then the penalty for any accomplice will be severe. You're a young woman with a highly successful career. Do you want to go to prison?'

She stood tight-lipped.

'This man has manipulated you. Is he worth being dragged down for?'

Something kindled in the back of her eyes. She ground the cigarette into a marble ashtray and clenched her teeth.

'You're way off beam, Inspector. No one manipulates Vanda Pitts! I do what I like when I like!'

Revelation burst over Montgomery. This little girl from the East

End wanted Neil Thornton – at any price. Whether or not she had known the full story, she had agreed to provide him with an alibi for the night of Maureen O'Donnell's death. And in return . . . she would expect marriage. Not straight away, though: Montgomery couldn't imagine Neil Thornton consenting to any such thing. Vanda would keep her information as a blackmail card, to be produced when pressure would bring the best results. She was a hard bitch – but not in Thornton's league. Her ambitions were potentially suicidal.

'You're fooling yourself, Miss Pitts,' he said, shaking his head wearily. 'You think that now Thornton owes you a favour you can extract a requital whenever you like. But people of his sort can't be blackmailed. Try it and you could well find yourself the victim of another "accidental death".'

Her cheeks paled, then flushed with rage.

'I don't have to listen to this,' she said in a loud, aggressive voice. 'You've got no right to be here. You're just filth, no better than those two stupid jerks you sent round last time! I want you to leave – now.'

'Where is he, Miss Pitts?'

'I don't know, and if I did I wouldn't tell you. Get out of here!' Her careful accent was in tatters, the Bow Bells clanging harshly through every syllable. She bundled them towards the door, where Montgomery paused with his fingers on the handle.

'One final piece of advice, Miss Pitts. Don't leave Nottingham, will you?'

'We should have arrested her,' said Sergeant Bird. 'She's probably packing at this very minute!'

Montgomery swung the car out on to the main road and headed at speed for Trent Bridge. 'Thornton's more important,' he answered. 'I don't like this disappearance of his. Yell out when you see a phone-box; we must warn Coleman to be on his guard.'

The box, when they came to it, had been vandalized. Montgomery swore and raced back to the car, his stomach hollow with anxiety.

'We've wasted enough time,' he breathed. Let's go straight for the hospital ourselves. Ten to one that's where Thornton's gone.'

The Sierra's tyres screamed as they roared away into the night.

19

Philippa had been dreaming, a dream of whirling dark visions and clutching hands, so terrifyingly realistic that she thought she must have died and been sent in the wrong direction. Now, partially awake and confused, she followed with her eyes the vertical line of the giving set leading from her arm to the drip bag above.

So she was still in hospital . . . at least that meant she was alive. Something must have happened to make them revert to intravenous fluids. Oh yes . . . Neil was convinced she had an infection. He'd been taking all those blood tests. Perhaps they'd found out what it was and changed her treatment. If so, it was working. She felt better than before. Must tell him . . .

Outside the window of her room the sky was livid, and a steady stream of water droplets kissed the pane. The corridor light, however, provided sufficient illumination for her to make out the shape of each piece of furniture and equipment; the light above her bed, which was set to 'dim', completed the ghostly delineations.

She sighed, and nestled down among the bedclothes. No one about. Nothing to do but sleep. Half of her mind was reluctant to risk facing the nightmare kaleidoscope again, but the other half told her that those images had passed, and she would feel even brighter when she next woke. Her optimism, which had flagged over the previous few days, was reasserting itself. She began to doze again . . .

'One for you, Philippa!'

Jack, the most irreverent of the haematology lab technicians, flashed her a wicked grin as he handed over the slide.

She was immediately suspicious. 'What is it?'

'Your favourite. Eosinophilia. Lots of plump, juicy, *ripe* eosinophils just panting for your perusal.'

She clipped the slide under the lens of the microscope and turned the serrated focusing knob delicately between finger and thumb. Under her gaze, the 'ground glass' blur of the field drew into sharp relief and there, winking up at her like amber jewels, were the blood cells Jack had promised.

'*Glorious*!' she breathed.

'Hah!' he crowed to his colleagues. 'Her Achilles heel is demonstrated. Behold the paroxysms of ecstasy! Our Philippa will do anything for an eosinophil – won't you, Phillo?'

'Name it, and it shall be done,' she agreed. 'I need my daily fix. Just *look* at this! What does the request form say? Has the patient got some sort of allergy or parasitic disease?'

She was engaged in writing a helpful comment for the clinician when an apologetic cough sounded from the doorway. Glancing up, she saw Gilbert Bradshaw standing there indecisively, his face a concertina of anxious creases.

'Come in, Gil,' she greeted him. 'What can we do for you?'

'Er, sorry to disturb you like this . . . ' He cast a beseeching look towards the clutch of technicians seated at their microscopes down the long bench, and lowered his voice. 'I don't suppose . . . could we possibly have a word in private?'

'Of course,' said Philippa warmly, hiding her mystification. 'Let's go into the corridor.' She slid off the stool and followed him out of the door, careful not to attract Jack's attention; Gilbert was obviously in no mood for banter.

Between Haematology and Biochemistry was a quiet stretch of corridor where the chances of being overheard were small. They paused there while Philippa waited for Gilbert to voice his request. For several seconds he was silent; to her growing concern, she noticed that his hands were trembling uncontrollably.

He bit his lip, then swallowed. 'Philippa . . . I – I hate to impose on you, but I need your help with a – a serious matter. I can't explain it now – it would take too long – but you're the only person I can ask.'

'I'd be glad to help, Gil,' she assured him, worried by his agitation and pallor. 'When do you want to talk?'

'Could you – ' A shudder passed down his frame, and he swayed. 'I'm sorry . . . Do you think you could manage tonight, after work? In fact, are you free for most of this evening?'

In other circumstances, that would have sounded like a proposed date, but clearly nothing was further from Gilbert's mind. Clamping down on her curiosity with more difficulty, Philippa nodded.

'Yes, I am. I had nothing special planned.' Gratitude flared across his face, but he seemed incapable of further speech. 'Shall we meet somewhere off the beaten track?' she suggested. 'I should be finished by twenty to six, barring emergencies. What about the "quiet room"?'

He nodded jerkily in his turn, then thanked her in a voice which was little more than a whisper, before trailing unsteadily down the corridor away from the laboratories.

'We thought you'd gone home for the weekend,' announced Jack when Philippa returned to her place at the bench. 'Who was at the door? One of your admirers?'

'You guessed.' She was relieved to find that they had been too engrossed in their work to identify Gil. He needed protection, even if only from idle gossip.

Philippa frowned as she picked up a bone marrow slide and adjusted the microscope. Gilbert was in deep trouble, the nature of which she could only surmise at this stage. The last male colleague she had seen in such a state of terror had failed to prevent the death of a patient because of a small oversight, and had just learned of the family's intention to sue. Perhaps Gil was in a similar predicament? While medico-legal entanglements could be regarded as an occupational hazard, they could also blight the lives of sensitive individuals for years.

Poor old Gil, she thought, then made a determined effort to concentrate on haematological matters.

He still looked ill at ease when they met in the Quiet Room at the end of the afternoon, but had managed to control the more overt manifestations of his anxiety.

'Philippa, it's very good of you to give up your time like this. I wouldn't abuse the privilege, but I've had rather a shock and I need some impartial advice. May I drive you out to my house in Sylvia Vale and explain matters there?'

'I – well, yes, if that would be best,' she stumbled, surprised. 'Shall I come in my own car, then you don't have the bother of driving me back?'

'No, do let me drive you. You might find the route difficult.'

They left the Mess by a side door, and Philippa noticed the lowering menace of the sky as she crossed the car park in her green tweed skirt and matching lambswool jumper.

'Looks like rain,' she said.

'Yes. This is my car – the Maestro.'

It was typical of Gil not to have an ostentatious vehicle, she thought as she swung her feet into the passenger well. He was quiet and modest, despite the high bank balance ascribed to him by others. They had no reason to lie, in fact; his parents were both dead, and no one who continued to reside in Sylvia Vale could be short of cash. Philippa had to admit to herself that even she was inquisitive about his house.

They reached One, Beechcroft Lane before the rain fell, but the gloomy sky did nothing to ameliorate the drooping depression of the garden. Inside the house things were even worse: the drabness of the walls and the air of under-use seemed to sap Philippa's resilience, making her feel vulnerable for the first time.

'I'm sorry,' said Gilbert with a quick, shy smile, closing the front door behind her. 'It's not what you expected, is it? I know everyone thinks I live in a palace ... if only they knew. May I make you a cup of tea?'

'Yes, please,' said Philippa.

He led the way into an old-fashioned kitchen at the end of the hall, and plugged in an electric kettle before removing two mugs from a cupboard. When the tea was made, they sat self-consciously on hard wooden chairs, like strangers who were groping their way towards acquaintance.

'This house used to be beautiful,' he burst out suddenly. 'My parents poured years of work into it, making it a home to be proud of ... I grew up here, and I loved it as much as they did.' He dropped his gaze to the mug on the table, and ran his finger nervously along the rim. 'Out of the blue my father became – ill, and couldn't work. We stayed here anyway, doing the best we could, but when my parents died I found I couldn't keep up the maintenance ... my back was in terrible shape despite the operation. Every penny counted, so I couldn't employ a handyman.

'It's amazing how quickly a place can look dilapidated. We were just due to redecorate and fit a new kitchen when my father had his trouble, so of course all that went by the board. Lately, I've been making an effort, but it demands so much time, and everything I do indoors takes me away from the garden; it's now such a tangle that I despair of ever straightening it out.

'The ironic thing is, people have got the fixed idea that I'm loaded with money. No, it's true, Philippa, I know my reputation in the hospital. It ought to be laughable – if anyone needs money, I do – but it isn't. You see, Philippa ... ' he paused and looked right down at his knees ' ... I'm being blackmailed.'

Philippa was absolutely stunned. Of all the things she might have expected to hear, this was surely the last. Her brain seemed to freeze, just at the moment when a kindly word was essential to break through the cortex of agonizing shame in which Gil's hunched body was imprisoned. If only she knew him better! Questions like 'who?' and 'why?' were too crude to articulate.

'Are you sure?' she asked quietly. 'Could it be a mistake?'

He gave a short, bitter laugh. 'There's no mistake. The person involved isn't given to making mistakes. He knows the facts are on his side.'

She waited, then prodded him gently. 'Do you want to tell me about it?'

He raised embarrassed eyes to hers. 'Not really, but I know I must. You're a very kind girl, Philippa. You've listened to my garbled story with nothing but sympathy on your face. I hesitate to change that look to one of disgust . . . but I owe you an explanation of my behaviour. Here goes . . .'

He squared his shoulders. 'You know about my back trouble. It's been the bane of my life for over ten years. Every ward round, every session in theatre, every clinic used to provoke intolerable pain; tablets didn't help and they made my ulcer flare up. The operation was only a partial success, but I was frantic to stay in medicine, having invested so much in study and training, and my income was vital if we weren't to lose the house.

'Anaesthetics was a little easier than surgery, because I could sit down for longish periods, but it wasn't the whole answer. There were still days of pain so sickening I thought I would go mad. I dared not take any more time off work for bed-rest; Dr Jones was starting to give me ominous looks. So I did a very foolish thing . . .'

Philippa knew what was coming.

'I took pethidine,' he said.

'Oh, Gil.' She reached out a hand and touched his knee in a gesture of support. She felt desperately sorry for him. Pethidine was a narcotic pain-killing drug given daily by anaesthetists to unconscious patients. Syringes and needles were readily available in the theatres and their adjacent rooms. Gil would simply have injected himself and recorded the dose on the patient's drug card so that the stock counts would tally. Or he might have pocketed the vials for later use. A doctor with his experience

221

knew how to use the tiniest needles and leave no scars. But once started . . .

'It helped,' he said in a flat, resigned way. 'I could get through the days, and even do a bit of physical work at home. But I knew it was wrong. Every dose I took was medicine which should have gone to a patient. You can't imagine how I despised myself for that. And of course, I became addicted.

'This went on for two whole years. I even used eye drops so no-one would wonder about my small pupils and guess what I was doing. I diluted them specially. It's horrifying how cunning addicts become.

'One day this summer I looked at myself in the mirror and said: "This has got to stop." I set a date and stuck to it. No tailing down, nothing. Just stop. It was ghastly; I won't harrow you with the details. But I did it – and I haven't taken any since.'

'How can anyone threaten you, then?' asked Philippa, puzzled.

His face set grimly. 'Because the person concerned has been sitting on this information for months. I evidently wasn't as careful as I thought; he seemed to know all about it.'

Her brain forced the question out while her stomach drew back. 'Who, Gil?'

'Neil Thornton.'

'Neil? Neil from surgery? I can't believe it!'

'Neither could I. I thought I was having a bad dream. He drifted up to me after lunch today and in a few well-chosen words made it abundantly clear that he was aware of my habit, and would consider it his duty to inform the General Medical Council unless we reached some "arrangement". I was so staggered I could hardly speak. He suggested we had further words tonight, and invited himself round here.'

'Here? When?' Philippa felt a stab of panic, and darted an involuntary glance at the kitchen clock.

'Don't worry: not yet. He said half-past seven. There's still an hour to go.' Despite his attempt to sound reassuring, Gilbert's own face was once more drained of colour. He clasped his hands together. 'Philippa – it's not been very fair of me, bringing you here to tell you all about it. This afternoon I made a decision. I'm going to stand up to Neil Thornton. He's not taking away every-thing my family has built up over decades. You've helped me enormously tonight just by listening, and I wonder if I dare ask you an even greater favour . . . I thought – if I had an independent witness, who could monitor the proceedings secretly from another room, it would give me a weapon to counteract his blackmail . . . '

'I'll do it,' she said at once.

'No, wait, Philippa. Think carefully. You're under no obligation at all. I can easily drive you back to the hospital before he comes; I've already trespassed on your time quite enough.'

'Nonsense!' she said vigorously. 'If Neil really intends anything so monstrous, then he should be thwarted by all available means.'

'Are you quite sure?'

'Yes.'

'I can't begin to thank you . . . I promise there'll be no danger. He won't even know you're here.'

'You'll just tell him later that someone was listening, and he risks being exposed as an extortioner?'

'That was the plan. I've hardly had time to think it through. My brain's been whirling round!'

Philippa stood up and carried the tea-mugs to the sink, where she washed one of them and left it upside-down on the draining board. 'That was your earlier drink,' she explained.

'Goodness . . . yes. I'd make a rotten criminal. I haven't the least idea how to go about things.'

'It was just a precaution. Now – where will you be talking to Neil?'

'I'll invite him up to the den. It was a bedroom, but I'm using it as a sitting-room while I decorate downstairs. There's a door connecting with my bedroom; you could sit in there and we'll leave it ajar.'

'Mm,' she agreed. 'Have you got a tape recorder? One of those small cassette players?'

'No, sorry. I don't even have a television.'

Philippa sighed inwardly. It would be unproductive to tell him that he should have rushed out and bought a machine that afternoon; Gil's mind was cast in a mould innocent of pragmatism, strangely like Barnaby Fletcher's.

'Show me the room.'

The 'den' overlooked the long garden at the front of the house, but Philippa's attention was instantly claimed by the fish-tank standing against a partially veneered wall.

'How beautiful!' she cried, peering at the lively little bodies in their grotto of swaying plant fronds.

'If you like fish, there are fifteen more tanks downstairs,' he said eagerly, forgetting his predicament for a brief space of time.

'I'd love to – later,' she said. 'Perhaps we should check our positions first; it would be terrible if he came early!'

Gilbert shivered. 'Yes . . . I thought I might offer him one of these two chairs, because they're comfortable and they've got their backs to the bedroom door.'

'And would you sit opposite on a hard chair?'

'Yes.'

'Don't be too surprised, Gil, if he chooses a hard chair himself. I can only guess at the psychology Neil will employ, but he won't want to give the impression that he's here for a cosy chat. Besides, those chairs are higher than the others – the old interview trick.'

'But he'll be facing the bedroom door then. Shall I swap them round?'

'No. If he can see all the exits, it will probably give him confidence and allay suspicion. May I go through?'

'Please do.' He escorted her into a plain bedroom papered in a light shade of cornflower blue. She noticed that the bed was neatly made, and the counterpane free of creases. Not many men were so tidy.

'You could sit on the bed,' said Gil. 'I wouldn't normally pull the curtains this early, so the room will be in a kind of half-light. Are you sure you'll be all right in here?'

'I'll be fine.'

Philippa paced the den restlessly, willing herself not to check her watch yet again. It was funny how Gilbert now seemed the more composed of the two; perhaps he drew strength from the familiar environment of his home. In the lounge he had displayed his fish with pride, open in his affection for them, calling some of them by name. They seemed to know him; the catfish came to the front of the tank and finned placidly, quite unaware of the crisis their master was facing. He visibly relaxed in their presence. It was Philippa whose innards were slowly going through the wringer.

Now, once more in the den, she heard rain splatter against the window pane. Dusk was falling fast; angry black clouds blotted out the dull silver of the evening and shed their venom over the rolling fields of Sylvia Vale. It was a night to be indoors – and somewhere out there, Neil Thornton was approaching in a car, intent on blackmail.

'I'd better pull the curtains,' said Gil behind her. 'We don't want him seeing your silhouette.'

She moved towards the back of the room as he did so, wondering whether she should have gone to the bathroom earlier. It was asking for trouble to go now. Was she wearing perfume? She quickly sniffed her left wrist, and was satisfied to find that the bouquet of her lunch-time touch-up spray had worn off. Besides, men wore all sorts of things these days. What else might they have forgotten? She had left her white coat and keys in the Doctors' Mess, and brought nothing loose with her . . . No coat, hat or bag . . .

Gil suddenly cocked his head to one side and threw up a warning hand, palm outwards, as if to quieten her. Above the accelerated drumming of rain against glass came the sound of a car engine in low gear. It was a throatier, richer sound than Philippa had expected from Neil's Cavalier, but the vehicle responsible was unquestionably within the grounds and advancing towards the house. As gravel scrunched directly outside the window, her limbs were seized by a ghastly paralysis.

'Go through – now,' urged Gil in a whisper, his own face once again a sickly white colour, the cheeks hollow. She took a jagged breath and forced her recalcitrant legs to move. They felt heavy, yet at the same time, insubstantial. Her heart seemed to be thundering against her ribs, filling her chest so that air couldn't reach her lungs.

She turned in the doorway, and gave Gil a long, level look. 'Don't let him rile you,' she said. 'Just appear to go along with him. Remember there are two of us.'

His smile was spectral; the image stayed with Philippa as she padded into the bedroom and cautiously adjusted the door until only a crack remained to communicate with the den. The idea of sinking down on the bed was an inviting prospect, but she instinctively rejected it. A position behind the door was safest; Gil's manner might give something away.

Was Neil the visitor? What was he doing? Did she really believe this incredible story . . . ? She curled her fingers into tight fists; luckily the nails were short. Had he gone away again? What –

225

The doorbell vibrated loudly in the hall. She heard Gilbert's footsteps crossing the landing, then the sounds became fainter. Focusing all her concentration, she could just make out the click of a lock and the low murmur of voices. Supposing Neil refused to come upstairs? He might insist on staying somewhere like the kitchen. If so, she would hear nothing, and it would be very dicey to try to change her station.

Voices nearby startled her; they were right outside the den. Well done, Gil! She stood motionless, her back to the connecting wall, while Gilbert offered the newcomer a seat. To her dismay, the cool tones of acceptance did indeed belong to Neil Thornton.

'I'll sit here if you don't mind,' he was saying. 'This shouldn't take long. I presume you've thought about what I had to say at lunch-time?'

'Yes,' said Gilbert hoarsely, 'and before we go any further, I want to know exactly what you mean. You came out with some *disgraceful* allegations; I was completely stunned. What proof do you have?'

Neil gave a deep chuckle. 'Nice try, Gil. Do you think I'm only guessing? Sorry, old lad, but I don't work that way. I'm quite happy to tell you all I know – well, almost all. I'll keep just a little bit back as insurance.'

'This has got to be a mistake!'

'In that case, I shall look suitably foolish when I inform the GMC about your – unfortunate habit.'

There was a fraught silence.

'Neil – what makes you think I take drugs? Is it just because I'm an anaesthetist?'

'Oh, quit pussyfooting around!' snapped Neil. 'You know as well as I do that you're a junkie.'

'That's a lie!'

'Is it? Is it? Then listen to this. Last May a nice little nurse from theatre came to me, very worried. She'd seen you injecting yourself in one of the clinical rooms; when you'd gone, she'd checked the vial you'd thrown away, and found that it was pethidine. She was in a quandary. She told me she didn't want to destroy your career by telling the hospital authorities, but she couldn't just forget the matter because what you had done was wrong. I said I'd take care of it; she was most grateful. A fortnight later I assured her it was a transitory weakness, and you'd stopped.

'In fact, I was observing you myself, but you were very wily,

226

weren't you? I didn't catch you with pethidine; I even wondered if the nurse had made a mistake. Then I saw you in Outpatients one day, slipping a bottle of atropine eye-drops into your pocket. That was all the proof I needed.'

Philippa's heart sank, as she imagined Gilbert's was doing. She was in an awkward ethical position herself. If Neil intended to profit from Gilbert's lapse, then that was wholly reprehensible, but on the other hand, *should* it go completely unpunished? Had he voluntarily given up the habit, or was that part a fabrication?

Next door, Neil was waiting for comment. Eventually Gilbert spoke.

'You're right, Neil. I did take pethidine for a short while, because of my back. But I stopped doing it months ago . . . I came off it, of my own free will. Anyone who likes could take a blood test from me at this very minute, and they'd find nothing but traces of the Co-proxamol constituents.'

'That's irrelevant,' said Neil. 'The fact is, you took pethidine belonging to the hospital on at least one occasion, and two witnesses have all the details.'

'Who was the nurse?'

'Her name isn't important; what is important is your career. The waters have been choppy for some time now, haven't they? People are becoming sick of your unreliability, your ailments . . . personally, I wouldn't be sorry to see you go, from that point of view. But I think a mutual arrangement would be more – civilized. Why shouldn't we both benefit? You by remaining on the medical register, me by receiving a small token of your gratitude?'

'You mean money.'

'That's right. My racing sponsorship deal has just fallen through, and I'm acutely short of cash. You have far more than you need. A perfect case for symbiosis, I venture to suggest.'

'What if I refuse to have anything to do with your "civilized" idea?'

'Then I should regretfully have to bring your unpleasant habit to the attention of the authorities.'

'You're nothing but a parasite!' burst out Gil. 'Why should *you* take advantage of someone else's problems? What is it to you?'

'I happen to be the person in the know,' answered Neil mildly. His tone then sharpened. 'I wouldn't speak of parasites, if I were you. We've been carrying you as a passenger for years. You're the sort who'd rely on people's goodwill indefinitely. The broken reed.'

'You have no idea –'

'Yes, I have; every idea. But the state of your health doesn't interest me. I've come with a proposition: a straightforward exchange – my silence for ten thousand pounds.'

'You're crazy! I haven't got ten thousand pounds.'

'Maybe not lying around, but you can find it.'

'I can't. I don't have that kind of sum.'

Neil gave a small snort of disgust. 'Pull the other one, Gilbert. You live in Sylvia Vale. Sell some of your bloody stocks and shares, or take out a mortgage, like the rest of us.'

'I already have a mortgage.'

'Get a second one. I don't care how you do it. Just find the money by a week from today.'

Another silence followed. Philippa held her breath, willing Gilbert to stay calm and agree to the proposal. She felt intuitively that he was becoming angry, and her restraining presence was forgotten. If he lost his temper with someone as ruthless as Neil, the interview could turn very ugly indeed.

On the other side of the door, Gilbert spoke.

'Exposing me would hardly help your cash-flow,' he said slowly, 'but it would prompt me to tell the police about your attempted blackmail. I'd have nothing to lose at that stage. You would, though. Let me counter-propose. I'm prepared to forget this talk, pretend it never happened, provided you move out of the Nottingham area at the earliest opportunity. What do you say?'

'I say you're confusing check-mate with stalemate. I've got evidence to back up my story; you haven't any. Where and when did I blackmail you? At this moment I'm working hard in the Postgraduate Library, while Albert feasts his eyes on my Cavalier, which is parked right in front of his kiosk.' He paused. 'Your words don't worry me at all – but your cocky attitude does. Are you recording our conversation?'

Philippa only had a second to plaster herself against the wall before the door flew open. A wide bar of light fell across the floor and the bed, broken down its centre by Neil Thornton's menacing shadow. He stood in the opening, appraising the neat simplicity of the room, before turning back, apparently satisfied. The door swung to a right-angled position. Philippa remained motionless, her heart once more thundering in her chest, her hands trembling. A few feet away in the den, the sounds of searching were clearly audible.

'Okay,' said Neil at length. 'I didn't think you'd have the gumption. Now – where were we?'

'We've got to the point where you leave this house. I'm not making any bargains with a blackmailer. I resent your rummaging through my things. I resent your taking up my time. I'll see you to the door.'

'It's a bit late for dignity, Gilbert. You could have done with some of that before. But don't wet your pants – I'm going. You obviously need a day or two to get over the shock and see reason. We'll talk again on Monday.'

There was a sound of footsteps and the creak of a door.

'Christ, what a dump this is,' went on Neil, his voice fainter because of the increased distance from Philippa's place of concealment. 'So much for the worthy residents of Sylvia Vale.' He made an additional comment which she didn't catch, but Gil's furious reply rang out clearly.

'How *dare* you insult my parents! Get out of here, and take your slimy proposals with you! Go on –' Confused noises followed, reminiscent of a scuffle, then there was a sudden cry of alarm. As Philippa hastened anxiously towards the landing, a series of muffled thumps resounded through the core of the building, followed by total silence. She halted, terrified, just inside the exit door from the den; seconds later she heard the soft patter of footsteps going down the stairs. Someone emitted a single, vile expletive. It sounded like Neil. Then once again, no sound . . .

Philippa couldn't bear the suspense. Wrenching open the door, she strode boldly along the landing to the top of the stairs, and peered down at the two figures below.

Gil lay in the hall on his back, his neck twisted at a horrible angle, the face obscured from where she stood. Neil, crouched beside the body, looked up in shock as an involuntary 'Oh!' was torn from her lips. His own face was very white.

'Philippa –' he said blankly, then dropped his gaze back to Gilbert's lifeless form as she hurried to join him.

Philippa knelt on the other side of the body and shivered as she caught sight of Gilbert's eyes which were staring towards the lounge door unknowing, unblinking. Hopelessly, she reached out a hand and touched his neck, but no pulse throbbed against her fingers. Without doubt he was dead.

She levered herself numbly to her feet, still held in thrall by the sudden completeness of death, dimly aware that Neil had also risen and was standing behind her. When he put a hand on her shoulder, she misinterpreted the gesture; in her mind what had gone before was dwarfed by this unsought tragedy. He was wearing his black leather driving-gloves. She half-turned towards him, then abruptly his fingers were at her throat, clawing and squeezing with an unmistakably lethal intent.

Incredulous, she tried to twist out of his grasp, drawing a huge gulp of air into her lungs as the gloved fingers slipped from her larynx. Screaming would be useless here. There was no one to help in this isolated house. She had to act for herself.

She flailed at his face, but he seized her right forearm and yanked it behind her back in a tight arm-lock which made her cry out. Once more he came in close, his other hand seeking her throat. The premonition of her own death hovered, so near . . . If he kneed her in the back, she would have no chance at all . . . No!

Despite the pain in her shoulder, Philippa sagged against him, as if fainting. His hold barely loosened, but she was now near enough to inflict injury on him. With frantic strength, she ground the edge of her shoe down the front of his unprotected shin-bone then jabbed the heel down onto his instep and lifted her other leg, transmitting her entire body weight to his foot through an area of two square centimetres.

He yelled in fury and released her arm. She whipped the other one round and elbowed him forcefully in the solar plexus. As he doubled up with a grunt of agony, she rushed for the door, scrabbling with the locks, unaware of how far he might be incapacitated.

The night air was sodden and unfriendly. Hunched shapes of trees loomed dimly ahead; if she squelched through the garden, the mud would bear a trail as obvious as a furrow, and he could follow with a torch at his leisure while she cowered in the shrubbery. How convenient for him – the perfect place to leave a body.

That decided her. She plunged down the driveway, straining her eyes to penetrate the darkness, listening intently for any hostile sound above the monotonous drumming of the rain. She knew Neil's car must have been just round the corner, but he wasn't the type of person to leave keys in the ignition, and she doubted her ability to immobilize it quickly in near-darkness.

Please let him be crippled, she prayed. Please let me just reach Beechcroft Lane, and then the main road. I'm sure I saw a phone-box . . .

A branch of dripping leaves swished across her face as she hurried along. The uneven surface of the drive made speed hazardous, but a greater danger lay behind. She began to pant, harsh breaths searing in and out of her throat, and knew that panic was rapidly gaining the upper hand.

At last the driveway ended. Street lamps glowed faintly in the distance to the right; she turned towards these beacons of hope, new confidence trickling into her soul, her steps more elastic. She might yet succeed.

In the rain a girl was running . . .

20

Philippa opened her eyes. The overhead light was still set at 'dim' and the small window above the door provided the only other illumination – yet something was different.

A furtive sound came from the left. Lowering her lids, she swivelled her eyes round to the source of the noise, but could make out no more than an indistinct white form at the extreme edge of vision. In hospital, the presence of a white-coated figure was perfectly reasonable, but this time the primitive part of her brain shrieked silent warnings. Who was it . . . ? With infinite caution, she rotated the whole of her head to the side.

Neil Thornton stood there, a plastic kidney bowl in one hand. Even as she suppressed a gasp of horror he looked down at her and smiled.

'Sorry if I woke you, Philippa,' he said in a low voice. 'I just came to unblock your drip.'

Her mouth was dry, arid as Kalahari sand at midday, but she had to speak.

'What time is it?'

'Gone ten.'

'Where's Stewart?'

'He's busy. I'm helping him out.' He lifted a syringe out of the basin, held it up to the light and flicked it to dispel air bubbles.

Philippa felt deeply suspicious. She glanced at the transparent chamber where the drip rate could normally be seen and calculated, but he was right; there was no flow.

She struggled to sit up in the bed, her fears only partially allayed. She couldn't refuse to be treated; the best course would be to try and attract attention from the nursing staff.

'You'll need more light than that,' she told him loudly. 'Put it up to "full".'

'I can manage. You don't want to be dazzled.'

'No, really ... I've had all my sleep now. I think I'll read something when you've finished.'

From her new vantage-point Philippa could see the blue valve which controlled the flow of fluids through the giving set. It was closed. No wonder the drip wasn't working! Perhaps it wasn't blocked at all ...

'Look,' she said brightly. 'The nurses must have switched it off. There may be nothing wrong with it.'

He shook his head and spoke with exaggerated patience. 'It's blocked, Philippa. I tested it. And as for the valve, I closed it myself, to stop this injection tracking back up the tube.'

The explanation was so simple, so obvious. Why didn't she believe him? He was leaning over her now, uncapping the access point to the cannula lodged in a vein of her left arm. Would he dare risk another attempt on her life, in a hospital, with nurses so near?

'Show me anyway!' she tinkled capriciously.

He sighed. 'If you insist.' He put the syringe back into the kidney basin, which he had placed on a nearby chair, then reached out with his right hand and pushed the small blue plastic wheel until the valve was fully open. His left hand rested casually on the bed.

No fluid dripped through the chamber. For a moment, Philippa tasted reprieve, then the truth hit her with the blast of an explosion. The fingers of his 'nonchalant' left hand were pinching off the tubing, deliberately kinking it so that the dextrose couldn't flow. His talk of unblocking the drip was a blind; presumably he wouldn't have needed the ploy at all if she hadn't woken up. What was in that syringe?

She felt sick with fear. Neil calmly turned off the valve again and prepared to give his injection.

'Is it Nurse Hitchen on duty tonight?' she asked in desperation.

'The fat Jamaican one? Yes.'

'Please could you fetch her? I – I think I'm going to be sick. Sorry.'

'She's at the bottom of the ward with the drugs trolley. Have this.' He offered her the kidney basin. 'Bit small, isn't it?' he went on conversationally. 'But then I'm sure you'll find things settle down.'

In the dim light, his eyes were black and pitiless. He had seen through her procrastinations, and now all the cards were on the table; given their respective physical states, he held the straight flush while she lacked even the most miserable of pairs. Defeat dragged at her entrails.

'Hopefuly,' she replied, 'but I'm afraid I don't want the injection just now, thank you.'

'You're having it,' Neil said firmly, and clapped a hand over her mouth. With his knee he anchored her left forearm to the bed, then with his other hand he coupled the syringe and cannula. She looked wildly into his impassive face. He was going to kill her, right in the middle of a hospital full of people. He was going to pump a poison straight into her veins – probably potassium chloride, which would reach her heart in a matter of seconds. She was helpless. There was nothing she could use as a weapon to defend herself; pinned as she was to the bed, the plaster cast on her right arm was out of range.

He had cupped his hand to avoid her teeth, but in a frenzy of fear she tore her mouth free and nipped the ball of his thumb between her sharp incisors. She hung on like a terrier, forcing her jaws together as if they would meet in the middle. He remained grimly silent, but his face was contorted with pain, and when she suddenly let go, he withdrew the hand for a second, preparatory to improving his grip.

This was her chance. Rolling to her left, she awkwardly seized the exposed cannula and pulled on it. It was a clumsy, sideways pull, made by a hand and arm with strictly limited movement, but it was sufficient. Neil had slackened his grasp on the syringe, and the cannula was only anchored lightly by micropore tape. It slid right out of the vein, splattering blood on the coverlet; a dark plum bloomed beneath the skin of her forearm.

At the same instant, she screamed. The sound was not very loud, as she had hardly drawn breath, but it was her final moment of grace, the last opportunity to seek deliverance before his hand slammed against her lower face and thrust her head back into the pillow.

'You shouldn't have done that,' he said. His voice was quiet and level, but his eyes glared murder. Her outrage clouded into an odd kind of resignation; she had tried her utmost – and failed. Then she saw his gaze shift uncertainly towards the door.

From outside in the corridor came the clatter of running feet.

Montgomery heard a faint cry as he pounded along the passageway leading to Cavendish Ward. They had had trouble gaining access to the hospital; a night porter with no sense of urgency had engaged them in a lengthy pantomime of gesticulations from the other side of a glass door, then vanished; three side doors had been securely locked. Finally, Sergeant Bird had discovered a way in via the Doctors' Mess. They had checked the bar and television room as they passed, but Neil Thornton was not indulging in leisure pursuits.

'Quick, Will!' exhorted Montgomery as the sergeant lagged behind. There was no sign of DC Coleman; perhaps he was actually inside Philippa's room. They ran the last few feet towards the door only to see it fly open, as if in readiness for their entry. Neil Thornton stepped out, took one look at them, and swung round in the direction of the main ward. He pushed through the swing doors and let them slap shut behind him, baulking Montgomery who was in close pursuit.

The patients on Cavendish Ward had just received their medicines and drinks of Ovaltine. They gaped as their registrar flew down the central aisle between the beds, dodged nimbly round the drugs trolley and its attendant nurse, gave the bar on the fire-escape door a sharp knock and disappeared into the night. The same nurse effectively obstructed Montgomery as she stared after the apparition. He bundled her aside unceremoniously and arrowed to the doorway.

Rain fell on him as he peered down. The metal fire-escape led via a small courtyard into one of those warrens of mysterious alleyways common to hospitals and other public buildings to which new wings and outhouses have been added over the years. Thornton was just entering a passage on the right, his coat a white blur in the darkness. Sergeant Bird had gone to see Philippa; Montgomery had no option but to continue the chase alone. If Thornton reached his car . . .

He clanged down the fire-escape, making use of the handrail because the steps were so slippery. As he gained *terra firma*, he heard a shout above him. William Bird was silhouetted in the open doorway from the ward.

'Sir! Philippa's all right. Shall I try to cut him off?'

'Yes. Go out the way we came in and see if you can find the Vauxhall before he gets to it.'

'Will do.'

Montgomery hardly caught the last comment as he was running furiously, pumping air into his lungs like an athlete. He had already lost sight of Thornton. He dashed through the narrow alleyway and came out near a long laboratory. The place seemed deserted. He set off again, rounded a corner and spotted a white-coated figure flitting among the shadows.

'Stop – police!' he yelled, not hopeful of the outcome. To his amazement, the person did stop. He quickly recognized that it was a female doctor, who stared at him in alarm, perhaps doubting his claim.

'Did you see Mr Thornton?' he gasped. 'Which way did he go?'

The girl still looked uncertain, but his air of authority must have overridden any serious misgivings because she pointed to a paved footpath which curled round a tall building diagonally ahead.

'Over there.'

Montgomery grunted his thanks and followed the path. It ran past the kitchen area of the hospital, leaving a trail of impressions like a string of beads: steamed-up windows with someone singing loudly behind them, the heavy smell of frying, dustbins, a lean black cat . . .

Suddenly he emerged into an open space. It was a small, out-of-the-way car-park containing a couple of elderly vans. He stood still, chest heaving, wondering if Thornton was lurking in the vicinity. He didn't wonder for long. An engine burst into life just beyond the vans, and two headlight beams sliced through the darkness. A moment later a Vauxhall Cavalier swished away, the baleful red glow of its rear lights, like eyes, looking back at him.

'Damn it!' spat Montgomery into the impersonal drizzle. 'Damn it, damn it, damn it!'

He ran round the side of the hospital at a jog-trot, crossed the main car-park and jumped inside his own Sierra. It responded quickly to the starter motor; within twenty seconds he had picked up a disconsolate Sergeant Bird from the area of the Doctors' Mess and was swinging out of the hospital grounds.

'Do you think he'll head for the M1?' asked Sergeant Bird. 'He could get on it at the Nuthall junction; it's not far.'

Montgomery frowned. The Cavalier was nowhere to be seen, and decisions loomed in the shape of the Valley Road roundabout.

'No,' he said. 'Once on a motorway, you're trapped. One message from us, and every exit would be watched.' He gave an ironic smile. 'Not that we actually *have* any radio facilities here – but he doesn't know that. I say let's go left.'

There was a moderate amount of traffic on the roads, but Montgomery made the best speed he could in the absence of the klaxons and flashing lights so beloved of his junior officers. Sergeant Bird stared through the windscreen, watching for any clue as to the whereabouts of the Cavalier. They were rewarded more quickly than they expected. Less than half a minute after they had gained the Mansfield road, they heard an angry chorus of car horns up ahead. A vehicle had jumped the lights at the Arnold turn-off.

'That's him!' cried Montgomery triumphantly. He pushed his foot down and roared in pursuit, weaving between slower vehicles, anxious not to lose the visual contact. Sporadic hoots sounded behind him, but he was indifferent to the irritation of other drivers. He had found his quarry.

The Cavalier raced northwards through the suburb of Arnold, reached open countryside, then turned right towards Woodborough village.

'Woodborough's got two double bends and a thirty-mile-an-hour limit,' said Sergeant Bird. 'He'll come to grief if he carries on at this rate.'

Montgomery glanced at his speedometer. Yes; sixty-five was quite enough for these narrow roads. Thornton had tried to fool them by leaving the main routes out of Nottingham, but he almost certainly knew by now that he was being followed.

They descended a dark hill into the village, noting wryly the word 'Slow' painted twice on the roadway before the speed-limit sign flashed past. The Cavalier had vanished round the double bend. Montgomery, in his efforts to keep up, took the second portion too fast; the Sierra skidded alarmingly on the rain-slicked road surface, and avoided smashing into a stone wall by the slenderest of margins.

'Now I know how a cocktail feels,' said Sergeant Bird peevishly.

'If you think you can do better . . . ' Montgomery clutched the wheel, leaning forward as if that would help him penetrate the swirling curtain of rain ahead. It was coming down heavily again; Thornton would be in his element in conditions like these, using controlled racing skids to his advantage while they floundered helplessly, losing vital seconds. At least the atrocious weather was keeping pedestrians at home. As they snarled through Woodborough's attractive village centre the only individuals to be seen were a few stalwarts with hunched shoulders coming out of the Nag's Head.

Another sharp double bend, and they were once more in open countryside. Broad-leafed trees lined the road, and in the distance they caught tantalizing glimpses of a car's rear lights.

'We'll be at the main road soon,' commented Sergeant Bird.

'Which one? The 6197?'

'Yes. It's my guess that he'll turn right, which gives him a choice of three major roads within five miles or so. He could double back to Nottingham, zap down to Leicester, or aim for the A1 and get right out of the area.'

'That last one,' said Montgomery tersely. 'There are scores of small exits. We must stick with him.'

The car in front had now stopped for the junction; with dismay they identified it as a stately old Rover.

'Don't panic,' said Montgomery coolly, feeling panic-stricken. 'We'll go right as we planned. He can't be far ahead.'

The new road was fast, with a decent stretch of dual carriage-way. They swept past a number of cars, the speedometer registering well over eighty, but none was a Cavalier. A roundabout linking their road with the pleasant Nottingham-Southwell route dared them to slow down, to vacillate. Montgomery powered across it, glad that the Sierra had more than half a tank of petrol on board.

'We could do with a squad car,' he said. 'Perhaps we'll be done for speeding and pick one up that way.'

'Never around when you want them,' said William Bird, hanging on grimly to his seat-belt. He cringed as they traversed a bridge at a frightening pace, knowing the swollen waters of the Trent flowed unseen below. Street lamps no longer facilitated their progress; outside the confines of their own headlight beams was a sense of space and isolation, flat fields hidden in the blackness.

'Lights!' shouted Montgomery. Two red pin-pricks wavered in the rainy blur ahead, then vanished.

'He's turned left up the A46,' said Sergeant Bird. 'Straight road to Newark and the A1.'

'Not if we've got anything to do with it,' muttered his companion. A handful of seconds later they rounded the same corner; the twin glow-worms shimmered in the distance before a lorry thundered past on the opposite carriageway, blinding them with full headlights. Another one followed; Montgomery's eyes were dazzled. He blinked and peered – the will o' the wisp had gone.

'He's left the road,' stated Sergeant Bird with confidence. 'We'd see him otherwise. He's trying to shake us off with the trick he used before. Go right here!'

This area of the county constituted a network of small villages linked by narrow, winding roads. Slow down or die, thought Montgomery, reluctantly paying heed to his own advice. Careful negotiation of these by-ways would still lead Thornton to the A1, but he would have to curb his speed accordingly. If someone was out walking their dog . . .

It was a shock to come upon the accident scene. In fact, they almost compounded it, lurching to a stop inches from the back of the broken-down Dormobile which filled the road beyond a bend like a great beached whale, hazard lights flashing ineffectually. There had been no warning triangle. Neil Thornton must have swerved to avoid the obstruction and lost control; the Cavalier was wrecked, the whole of the front crumpled against an unforgiving wall. A hiss of steam mingled with the patter of rain. Spotlit in the Sierra's headlamp beams, an elderly man stood nearby, wringing his hands and muttering incoherently. When he saw Montgomery, he seized his raincoat in supplication, gabbling and trembling.

238

'We were booked in . . . Elmwood Farm . . . touring holiday . . . dinner near Belvoir Castle . . . never broken down before . . .'

Montgomery gently disengaged the clinging fingers and walked over to the wreck while Sergeant Bird arranged lights and warning signs in the roadway behind. He shone a flashlamp in at the driver's window. Neil Thornton's eyes were closed, his coldly handsome face marred by an ugly gash high on the forehead from which blood flowed in a steady trickle.

Together the detectives lifted him from the car, and laid him down on the road. He made no sound, but the eyes opened once and stared at them dully before he surrendered to oblivion. Rain fell from the skies and washed his face clean.

21

Sergeant Bird sat in front of a flickering fire, his legs stretched out, his stomach warmed by fine brandy. The use of solid fuel in a genuine fireplace was one of the things he liked best about the Montgomerys' house; another was the splendid quality of the meals on offer there. Carole was an accomplished cook. His wife Jean had also appreciated the importance of good food. At times like this, when he was part of a friendly gathering, he missed her badly.

'Thank you again,' he said to Carole. 'No – not another morsel. The inner man is full.'

'So is the outer man,' teased Montgomery.

William Bird gave a bland smile, but felt too mellow to be baited. They had been discussing elements of the Bradshaw case over dinner; he sensed that Carole was keen to hear more.

'It's poetic justice that Thornton broke his right leg, isn't it?' he observed idly. 'If Philippa was a vengeful kind of girl, she'd be pretty pleased.'

'She's not, though,' Montgomery replied. 'I think she's still stunned by his conduct. A lot of people are. If we'd sent him to the District Hospital for treatment, he would have been lynched by now.'

'What motivates a man like that?' asked Carole. 'On the face of it, he had everything – brains, good looks, a worthwhile career.

He sounds like a strong character, yet blackmail is such a cowardly crime . . . '

'I think it's a case of twisted morality,' said Montgomery. 'He regarded Bradshaw as hopelessly weak and flawed, the undeserving recipient of a pile of inherited wealth; blackmailing that sort of specimen was quite justifiable in his view. On the other hand, he wouldn't entertain the idea of asking his girlfriend for a loan. Presumably he thought that would be degrading, or would put him in an unwelcome position of obligation. But then the blackmail victim died.'

'Are you satisfied that it was an accident?'

'Yes; Philippa's testimony agrees with Thornton's, and let's face it, you don't go killing the goose *before* it's parted with the golden egg. That accident, however, sparked off a whole chain of cover-up events which became progressively more callous. From what we've learned from Thornton himself, from Philippa and other hospital personnel, I think the pattern went something like this:

'Thornton had been in tight financial straits for some time because of his racing, but was determined not to give up, being so close to winning the Championship. Early in September, a double blow fell. First, he had a smash at Snetterton when another Porsche lost control and spun in front of him; then a computer firm let him down over an important sponsorship deal. The time had come to make use of the information he had been harbouring on Bradshaw.

'It was unlikely that Bradshaw would bleat to the authorities that he was being threatened, but Thornton took thorough precautions. On that Friday he left his Cavalier as close to Albert's kiosk as possible, knowing Albert spent long periods staring out of the window and would be bound to notice it. He locked the library, left by the side door, and walked up the road to Arthur Wright's garage, where the Porsche was kept. He had his own key, of course. Arthur Wright was on holiday, and the front end of the car hadn't yet been repaired, but it was still drivable. The racing numbers – a '3' on each side – were peeled off. I only realized recently that they aren't all painted on; some people have only one car for both general use and racing. It was a dark, wet evening, and so the Porsche didn't attract much attention. In Sylvia Vale, there was no one around to see it.

'As you know, the blackmail attempt went wrong. Bradshaw

stood up for himself and tried to eject Thornton from the house. They had a skirmish at the top of the stairs, triggered by a shove from Bradshaw, and the result was tragedy. To compound matters from Thornton's point of view, Philippa Rowe suddenly appeared. He made a quick decision; he would extricate himself from the entire situation by killing her and deflecting the blame on to Bradshaw.

'He knocked her down with the already damaged Porsche, then ran over her using Bradshaw's Maestro. His driving-gloves left no fingerprints on the wheel or door-handle. At the house he calmly set the locks and slid the keys down to a position near Bradshaw's pocket; the only door he couldn't lock was the garage door. He returned to the hospital, convinced that Philippa could not have survived, picked up his briefcase from the library, and deliberately engaged Albert in a conversation which the old man would remember.

'The first of several rich ironies in this case occurred the next day. Neil Thornton's surgical team were on "take" for emergencies, when who should be brought in but Phiilppa Rowe? He had to assist Vernon Crowland in a theatre full of people, and make a good job of it, before she was admitted to the ward under the care of their team.

'It isn't easy for a registrar to gain access to a patient without a whole entourage of interested parties following him or her – students, nurses, etc. The routine tasks such as setting up drips traditionally belong to the houseman. So Thornton had a problem on his hands. He wanted Philippa to die in an apparently natural manner. To this end, he prepared the ground by emphasizing to me that trauma victims often die suddenly – which is perfectly true – and playing on Stewart Bridges' well-known carelessness. There was an episode with antibiotics which, while not fatal, drew attention to Stewart and his shortcomings; he was a potentially useful scapegoat. I think Thornton may well have spotted the prescribing error and chosen not to correct it.

'Time-wise, there was now a bit of leeway. Philippa could remember nothing of the events in Sylvia Vale. If she had done, presumably Thornton would have attributed her tale to delusions stemming from the head injury and her general condition. But while he was planning the regrettable loss of his patient, something unexpected happened. Maureen O'Donnell stopped him in the hospital corridor and told him she was anxious about Gilbert's death. The whole hospital was buzzing with the mystery. She wondered if he had gone back to drugs, and whether this could have caused his fall? Would tests show anything? Should they tell the police about his past history, or not? Might someone be blamed if they didn't?

'Maureen had probably watched Thornton with sheep's eyes for some time; a tall, handsome surgeon is perfect hero-worship material for an impressionable young nurse. In addition, she admired his prowess in theatre, and trusted him. That situation was ripe for exploitation.

'By chance, Thornton had heard about Maureen's fear of water. We think that was on the Thursday night when the subject was discussed in Philippa's side room. At any rate, he knew. He arranged to take her out to the Boatman the following evening to talk through the problem of Gilbert and decide what was best. She was flattered. He swore her to secrecy and picked her up a few streets away from her flat to avoid Coral's sharp interest. The rest of the night's events we know about. The method chosen carried some risk, but the death could have been construed as accident or suicide.

'Thornton felt he had to remove Maureen because her knowledge linked him uncomfortably with Bradshaw. It wouldn't take much astuteness for someone to think of black-mail. But no sooner had he responded to this particular jolt, than he received another one. Anne Markham passed on the "good news" that Philippa had begun to remember things that she did the day before Gilbert's death. It was time to concentrate on her.

'Vernon Crowland's team were looking after a woman in isolation on another ward, who was suffering from an unpleasant form of staphylococcal infection, resistant to most antibiotics, including those that Philippa was on at the time. He took material from this patient, and used it to infect Philippa. I don't know precisely how he did it, but Anne Markham had unfortunately played into his hands at that stage by asking him to take the blood cultures and other tests himself, rather than leaving them to Stewart whose sterile technique was considered dubious. He must have had various opportunities to inject the stuff.

'In Philippa's debilitated state, she quickly became moribund, which was just what he wanted. However, Anne Markham wasn't satisfied. She couldn't understand why all the blood-test results were coming back from the lab negative, when Philippa was so obviously septicaemic. She suspected trickery of some kind, and took Thornton into her confidence. That must have given him yet another nasty turn!

'His method had been to send another patient's blood out from the ward for culture under Philippa's name. Before you ask, blood *grouping* is a completely separate test, performed in a separate laboratory. These were bacteriological tests; there would have been nothing to indicate that the sample hadn't come from the patient named on the label of the bottle. At all costs, he had to deflect attention away from the ward end of the procedure, and towards the lab. He had no key to the microbiology lab himself, but David Stannard had once done a job there. With typical manipulation, Thornton directed Anne Markham's distrust toward Stannard.

'He very nearly succeeded in killing Philippa. But Anne believed in her own instincts. She personally took a sample from Philippa and sent it to the lab under a false name . . . it came back strongly positive. There had been no chance to discuss her plan in advance with Thornton – for which we can be grateful! – but she immediately told him about the result. For the second time, he had no choice but to save Philippa's life: he pumped her full of the correct antibiotic with Anne Markham breathing down his neck. When Anne insisted on involving us in this latest episode, he cunningly aligned himself with her, dropping reluctant hints about Stannard. During that session, he even had the gall to suggest that Philippa should be moved, whilst covering himself by saying she was still too ill. He left the hospital with us, and made sure that we saw him drive off in the Cavalier. But, of course, he came back . . .'

'Didn't you have a man on the ward to protect Philippa?' asked Carole.

'Yes; Coleman. He'd set up camp in the Interview Room with the door open, and watched everyone who passed. He was in radio contact with Haslam and Grange. Unfortunately, they sent him a message that Stannard and Chapman had gone safely to ground in their respective flats, so he felt he was entitled to a bit more freedom, like drinking tea in the kitchen and wandering off down the corridor to the gents. Thornton had been waiting for just such a chance. He went straight to Philippa's bedside armed with a syringe-full of potassium chloride – '

'Then you came on the scene!' interjected Carole proudly. 'Just in time to save her.'

'She saved herself,' said Montgomery, 'and if we'd read the clues more carefully she might not have been in danger at all. We got thoroughly side-tracked by Coral Chapman and her family history. We weren't logical; we should have realized that if she'd planned murder on the basis of an expected inheritance, she'd have read her legal tomes *before* the deed, not after.'

'Why did she want a book on law?'

Montgomery took a sip of coffee. 'She was afraid she would be landed with Bradshaw's debts. Maureen pointed out Pendle's newspaper enquiry for relatives; Coral appreciated the implications of this. She knew she was probably the main heir. But Milton Gale had blown the myths about the grand house in Beechcroft Lane. Whoever inherited might be liable for enormous debts, repair bills and such. She wanted to find out if that was the case, and was certainly not going to come forward without checking.'

'What is she entitled to?'

'The house, grounds and not much else. The mortgage was covered by Bradshaw's life insurance policy, but there's no surplus cash because his premiums were high and he ploughed the rest of his earnings back into the maintenance of the building. It's still a sizeable inheritance, though. Even in its present state, it would fetch a handsome price; Sylvia Vale's a sought-after area. I imagine Coral will sell.'

He frowned thoughtfully before continuing. 'Coral wasn't the only mistake we made. There was an unlikely component in Thornton's first alibi which he glossed over so smoothly that we didn't notice it. When he returned the Porsche to Arthur Wright's garage, the rain was coming down quite heavily. He didn't have an umbrella, so he got soaked walking back to the hospital. But he had to meet as many people as possible in order to bolster his alibi; remember, blackmail had now turned into murder – or at least he thought it had. So he needed a reason to be wet. He told us he'd finished his work in the library and stowed his briefcase in the car before going to the Mess to watch television. Was that necessary? Was that likely in a rainstorm? He could have taken the indoor route and kept the case with him. But he didn't, because he wanted to be seen by Albert, to draw his attention to the Cavalier, and subconsciously remind him that it had been there all evening.'

'Of course!' said Sergeant Bird. 'We rationalized that his first trip, from the library to the canteen, would be outdoors because he would want a breath of fresh air – but that would have been reasonable since the rain hadn't started then.'

'Right. He never went to the canteen anyway; he went straight for the Porsche.' Montgomery fiddled moodily with his tea-spoon. 'I wish we'd known how close Arthur Wright's garage was to the hospital. It would have alerted us to the possibility of the Porsche being used. Haslam and Grange didn't emphasize the geographical aspect at all.'

'They felt that Arthur Wright was honest,' said Sergeant Bird, 'and in that they were correct. When they asked him about damaged cars, he immediately volunteered information on the only one he thought was relevant. The Porsche was already "legitimately" damaged, so he didn't mention it. If he had done, that would have put a whole new complexion on the case.'

'You picked up that fact from Mark, didn't you?' Carole asked Montgomery.

'Yes. He made a passing comment at Donington, but I only realized the implications much later. It's funny – all along, apart from one occasion, I felt that Thornton possessed the kind of character we were looking for. The single exception was his unfeigned anger when he described Philippa's injuries to me. I thought it was directed towards the hit-and-run driver, but really he was furious with *himself* for not making certain that she was dead when he had the chance. I can only imagine he was afraid a resident from Beechcroft Lane would come sweeping round the corner while he was crouched in the road.

'Evidence-wise, though, he appeared to be ruled out. His car never moved from the car-park on the night of Bradshaw's death. Vanda Pitts lied for him about the following Friday; Jackson was actually right when he described her as self-centred and career-minded, but he drew the wrong inferences. Finally, our big red herring – or should I say our second red herring after Barnaby Fletcher? Philippa Rowe's mysterious collapse. Thornton was provably at Donington Park that Saturday afternoon, so it did us no favours at all.'

'Did you ever solve the mystery?' asked Carole.

Montgomery shook his head. 'No. I don't like loose ends, but we have to conclude by now that it wasn't relevant to our investigation. Anne Markham still believes the incident was a definite attack on Philippa. Personally, I think some junior nurse made a mistake and is keeping a low profile. It served one useful purpose; attention was focussed on the possibility of harm coming to Philippa within the hospital. Neil Thornton can't have been very pleased about that!'

'What will happen to him now, Richard?'

Montgomery stared at the dancing firelight, orange pin-pricks reflecting from his eyes.

'He'll face a jury when he's fit and the machinery of law is ready for him. He'll be tried for manslaughter, attempted murder and murder. And if there's any justice, he'll be shut away for a long time to come.'

'So Coral inherits a great big house in Sylvia Vale!'

Audrey sounded personally aggrieved, and David gave an inner sigh. He looked at her face across the table – at the heavy make-up and small mouth twisted in displeasure – and saw there fuel for his resolve to finish their association once and for all. They had finally realized their trip to the Trattoria Sorrento; he had owed her this outing. Perhaps it was craven to consider broaching such a subject during a quiet dinner in a public place, but those very features would protect them both from the futility of a stormy scene. Surely it would be obvious to Audrey that they had no future together.

'Coral's had a rough time,' he said. 'Don't you remember how upset she was on the day Philippa collapsed? I'm glad something's going right for her at last.'

Behind him, a table of revellers erupted into laughter, but Audrey didn't appear to notice. Her expression was queer and glazed, as if she had been woken up from the middle of a deep sleep and didn't quite understand what was going on.

Avoiding his eye, she reached out and picked up her wine glass. To David's surprise, her hand seemed to be afflicted with a fine tremor; the red liquid quivered ominously, and she hastily replaced the glass without drinking.

'Is something wrong, Audrey? he asked.

'No . . . no. It was just those people. They startled me.'

That was patently untrue. David frowned as he chewed his

lasagne. Could some presentiment of his intentions have touched her narrow-minded cocoon? It would hardly produce such an effect ... Audrey was not only distracted; he would swear that she was frightened. What could possibly be the cause?

Her voice cut into his speculations. 'You were saying something about Philippa before we were interrupted.'

'Coral,' he corrected.

'Well, yes, but you mentioned that Philippa had collapsed. I never heard of that at the time; we were all thinking of Maureen. What happened?'

'There isn't much to tell. It was on the Saturday afternoon after we left. She suddenly started passing far too much fluid, which made her faint. She fell out of bed, but luckily didn't sustain any serious damage.'

'Oh, I see.' Audrey picked half-heartedly at her food for a few moments, then cleared her throat. 'I suppose it was all part of the illness.'

'What was?'

'This fluid thing of Philippa's.'

'I don't think so. It didn't fit in – she was getting better. I heard from Anne recently that they found a vial of frusemide on the ward, which could have accounted for the signs if someone had been daft enough to give it to Philippa. But there was no clinical indication at all. That's why Anne involved the police. They wanted to know about anything unusual connected with Philippa's management in the hospital; they were already on to the fact that a medical person was their most likely suspect.'

'Did they – take fingerprints?'

'I've no idea. That particular incident fizzled out, swamped by more serious events ... Look, Audrey, you've hardly touched your tagliatelli. Would you like something else?'

'No. Let's go, David. Please.'

'What, right now?'

'Yes. I don't want to stay here. I'm not enjoying it.'

'If the food isn't right, I'll send it back.'

Audrey tore her napkin down the middle. 'There's nothing wrong with the food. I just want to go home. Please ask for the bill.'

'If you insist.' David suppressed his irritation with difficulty. Audrey was acting very strangely. He was going to get to the bottom of this.

It was cool and dark in the car, a quiet, anonymous environment. Audrey leaned her hot cheek against the window pane and wearily parried David's string of questions. Their clothes smelt of smoke from the restaurant. She wanted to go home and have a bath.

'We aren't going anywhere,' David was saying, 'until you tell me what's wrong. There's no hurry. We can stay here all night.'

'Don't be cruel,' she pleaded. 'I just don't feel well.'

'I'm afraid I don't believe you. You were fine until we started talking about Philippa. Then you had a sort of *petit mal*.'

'It's enough to give anyone a *petit mal*,' she answered with spirit, 'the way everything comes back to Philippa. Philippa this, Philippa that . . . '

'Oh, act your age, Audrey! I'm not a fool. That wasn't the reason.' He broke off as her eyes filled with tears. Resignedly, he patted her back. 'I'm not trying to torment you. I just don't know what's wrong. Tell me.'

She bit her lip. Kindness was perilously close to succeeding where hostility would have failed, but for how long would his kindness last once he knew the truth?

'You'll hate me,' she whispered.

'No, I won't. I don't think we're entirely suited, but that's a different matter. I hope I'll always be able to help you if you need it.'

'You can say that now . . . but you'll change your mind. I did something really irresponsible; you'll never understand.'

'Try me.'

'All right – but remember what I said.' Her speech wavered and her hands clenched into fists. 'I gave that frusemide to Philippa. It was in the lemon squash.'

If she had wanted to shock David, she could scarcely have hit upon a better method. A variety of emotions crossed his face, but he restrained himself with an effort, and in the end voiced only the simplest of questions:

'Why?'

Why, indeed, she thought bitterly. Because it seemed like a good idea at the time. Because Philippa looked so infuriatingly *saintly* and frail and vulnerable in that room, appealing to the knight errant in every male around, drawing David back to her with a web of hospital bed-linen . . . How did you fight an invalid?

So she had acted on a story of Coral's, the one about the

frusemide in the punch-bowl. Her intention had been humiliation; she had visualized Philippa asking for constant bed-pans, interrupting David's visit, tarnishing the image of patient holiness. But then Coral had burst in . . .

'You haven't answered, Audrey. Why did you do it?'

She turned to him. 'It was meant as – a joke. I didn't know it could be dangerous. I didn't even know there'd been any consequences until tonight.'

'But, Audrey – '

'Please, I don't want a lecture. I know it was wrong. I'm ashamed. Let's leave it at that.'

He shook his head sadly. 'It's not so easy. You were right – I don't understand, although I'm trying to. Philippa never did you any harm. If you were angry with anyone, it should have been me. I'm the one who's treated you badly, and I'm sorry. I misled you into thinking I was a free man, when I suppose I was just trying to convince myself. Compounding the mistake has been wrong for both of us.'

Audrey felt sick. So this was it: the boot. No marks for honesty. She had surprised herself by telling him; now the same honesty was forcing her to examine other truths. Deep down, she had always known that David's affections were elsewhere. A parting was inevitable. Convenient though the fiction would be, she was not being penalized for one single act of stupidity.

Her eyes began to sting, but she set her jaw and controlled the impending self-pity. When she spoke, it was in rational tones.

'Yes, it has,' she agreed, 'and I take my share of the blame. Just help me with one thing, please . . . Do you think I should tell the police?'

'Yes.'

'Then I shall, tomorrow. Would you come with me?'

'Of course,' he said without hesitation.

She gave him a watery smile. It was the first time he had looked at her with respect.

'This has just come for you,' announced Coral, dancing into Philippa's side room with a flat brown package. 'Anne has allowed me to act as delivery-person. To put you out of any misery you may be in, the postmark says Sussex.'

'You don't miss much,' laughed Philippa, holding out her

249

hand for the parcel. It had been a busy morning. Barnaby had just left, clutching his latest batch of photographs, and Vernon Crowland had earlier called by to pronounce her progress 'very satisfactory' and introduce his new locum registrar. At least she had been able to receive them with some semblence of dignity, having graduated to a chair and footstool.

She deciphered the postmark. Yes, Sussex – where her father was recovering from the heart attack they hadn't wanted to tell her about. How paranoid she had been!

'Quick, quick!' exhorted Coral, rubbing her hands together. 'It's obviously something to wear. A blouse, perhaps, or an underskirt.'

'Tea-towels, I should think,' said Philippa. 'I've certainly been waited on long enough.' She carefully slit open the brown paper covering, and drew out the contents. A cascade of amethyst silk slithered across her lap, the colour rippling richly like waves on a great purple pool. Coral exclaimed in delight.

'A nightdress! Do let me hold it up, Pippa! Isn't it lovely!'

'Beautiful. How kind of them . . . ' The letter was Valerie's, but there was a note from her father, as well, in encouragingly firm handwriting. She ran her eyes down it quickly before deciding to savour it as a treat in store for later. Odd phrases stood out from the rest: ' . . . *told them exactly what I wanted; young Jonathan spotted it, although Val did the honours . . . We all send our love. I'm coming north as soon as these damned doctors let me travel. Until then, remember you're my special girl . . . '*

'A man should see this,' said Coral emphatically, tracing with her finger the delicate spume of lace which bordered the hemline.

'One already has.'

'You know what I mean. A *young* man should admire you in this nightdress . . . a lover.'

'Have you looked at my leg recently, Coral? The one that's now rigid in three feet of plaster?'

'I didn't mean anything *crude*. The more ephemeral side of love . . . '

'I don't think that's quite the word you want.'

'Ethereal, then. You know. You're just being difficult.'

'How so?'

'You won't discuss David.'

'You're right, Coral, I won't. How *is* your house in Sylvia Vale? Have you thought what you're going to do with it?'

'Yes.'

'Do tell me.'

'Only if you promise we can talk about David afterwards.'

'There's nothing to say, but if you really want to, we can.'

'Good.' Coral handed back the nightdress with reluctance and perched on the side of the bed. She took a deep breath. 'I'm going to live there. I want to turn it into decent rented accommodation for nurses who don't enjoy stifling in a hospital environment all day long. Junior doctors, too, pharmacists, anyone. It's going to come alive and be used.' She saw Philippa's look of doubt. 'Don't worry, I've no intention of presiding over a noisy commune. They'll be the right sort of people. People who can both respect the rules *and* enjoy the freedom of the countryside. We can give each other lifts, so no one is walking through town on dark nights alone. What do you think?'

'You've obviously considered many of the aspects,' said Philippa carefully, 'but do you feel that enough suitable people will want to live out of town?'

'Yes. It's not far really, and I've already canvassed several of my friends. They think it's a great idea. They can't wait to join in.'

'What about finances? Have you thought how much the conversions will cost? You can only start charging rent once the bedrooms are actually finished.'

'I know. I shall have to get a loan, but it's worth it. I only need to buy second-hand furniture – you should see the junk in the Nurses' Home! – and my friends will help with curtains, cushions and bedspreads. We'll buy material in bulk at the market. It can be done, Pippa!' Coral's eyes shone with enthusiasm, and Philippa realized that here was a sense of mission, a project to fill the appalling gap left by Maureen. Coral had relied on her mouse-like friend more than she had ever realized while Maureen was alive.

'Good luck,' said Philippa warmly. 'As soon as I'm up and around, I'll help you. You can have a croquet lawn at the front. The nearest neighbours are hundreds of yards away ... ' She paused, as a vision of a dark, wet night corkscrewed through her mind. She felt a sudden deep sadness. 'Lay the ghosts, Coral,' she said. 'Make that house a merry one. I'm sure Gil would have wanted it.'

Coral scanned her friend's face earnestly, her own pointed like a young vixen's. 'That's one of the reasons why,' she said. 'You told me what he said – and what he did. He fought for his home. I'm going to keep it in the family. Who knows, maybe one day . . . Anyway, that's why. And I want to make amends, too. I never knew him, I never even wanted to know him, yet he was my cousin and the only family I had. I made judgements and I was wrong.'

Her head dropped; she contemplated the floor for a few seconds before sitting up abruptly and flicking a vagrant russet curl away from her eyes. 'I've kept my side of the bargain,' she said. 'Now it's your turn. You never did tell me why you left David when you were so obviously suited for each other. I wish I could understand it.'

Philippa gave a rueful smile. '"Obviously suited" . . . I wonder, is any couple really "obviously suited", or do they just conceal their disagreements from the public eye rather more effectively than do others? I think I was naïve. My expectations of domestic life with a man from my own generation were unrealistic, but it took me a while to discover that.'

'Didn't David pull his weight in the flat?'

'At first, yes. But it wasn't long before he was talking about "helping me" with washing-up and such, and I came to appreciate that he wasn't as enlightened as I'd thought. When I went to stay with his family I could see why: his father is very old-fashioned, just like mine, and doesn't lift a finger once he gets home from work. His mother and sisters take care of everything. So in a way, it's not really David's fault; for years that's been the norm from his point of view. But it didn't stop me resenting the "*hausfrau*" role he was forcing on me.'

She stopped, and shook her head. 'You've got me going, Coral. You don't really want to hear all this. Let's just say that David doesn't need a career woman as a wife – yes, he was muttering about marriage; he needs some malleable person who will enjoy putting him first.'

'Someone like Audrey?' Coral's eyes were unfathomable.

'Perhaps. Yes, perhaps he's landed on his feet there.'

'Mm. But you still haven't told me what made you actually leave. There must have been some trigger.'

'Oh, there was. A silly little thing in retrospect, but it was upsetting at the time. He often joined in with the cooking if we had guests, which was helpful on the one hand, but a bit hypocritical on the other. Well, one Saturday when two old friends of

252

his – both men – were coming down from Kilmarnock, he offered to cook the whole meal. I said no, I'd do it myself so he could catch up on all their news. To be honest, I knew I'd make a better job of it.

'I decided on pork in sour cream, a casserole that most people seem to like. His friends came at six . . . we chatted, had drinks . . . I served the meal at eight – and neither of them could eat it!'

'Whyever not?' Coral was astonished. 'Didn't the oven light?'

'Nothing so simple and mechanical. It was the visitors themselves. One was a vegetarian, the other was Jewish.'

'No!'

'I'm afraid so. It was awful, because they were hungry and they'd travelled a long way . . . David offered to bring in some takeaway food; they chose to eat the vegetables instead. We did find a bit of cheese, but the meal was ruined.'

'Didn't David know about them beforehand?'

'That's just it: he'd forgotten. Not being geared to the importance of other people's eating preferences, he hadn't given it any thought. I felt a total failure as a hostess. He laughed and said, "Never mind, Philippa," as if it was nothing to do with him! I was so angry, I nearly choked.' She looked down at her knees. 'We had a colossal row the next day, after they had left. I saw the incident as symptomatic of everything that had been going wrong, while he thought I was making too much of it.'

Coral was thoughtful. 'Perhaps you should have *let* him cook for his friends,' she said. 'Don't you think it was your pride which took a knock that night?'

'Oh, partly. I'm sure that we're all rather ambivalent about the female role – we don't want our domestic compliance to be assumed, and yet we want to excel at those very tasks! At the same time, I was having doubts about the broader issues of marriage, the potential conflict of careers, Establishment attitudes to married women – all those problems which no one has managed to solve yet. It seemed like the right time to leave.'

'I see,' said Coral slowly. 'Presumably, then, you're happy on your own, and glad that David found someone like Audrey so quickly?'

'I wouldn't quite say that.'

'Neither would I. Listen, Pippa – David still loves you! I know he does. Audrey isn't a factor any more – truly. They've gone

253

their separate ways. He wants to try again with you, if only you'll give him a sign of encouragement . . . Don't you want him back!'

She was so vehement that Philippa smiled in spite of herself. 'Half of me does, Coral. I must admit, I never thought I'd miss him as much as I did. And he's been so kind these last few weeks. But that's exactly the reason why it would be rash to make any decision now. Sitting here with my leg in plaster, feeling vaguely bemused and grateful . . . I could make a terrible mistake. All my life I've tried to use my brain whenever there were difficult options to consider, only just now it doesn't seem to be in gear. I don't know why.'

'But you'll at least think about it? You will, won't you, Pippa? I'm sure he'll try harder this time. Picture yourself in a nice house with David – not as nice as mine, of course – each of you with your own sphere of influence. You might well be cooking banquets in the kitchen, but he'd probably be doing some filthy job in the garage. It'd work, you'd see. Promise me you'll think it over!'

Philippa laughed. 'He's got himself a persistent advocate, I'll say that for him. Am I likely to get any peace if I don't?'

'I can't envisage it.'

'Neither can I. All right, then, I promise I'll give the matter serious thought. I'm sorry I can't be more specific just yet. Will that do?'

Coral beamed. 'That'll do to be going on with.'

Montgomery was reading his newspaper when the telephone rang. He sighed and ignored it; Carole had just gone into the hall with the vacuum cleaner. He heard some muted conversation before the door opened and she appeared, holding her hand over the lower part of the receiver, a quizzical expression on her face.

'It's Mark,' she said. 'He's got the Fiesta roadworthy again, and he'll be racing at Oulton Park this Sunday. He wonders if we'd like to come and watch . . . no obligation . . . Hm.' She grinned. 'Oh, well. It was just a thought.'

X